QUATERNARY DATING METHODS – A USER'S GUIDE

Edited by
P.L. SMART & P.D. FRANCES

Quaternary Research Association

Technical Guide No. 4

Edited by Peter L. Smart and Peter D. Frances

Department of Geography,
University of Bristol,
University Road,
Bristol BS8 1SS.

© Quaternary Research Association: London 1991
Reprinted 1994

ISSN 1264-9241
ISBN 0-907780-03-3

Typeset by University of Bristol Printing Unit, 1/9 Old Park Hill, Bristol BS2 8BB

Printed by Carneval Printers and Publishers Ltd, Unit 4, The Old Dairy, North Street, Melton Mowbray, Leicestershire, LE13 1NL

Series Editor Dr. W. A. Mitchell, Publications Secretary.

Recommended reference:
SMART. P.L. and FRANCES. P.D. 1991. *Quaternary Dating Methods: a Users Guide*. Technical Guide 4. Quaternary Research Association, London. 233 pp.

LIST OF CONTRIBUTORS

A.J. Hurford   Department of Geological Sciences, University College, London, WC1E 6BT.

D. Kroon   Department of Geology and Geophysics, University of Edinburgh, Edinburgh EH9 3JW.

A.J. Patience   Department of Geology and Geophysics, University of Edinburgh, Edinburgh EH9 3JW.

J.R. Pilcher   Palaeoecology Centre, Queens University of Belfast, Belfast BT7 1NN.

D.A. Richards   Department of Geography, University of Bristol, Bristol BS8 1SS.

P.L. Smart   Department of Geography, University of Bristol, Bristol BS8 1SS.

G. Sykes   Institute of Earth Studies, The University College of Wales, Aberystwyth, Aberystwyth SY23 3DB.

R. Thompson   Department of Geology and Geophysics, University of Edinburgh, Edinburgh EH9 3JZ.

A.G. Wintle   Institute of Earth Sciences, The University College of Wales, Aberystwyth, Aberystwyth SY23 3DB.

PREFACE

This manual is intended primarily for those who are 'users' rather than 'producers' of dates. Technical detail of the instrumental and other methods involved has therefore been kept to a minimum, readers being referred to the appropriate specialist literature. Emphasis has been placed on clear explanations of the theoretical basis of the methods, with more detailed treatment of their application to specific examples, of sample suitability and collection, and the evaluation of the reliability and accuracy of the age estimates. The latter is also covered in a more general manner in Chapter 1, which illustrates this theme using a deliberately provocative example.

Quaternary geochronology is a rapidly changing field due both to improvements in instrumental technology and the increasing number of laboratories that are engaged in methodological development and application. There are thus frequent improvements in the reliability and applicability of existing techniques and novel methods continue to be introduced. This manual has had a long and chequered history, and a succession of editors. In finally bringing it to press we hope to have encapsulated the current state of the art (or science?), but we have made no attempt to standardise the content of individual contributions. These therefore reflect the emphasis of the individual authors.

ACKNOWLEDGEMENTS

We would like to thank all the contributors for their patience during the long delays in the preparation of this volume. We would also like to acknowledge the help we recieved from members of staff in the Geography Department at the University of Bristol, especially Liz Owen, Anna Kaleta and Sarah Howell for their help with the typing, Simon Godden for his assistance with the figures and Patricia Lane and Julie Rigg at the Printing Unit for typesetting the text.

Peter Smart
Peter Frances.

CONTENTS

Chapter 1

GENERAL PRINCIPLES

P.L. Smart

WHY DO WE NEED DATING TECHNIQUES?

Much of the terrestrial Quaternary geological record is derived from spatially variable, fragmentary and discontinuous deposits. In the British Isles, Rose (1989) has argued that stadial deposits are considerably more useful than the interstadial deposits, which have formed the focus of previous subdivisions, because they may be traced extensively across large areas. However, correlation using conventional lithostratigraphic criteria becomes increasingly unreliable as one moves from the local to the continental scale (Richmond and Fullerton, 1986). To overcome these problems, Quaternary geologists have turned to faunal and floral evidence to characterise deposits of a particular age; the work of West (1963, 1984) on British interglacial sites is a classic example. Unfortunately, rates of biological evolution are relatively slow, and thus while a series of micropalaeontological datum levels are recognised in the ocean cores, and prove useful over long time scales (O − >1 Ma, Berggren et al., 1990), this technique becomes of limited utility at the shorter scales often of interest in Quaternary studies. In some cases, distinctive floras or faunas may be associated with deposits of a particular age, as suggested for the UK interglacial mammal fauna due to differential immigration from the continent across the English Channel land bridge (Currant, 1989). However, differences in interpretation arise, as shown by the alternative chronology of Stuart (1982). Furthermore, in many cases very similar assemblages may derive from periods of similar palaeoclimate, but different age. The confusion over palynologically similar ''Ipswichian'' sites in Britain, which appear to display different mammal faunas and are probably associated with both oxygen istope stages 5 and 7 (Shotton et al., 1983), is a classic example, and similar problems are reported from elsewhere (Frenzel, 1989). Correlation between terrestrial deposits can therefore only be reliably achieved by dating individual sites.

In the oceans, deposition is often more continuous, particularly as one moves from deposits on the continental shelf which may be directly affected by glaciation at low sea level (Eyles and McCabe, 1989) to the deep ocean basins. Thus the record of Quaternary events provided by deep sea cores (Shackleton, 1989, Jansen, 1989) has come to provide a yardstick employed by all Quaternary scientists. There is, however,

Table 1.1 Caveat Emptor — a careful users guide to intercomparison of age estimates, illustrated by the 'dating' of UK interglacial sites from the different aminostratigraphic zones of Bowen et al. (1989). The amino acid ratios are given in column 1 for sites where isotopic or radiogenic age estimates are also available. The reader is invited to assess the reliability of the chronology using criteria discussed in the text. Note that in many cases standard deviation quoted for multiple determinations and/or samples is considerably greater than mean quoted uncertainties (MQU). For individual techniques there is often good mutual agreement between multiple ages (stratigraphic criteria 1), although special pleading has been advanced for the range of ^{14}C dates from Tattershall Castle. These analyses are typical of very old material variably contaminated with modern carbon. Stratigraphic criteria 2 is, however, met at this site, the ^{14}C dates being above and younger than the U series and TL dated samples. Furthermore, because of the relatively large uncertainties, stratigraphic criteria 3 appears also to be met; it is only recognition of the probable open system nature of the mollusc uranium series results that urges caution (methodological criteria 2). The ESR result from Hoxne should be regarded as 'experimental', as the technique used, whilst theoretically sound, has not been validated (effectively methodological criteria 3). Finally, there is considerable debate as to the stability (saturation state of the traps) involved in feldspar TL, which raises questions regarding the accuracy of the older TL dates quoted. Amino acid ratio for species: B Bithynia, L Lymnaea, C Cepaea, V Valvata, determined at Royal Holloway and Aberystwyth laboratories; square brackets indicate determinations made at INSTAR (University of Colorado). Ages are in ka; Bold mean and standard deviation for multiple determinations and MQU: T Top, M Middle, Bo Bottom.

Site and Unit	Amino Acid Ratio[1,2]	Uranium Series Age[3,4]	TL Age[2,5]	ESR Age[6]	^{14}C Age[7]
Bobbitshole Beds B+C	B 0.09 ± 0.14a(4) L 0.10 ± 0.014(2)	—	—	—	—
Bacon Hole Shelly Sand	—	116 ± 18c 122 ± 11 T 129 ± 16 M 125 ± 26c Bo 129 ± 30c **126 ± 5(2)d (MQU ± 14)**	—	—	—
Sandy cave earth	C 0.122 ± 0.02(5)	—	—	—	—
Tattershall Castle Higher Silts	—	—	—	—	>40.5 43.0 ± 1.3/-1.1 42.2 ± 1.0 30.8 ± 0.36i 28.0 ± 0.80i 39.4 ± 0.80i >46.3i
Detritus Mud	C 0.091 ± 0.005(3)b C 0.115 ± 0.03(4)	76c +10/-9 94 +10/-9 93 +18/-16 101 +25/-20 **91 ± 11(4) (MQU + 116/-14)**	—	—	—
Calcareous Silt	—	—	114 ± 16e	—	—

Hoxne

Layer e	V 0.26 ± 0.01(4)	—	—	295 ± 25(4)g **330 ± 50**h	—
	[V 0.243 ± 0.023(3)]			365 ± 14(2) **MQU ± 17**	—

Swanscombe

Upper Loam	—	—	206 ± 19f (**MCU ± 27**)	—
Upper Middle Gravel	B 0.312 ± 0.017(4)	—	—	—
Lower Middle Gravel	B 0.296 ± 0.01(4)	—	—	—
Lower Loam	[C 0.30 ± 0.04(3)]	—	231 ± 20f (**MCU ± 33**)	—
Lower Gravel	B 0.30 ± 0.015(5)	—	—	—

Sources: 1. Bowen et al. (1989)   2. Holyoak and Preece (1985)   3. Ivanovich and Holyoak (1982)   4. Currant et al. (1984)   5. Bridgland et al. (1985)   6. Grun et al. (1988)   7. Girling (1980).

Notes:

a Quoted uncertainty for *Bithynia* very large compared with results from second species (*Lymnaea*) from same site (typesetting error?).

b Note significant difference between ratios quoted by same laboratory using 2 different preparation techniques (see Sykes this volume).

c 230Th/232Th ratios indicate contamination with 'detrital' thorium; ages should be considered unreliable.

d 122 ka (no uncertainty) quoted by Bowen et al. (1989).

e No *in situ* measurement of water content, but this included in quoted uncertainty.

f Figures are arithmetic means of 3(2) techniques for same sample quoted in Table 2 Bridgland et al. (1985). These values differ from values of 202.0 ± 15.2 and 228.8 ± 23.3 quoted in text by these authors. Figures probably represent minimum dates because of uncertainty regarding saturation of TL traps (Mejdahl, 1988).

g Age is critically dependent on radiation dose derived from U, Th and K analysis of adhering soil.

h 319 ± 38 ka quoted by Grun et al. (1988) as arithmetic mean and standard deviation of all measurements (not mean of two sample averages); 309 ka (no uncertainty) quoted in Bowen et al. 1989 (typesetting error?).

i Considered to be contaminated by modern carbon (Flandrian rootlets) Girling (1980).

j Considered to be contaminated by interglacial material (Girling, 1980).

3

still a need for dating of these cores in order to correct for variations in deposition rate, and to provide distinctive time horizons for intercorrelation of different records (the stage 5e (5.5) high sea level and raised coral reefs for example, Edwards et al., 1987). Palaeomagnetic (Shackleton and Opdyke, 1973), uranium series (Kominz et al., 1979) and radiocarbon dating (Pisias et al., 1984) of ocean cores has provided an independent numerical time scale for Quaternary events, and has been critical in confirming the role of astronomical forcing, where the physical processes provide a periodicity clearly defined and calculable in calender years (Berger, 1980, Hays et al., 1976). Indeed the matching of astronomical periodicities is now used as a method for refining the time scale of the oxygen isotope record in cores (Martinson et al., 1987).

WHAT CONSTITUTES AN ACCEPTABLE AND RELIABLE AGE ESTIMATE?

Many numbers generated by dating laboratories are accepted uncritically by Quaternary scientists, and worse, are systematically sifted to yield the "correct" result. The former can be avoided by always applying a series of general criteria before accepting age estimates as reliable, the latter is simply unscientific. In some cases specific criteria apply to specific methods, but there are in fact several universally applicable criteria which any reliable age estimates should meet, a point emphasized here by discussing them prior to the individual dating techniques. These criteria are broadly in two groups, here termed stratigraphic and methodological criteria. Their application is illustrated in Table 1.1 by consideration of difficulties in the calibration of the aminostratigraphy of Bowen et al. (1989) for UK interglacial sites.

Statigraphic Criteria

1) For a specific dating technique there should be good agreement between multiple age determinations within a single chronostratigraphic geological unit.

2) For a specific dating technique there should be concordance between age determinations from stratigraphically related samples in a geological sequence. Thus the basal layers in a deposit should be older than overlying units.

3) There should be concordance between ages derived from essentially independent dating techniques for the same chronostratigraphic unit.

In many cases only criteria (1) and (2) can be used because there is a lack of suitable material in the deposit on which to apply several dating techniques. In other cases, the methods applied may not be truly independent. An example is the dating of speleothem calcite using ESR and uranium series techniques; the former technique uses radioisotope concentrations which may well be derived from the uranium series analysis. It is however an important consideration for those selecting samples for dating to ensure that they are able to apply the first two criteria.

Tests for agreement or stratigraphic concordance of ages must take account of the inherent uncertainties associated with the age estimates. In some cases these may be stated, normally as a $\pm$ 1 standard deviation range calculated from analytical and other uncertainties. In others, such as correlative methods, no uncertainties are quoted and statistically rigourous evaluation is thus not possible. For example in discussing amino acid racemization dating of UK interglacial sites, Bowen et al. (1989) quote ratios for the "Ipswichian" last interglacial sites of Bobbitshole and Bacon Hole (sandy cave earth) which are statistically derived from two separate populations (Table 1.1). Yet they use a uranium series age estimate from Bacon Hole to calibrate the amino acid racemization rate for the Bobbitshole type site. In fact, the uranium series age is from broken speleothem incorporated into the overlying shelly sand deposit, and thus cannot even be considered to be truly contemporaneous with the amino acid "date". It is important to remember that even adjacent sediment units may be separated by significant hiatuses, and that it may in fact only be possible to suggest that the sediment body of interest pre or post dates the material actually dated (a problem discussed further below). It must also be stressed that agreement between an age estimate and the geologically expected "age" is not adequate unless the latter is based on very firm evidence, for example a distinctive, dated fauna. The reader should also beware of papers "validating" new dating techniques by comparison with dubious and thoroughly insecure geological ages.

Methodological Criteria

1) The "event" recorded by the date should be the same as the "target event." For instance, the setting of an isotopic clock to zero should occur at the time of deposition of the sediment unit of interest. Thus, as discussed by Dunnell and Readhead (1988), a fragment of wood incorporated into a sediment body may already have a significant radiocarbon age, the isotopic clock having been set once tree growth stopped, not when the sediment was deposited.

2) There should be no evidence for post-depositional disturbance of the dating system. This is frequently called the "closed system" assumption, and in essence is that after setting of the clock at time zero, only time affects the parameter measured. Thus, post-depositional uptake of uranium in molluscs for example, alters the $^{230}Th/^{234}U$ ratio and gives unreliable uranium series ages.

3) The rate of change of the dating signal with time should be known. For example, in the case of an isotopic technique, the half life should be well known; in fact, with the development of mass-spectrometric analysis techniques, significant uncertainty may derive from imprecise knowledge of the half life because the isotope ratio may be measured with a very high precision.

In discussing dating evidence for Quaternary deposits, it is important that geologists state criteria for acceptance and rejection of specific age estimates, rather than simply ignore evidence they do not believe — a practice unfortunately far too common. For example, in interpreting amino acid racemization ratios for interglacial sites in the United Kingdom, Bowen et al. (1989) ignored the TL age estimates in excess of 100 ka derived from Bridgeland et al. (1985). In fact the validity of these ages is hotly debated in the TL dating community because of concern with trap stability and saturation, and the mutual disagreement between these results, the amino acid, ratios and the ESR results from Hoxne (Grun et al., 1988) may thus be acceptable (Table 1.1).

WHAT ARE THE TYPES OF QUATERNARY DATING METHODS?

The two-fold classification of dating methods following Colman et al. (1987) has much to recommend it. Methods which share similar mechanisms, assumptions and applications form one division, while the type of result they produce forms an essentially parallel but conceptually distinctive second classification (Table 1.2):

1) **Numerical age methods** produce quantitative estimates of age (and uncertainty) on a ratio or absolute scale. Note that the term "absolute" sometimes used to describe this category should be avoided because there are inherent uncertainties applying to all numerical methods which may invalidate the derived ages. Example: Radiocarbon and other isotopic dating methods.

2) **Calibrated age methods** measure systematic changes in a parameter with time, but this rate of change may depend on other (unknown) variables, and thus an independent chronological control must be used for calibration. Example: Lichenometry where grave stones, walls and buildings of known age and radiocarbon-dated morraines must be used for calibration.

3) **Relative age methods** provide ordinal (ranked) ages, but only an approximate indication of magnitude. Such estimates may be converted to calibrated ages if suitable independent chronological controls are available. Example: Amino acid techniques, where past changes in climate make determination of long term racemization rates difficult to calculate.

4) **Correlated age methods** only provide evidence of equivalence, essentially nominal data. Example: ^{18}O ratios in foraminifera from deep sea cores.

Of the six methods suggested by Colman et al. (1987), sidereal (calender) and geomorphic methods are not discussed in detail in this text. *Geomorphic methods* rely on rates of weathering at scales from individual crystals to landforms, as reviewed by Brooks (1985). The development of hydration rims on obsidian, a volcanic glass widely used for prehistoric tools, provides an example of a particularly well-developed

Table 1.2. *Classification of Quaternary Dating Methods; those methods reviewed in detail in this volume are in bold (after Colman et al., 1987)*

Type of result*

===== =Numerical-age= = = = =

---------------- = = = = = = = Calibrated-age = = = = = = = --------------------

-------------------- = = = = Relative-age = = = = --------------------

-- = Correlated-age =

Type of method

Sidereal	Isotopic	Radiogenic	Chemical and Biological	Geomorphic	Correlation
Historical records	^{14}C	**Fission-track**	**Amino Acid racemization**	Soil-profile development	Lithostratigraphy
Dendro-chronology	**K-Ar and ^{39}Ar-^{40}Ar**	Luminescence	Obsidian and tephra hydration	Rock and mineral weathering	Tephrochronology
Varve chronology	**Uranium-series**	**Electron-spin resonance**	Lichenometry	Progressive landscape modification	**Paleomagnetism**
	Uranium-trend		Soil chemistry	Rate of deposition	Fossils and artefacts
	Cosmogenic isotopes (^{210}Pb, ^{10}Be, ^{36}Cl, etc.)		Rock varnish chemistry	Rate of deformation	**Stable isotopes**
				Geomorphic position	**Orbital variations**
					Tectites and microtectites

Double dashed line indicates the type of result most commonly produced by the methods below it; single dashed line indicates the type of result less commonly produced by the methods below it.

geomorphic method in an archaeological context (Michels, 1986). *Sidereal methods* include varve chronology and dendrochronlogy (Baillie, 1982), and are both of importance because they provide a calendrical calibration of radiocarbon ages. They are not, however, at present capable of providing a time scale extending far beyond the upper boundary of the Quaternary.

A distinction is made in Table 1.2 between *Radiogenic methods* which measure the cumulative non-isotopic effects of radioactive decay (as in TL dating), and *Isotopic methods* which utilise measurement of changes in isotopic ratios. The latter are also sometimes also called radiometric techniques. (Note that isotopes are usually referred to by quoting their atomic mass number, followed by the elemental symbol, e.g. ^{14}C. Occasionally, the mass number is placed after the name of the element in full, as in carbon-14). Details of these and other techniques are given in specific chapters below.

HOW DO I SELECT A DATING METHOD?

Of the large number of criteria which might apply in selection of a dating method, only three are of prime importance:

1) Applicability — is there something dateable in a particular deposit?

2) Time range — does the time range of the method match the probable age of the deposit?

3) Precision/accuracy — is the method capable of resolving the age difference of the events of interest?

In practice, other more mundane criteria such as cost often intervene, and individual Quaternary scientists tend to have access only to specific techniques via facilities in their own laboratories or via contacts in other institutions. Furthermore, as advances in dating techniques generally depend on developments in basic physics and instrumental technology, there is a tendency for the most sophisticated techniques to be inaccessible to Quaternary scientists until the procedures become routine and instrumentation widely available.

Applicability

The physical and chemical basis of each dating method effectively determines which type of geological materials may be dated. For instance, in the case of ESR dating, some minerals such as calcite have usable dating signals (Smith et al., 1985), while others do not. The technique may thus only be used if calcite (or some other mineral with a stable ESR signal sensitive to radiation) is present in the deposit. In practice, there tends to be a continuum of dateable materials ranging from those generally considered as highly reliable, through those capable of yielding reliable ages under some conditions (when certain assumptions are met), to those which yield analytical results which cannot be considered reliable age estimates. Thus in the case of ESR dating of calcite, age estimates based on secondary soil concretions are unreliable, both because the clock is not set to zero on deposition, and because the concretion may result from protracted and intermittent growth over an extended geological period after initial sediment deposition (Radtke et al., 1988).

Quaternary scientists have adopted two "end member" approaches to the problem of applicability. The "*daters*" deliberately seek out deposits which are ideal for a particular method, and which have potential Quaternary significance, while the "*stratigraphers*" try to find dateable materials in the Quaternary sediments which are their starting point. It is a fundamental problem of terrestrial Quaternary geology that studies by "daters" provide our quantitative Quaternary chronology, while "stratigraphers" provide the bulk of the palaeoenvironmental information. Figure 1.1 provides a summary matrix relating the reliability of dating methods to the types of available geological materials. The reader should consult specific chapters to determine the extent and nature of limitations on the reliability of each method for specific materials.

Time Range

Most dating methods have both a minimum and maximum determinable age, fixed by the physics of the clock and the sensitivity of the measurement technique used. Table 1.3 presents the effective time range of the dating methods available to the Quaternary scientist, enabling a suitable technique to be selected for the expected age and dateable materials present in the deposits of interest. While in principle it is useful to know that particular deposits are beyond the age range of a dating technique, there is often a very low precision (or reliability) of age estimates near the upper (and lower) age limits, and spurious finite ages may be obtained; the large numbers of ^{14}C ages of about 35 to 40 ka reported are a case in point (as illustrated in Table 1.1). In many cases these probably result from trace contamination with modern carbon, but are often interpreted as valid age estimates, as in the example of the mid-Wisconsin age for high sea-stand deposits reported by Finkelstein and Kearney (1988) and discussed by Colman et al. (1989).

Table 1.3. *General effective range of application of different dating techniques (α = alpha spectrometric analysis, MSU = mass spectrometric analysis). Lower limits depend on level of analyte in sample and analytical technique; upper limits depend on analytical technique and stability of samples. Brackets indicate extensions to range under particularly favourable conditions.*

Method		Age Range (ka)
Radiocarbon		0.3 - 45
Potassium-argon		(1) 30 - <20000
Uranium series	$^{234}U/^{238}U$ (α)	100 - 1500
	$^{230}Th/^{234}U$ (α)	3 - 350
	$^{230}Th/^{234}U$ (MSU)	0.05 - 500
	$^{231}Pa/^{235}U$ (α)	5 - 150
Helium-uranium		100 - >2000?
Uranium trend		10 - 1000?
Thermoluminescence		0.1 - 100 (500)
Electron Spin Resonance		(1) 5 - 900
Fission track		(0.1) 50 - >2000
Palaeomagnetism		0.05 - >2000
Orbital tuning		1 - >2000

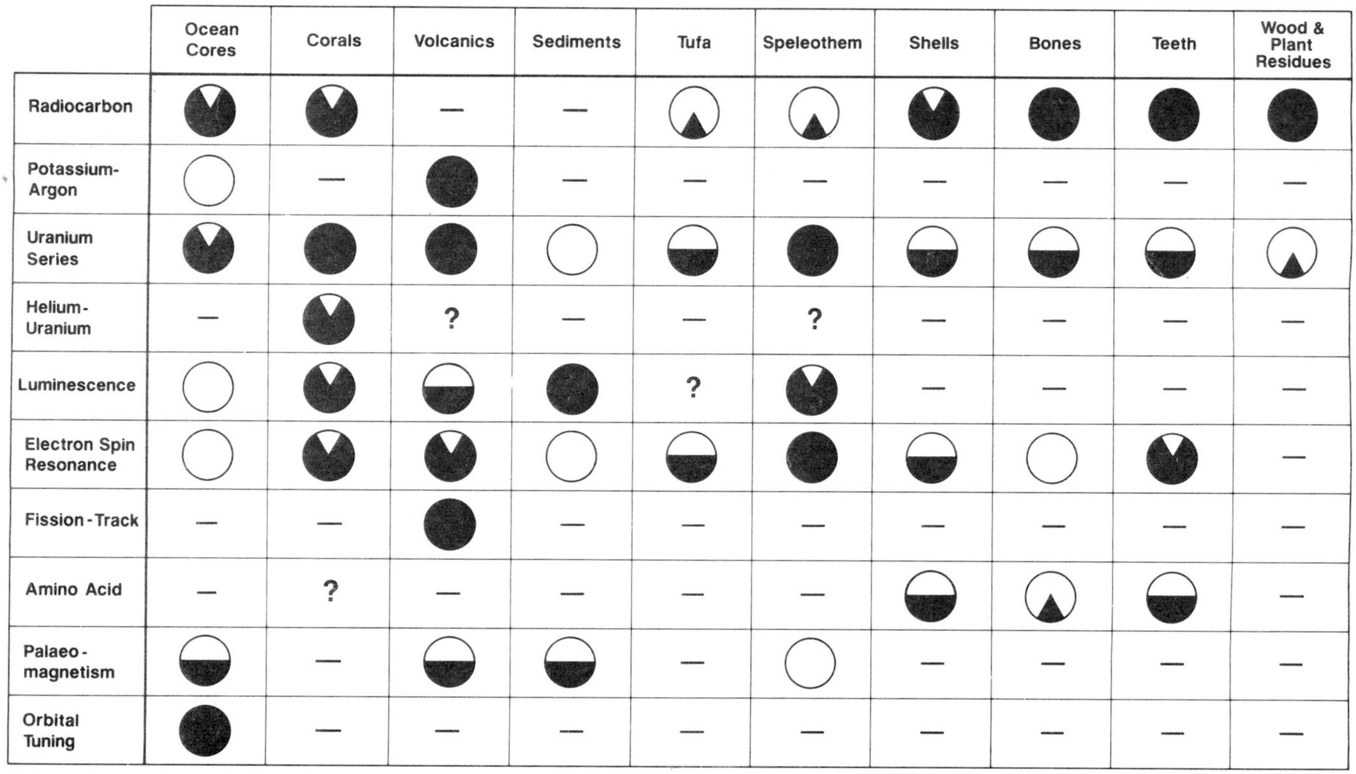

	Ocean Cores	Corals	Volcanics	Sediments	Tufa	Speleothem	Shells	Bones	Teeth	Wood & Plant Residues
Radiocarbon										
Potassium-Argon										
Uranium Series										
Helium-Uranium		?	?		?	?				
Luminescence										
Electron Spin Resonance										
Fission-Track										
Amino Acid		?								
Palaeo-magnetism										
Orbital Tuning										

Figure 1.1 *Applicability of dating methods in this text to different geological materials. Reliability is indicated by proportion of dark shading. Question marks indicate a lack of information on applicability, dashes that the method is unsuitable for the particular material. (Based on Aitken, 1990.)*

Precision/Accuracy

There are many sources of error in obtaining age estimates; some of these are *systematic* (considered below), while others are essentially *random* and control the reproducibility of a particular age estimate. In some cases these uncertainties may be routinely estimated for each date, as is the case for the counting of decay products or atoms in isotopic dating techniques. In others, such as amino acid determinations, they may only be derived from repeated determinations performed on each sample. The precision obtainable by a particular dating technique controls the events which are resolvable, and is often directly related to the sophistication of the measurement system available. Thus alpha spectrometic measurements of stage 5e high sea-levels with a typical precision of 5-10% ($\pm$ 1 standard deviation) are not capable of differentiating the age of possible multiple peaks unless these differ in age by more than 10 ka (Kaufman, 1986). However, this would be readily achieved using the mass-spectrometric analysis techniques now becoming available which have ($\pm$ 2 standard deviation) precisions of 124 $\pm$ 1 ka (Edwards et al., 1987).

Other errors may be systematic resulting from differences in calibration, sample preparation and analytical techniques between individual laboratories. Interlaboratory calibration schemes attempt to assess, control and eliminate systematic differences between laboratories. Frequently, inter-laboratory variance is found to be significantly greater than within-laboratory error, as was the case with Phase 1 of the Uranium Series Inter-laboratory Comparison Project (Harmon et al., 1979). Subsequently, the collaborating laboratories identified potential sources of error, agreed on standardised ways to calculate and express results (for instance the half-life to be used) and distributed a common spike, which reduced inter-laboratory variance significantly (Ivanovich et al., 1984). Despite such schemes which have been run for many of the methods (discussed further in subsequent chapters), systematic differences between laboratories may persist.

Environmental and geological factors may also cause systematic differences between individual samples or sample sites defining the same time event, and must be adequately assessed by multiple sampling. Thus, for instance, molluscs from an individual outcrop may give higher amino acid racemization ratios because they have remained unburied and exposed to solar insolation, a systematic difference of about 1.5 °C causing a difference as large as 25-30% in the effective age (McCoy, 1987). They may also record the aggradational phase of the high-sea level event represented, whereas others represent the recession. In practice the low temporal precision of amino-acid racemization techniques would not discriminate this difference, although it might be reflected in precise uranium series ages on corals (Ku et al., 1990).

EXPRESSION OF AGE ESTIMATES

The term ''date'' is firmly entrenched in the literature, but strictly defined this refers to a specific point in time, and should only be used for sidereal dating methods

(Colman et al., 1987). Most "dates" are best described as "age estimates" or "ages" defined as an interval of time measured back from the present. The term "age estimate" indicates there are inherent uncertainties associated with the determination, such that there may be differences between the quoted age and the real age, something often ignored in the Quaternary user community. The SI-derived abbreviations ka and Ma (thousand and million years) should be used for ages; measurement from the present is implicit and "before present" or "ago" should not be included in these abbreviations. In the case of radiocarbon dating, the internationally agreed form is "yr BP", indicating that the age is in radiocarbon years calculated from 1950 AD using the original half-life of 5568 ± 30 years. Conversion to the more accurately defined half-life (5730 ± 30 years), which has subsequently been determined can be made by multiplying by 1.03. In addition radiocarbon ages may be corrected to yield calendrical years using a calibration curve (see below) as indicated by the form "cal yr BP" (International Radiocarbon Conference, 1985). Very recently this calibration curve has been extended by calibration with high precision mass-spectrometric uranium series determinations on corals form a Barbados core (Bard et al., 1990).

The uncertainties quoted for numerical age estimates are normally expressed as ± 1 standard deviation, indicating that there is a 68% probability that the true age lies within this range (assuming that no other factors affect the relation between estimated and true age). More recently, with the advent of high precision mass-spectrometric methods, two standard deviation uncertainties have been quoted (95% probability), which are a rather more satisfactory basis for intercomparisons. There are often significant differences in the sources of error incorporated in the quoted uncertainties for age estimates between individual laboratories.

When several age estimates are available from multiple analyses for individual samples or coeval samples, they may be combined once they have been rigourously statistically screened for outliers. The mean age (or error weighted mean) may then be calculated, together with an estimate of the combined uncertainty. Details are given in Ward and Wilson (1978). It is also possible to combine numerical age estimates to produce probability density functions (Gordon and Smart, 1984) which are superior to histogram techniques for graphical representation because they do not suffer from class boundary effects, and incorporate the quoted uncertainties.

REFERENCES

Aitken, M.J. 1990. *Science-based Dating in Archaeology*, Longman, London, pp. 274.

Baillie, M.G.L. 1982. *Tree-ring Dating and Archaeology*, Croom Helm, London, pp. 274.

Bard, E., Hamelin, B., Fairbanks, R. G. and Zindler, A. 1990. Calibration of the ^{14}C timescale over the past 30 ka, using mass spectrometric U-Th ages from Barbados corals. *Nature*, **345**, 405-409.

Berger, A. 1980. The Milankovitch astronomical theory of paleoclimates. A modern review. *Vistas in Astronomy*, **24**, 103-122.

Berggren, W.A., Burckle, L.H., Cita, M.B., Cooke, H.B.S. Funnell, B.M., Gartner, S., Hays, J.D., Kennett, J.P., Opdyke, N.D., Pastouret, L., Shackleton, N.J. and Takayanagi, Y. 1990. Towards a Quaternary time scale. *Quaternary Research*, **13**, 277-302.

Bowen, D.Q., Hughes, S., Sykes, G.A. and Miller, G.H. 1989. Land-sea correlations in the Pleistocene based on isoleucine epimerization in non-marine molluscs. *Nature*, **340**, 49-51.

Bridgeland, D.R., Gibbard, P.L., Harding, P., Kemp, R.A. and Southgate, G. 1985. New information and results from recent excavations at Barnfield Pit, Swanscombe. *Quaternary Newsletter*, **46**, 25-39.

Brookes, I.A. 1985. Dating methods of Pleistocene deposits and their problems: VIII Weathering. *Geoscience Canada Reprint Series*, **2**, 61-71.

Colman, S.M., Mixon, R.B., Rubin, M., Bloom, A.L., Johnson, G.H. and Toscano, M.A. 1989. Comments and reply on 'Late Pleistocene barrier-island sequence along the southern Delmarva Peninsula: Implications for middle Wisconsin sea levels'. *Geology*, **17**, 84-87.

Colman, S.V., Pierce, K.L. and Birkeland, P.W. 1987. Suggested terminology for Quaternary dating methods. *Quaternary Research*, **28**, 314-319.

Currant, A. 1989. The Quaternary origins of the modern British mammal funa. *Biological Journal of the Linean Society*, **38**, 23-30.

Currant, A.P., Stringer, C.B. and Collcutt, S.N. 1984. Bacon Hole Cave. In *Field Cuide to Wales, Gower, Preseli and Forest Fawr*, (eds Bowen, D.Q. and Henry, A.), Quaternary Research Association, Aberystwyth, 38-44.

Dunnell, R.C. and Readhead, M.L. 1988. The relation of dating and chronology: comments on Chatters and Hoover (1986) and Butler and Stein (1988). *Quaternary Research*, **30**, 232-233.

Edwards, R.L., Chen, J.H., Ku, T.L. and Wasserburg, G.J. 1987. Precise timing of the last interglacial period from mass-spectrometric determination of thorium —230 in corals. *Science*, **236**, 1547-1553.

Eyles, N. and McCabe, A.M. 1989. The late Devensian (<72 000 BP) Irish Sea Basin: the sedimentary record of a collapsed ice sheet margin. *Quaternary Science Reviews*, **8**, 307-351.

Finkelstein, K. and Kearney, M.S. 1988. Late Pleistocene barrier island sequence along the southern Delmarva Perinsula: Implications for middle Wisconsin sea levels. *Geology*, **16**, 41-45.

Frenzel, B. 1989. Theoretische Grund probleme der botanischen Biostratigraphie des Eiszeitalters. In *Quaternary Type Sections, Imagination or Reality?* (eds Rose, J. and Schlüchter, C.), Balkema, Rotterdam, 33-39.

Girling, M. 1980. Late Pleistocene Insect faunas from two sites. Unpublished Ph. D. thesis, University of Birmingham.

Gordon, D. and Smart, P.L. 1984. "Comments on Speleothems, travertines and palaeoclimates" by G.J. Hennig, R. Grun and K. Brunnacker. *Quaternary Research*, **22**, 144-147.

Grün, R., Chadam, J. and Schwarcz, H.P. 1988. ESR dating of tooth enamel: coupled correction for U uptake and U series disequilibrium. *Nuclear Tracks*, **14**, 237-241.

Harmon, R.S., Ku, T.L., Mathews, R.K. and Smart, P.L. 1979. Limits of uranium series analysis: Phase 1 results of the Uranium Series Intercomparison Project. *Geology*, **7**, 405-409.

Hays, J.D., Imbrie, J. and Shackleton, N.J. 1976. Variations in the earth's orbit: pacemaker of the ice ages. *Science*, **194**, 1121-1132.

Holyoak, D.T. and Preece, R.C. 1985. Late Pleistocene interglacial deposits at Tattershall, Lincolnshire. *Philosophical Transactions of the Royal Society of London*, **B311**, 193-236.

International Radiocarbon Conference. 1985. *Radiocarbon*, 28-2B.

Ivanovich, M., Ku, T.L., Harmon, R.S. and Smart, P.L. 1984. Uranium series intercomparison project (USIP). *Nuclear Instruments and Methods in Physics Research*, **223**, 466-471.

Ivanovich, M. and Holyoak, D. T. 1982. The $^{230}Th/^{234}U$ disequilibrium dating method applied to shells of non marine Mollusca from British Pleistocene deposits. *Proceedings of the 5th International Conference on Geochronology, Cosmochronology and Isotope Geology*, Nikko Park (Japan), 168-169.

Jansen, E. 1989. The use of stable oxygen and carbon isotope stratigraphy as a dating tool. *Quaternary International*, **1**, 151-166.

Kaufman, A. 1986. The distribution of $^{230}Th/^{234}U$ ages in corals and the number of last interglacial high sea-stands. *Quaternary Research*, **25**, 55-62.

Kominz, M.A., Heath, G.R., Ku, T.L. and Pisias, N.G. 1979. Brunhes time scales and the interpretation of climatic change. *Earth and Planetary Science Letters*, **45**, 394-410.

Ku, T.L., Ivanovich, M. and Luo, S. 1990. U series dating of last interglacial high sea level stands: Barbados revisited. *Quaternary Research*, **33**, 129-147.

Martinson, D.G., Pisias, N.G., Hays, J.D., Imbrie, T.C. and Shackleton, N.J. 1987. Age dating and the orbital theory of ice ages: Development of a high-resolution 0 to 300,000 year chronostratigraphy. *Quaternary Research*, **27**, 1-29.

McCoy, W.D. 1987. The precision of amino acid geochronology and paleothermometry. *Quaternary Science Reviews*, **6**, 43-54.

Mejdahl, V. 1988. Long term stability of the TL signal in alkali feldspars. *Quaternary Science Reviews*, **7**, 357-360.

Michels, J.W. 1986. Obsidian hydration dating. *Endeavour (New Series)*, **10**, 97-100.

Pisias, N.G., Martinson, D.G., Moore, T.C., Shackleton, N.J., Prell, W., Hays, J. and Boden, G. 1984. High resolution stratigraphic correlation of benthic oxygen isotope records spanning the last 300,000 years. *Marine Geology*, **56**, 119-136.

Radtke, U., Bruckner, H., Mangini, A. and Hausmann, R. 1988. Problems encountered with absolute dating (U. Series, ESR) of Spanish calcretes. *Quaternary Science Reviews*, **7**, 439-445.

Richmond, G.M. and Fullerton, D.S. 1986. Introduction to Quaternary glaciations in the United States of America. *Quaternary Science Reviews*, **5**, 3-10.

Rose, J. 1989. Stadial type sections in the British Quaternary. In *Quaternary Type Sections, Imagination or Reality?* (eds Rose, J. and Schlüchter, C.), Balkema, Rotterdam, 33-39.

Shackleton, N.J. and Opdyke, N.D. 1973. Oxygen isotope and palaeomagnetic stratigraphy of equatorial Pacific core V28-238: Oxygen isotope temperatures and ice volumes on a 10^5 year and 10^6 year scale. *Quaternary Research*, **3**, 39-55.

Shackleton, N.J. 1989. The Plio-Pleistocene ocean: Stable isotope history. In *Quaternary Type Sections: Imagination or Reality?*, (eds Rose, J. and Schluchter, C.), Balkema, Rotterdam, 11-24.

Shotton, F.W. 1983. United Kingdom contribution to the International Geological Correlation Programme; Project 24, Quaternary Glaciations of the Northern Hemisphere. *Quaternary Newsletter*, **39**, 19-25.

Smith, B.W., Smart, P.L. amd Symons, M.C.R. 1985. ESR signals in a variety of speleothem calcites and their suitability for dating. *Nuclear Tracks*, **10**, 837-844.

Strömberg, B. 1985. Revision of the late glacial Swedish varve chronology. *Boreas*, **14**, 101-105.

Stuart, A.J. 1982. *Pleistocene Vertebrates in the British Isles*, Longman, London, pp. 212.

Ward, G. K. and Wilson, S. R. 1978. Procedures for comparing and combining radiocarbon dates. *Archaeometry*, **20**, 19-32.

West R.G. 1963. Problems of the British Quaternary. *Proceedings of the Geologists Association*, **74**, 147-186.

West, R.G. 1984. Interglacial, interstadial and oxygen isotope stages. *Dissertationes Botanicae*, **72**, 345-357.

Chapter 2

RADIOCARBON DATING

J. R. Pilcher

This chapter is written for those who are interested in radiocarbon dating as a tool that might be used to further their Quaternary research. By way of introduction, the briefest explanation of the method will be given in so far as it affects the user. Then consideration will be given to selection of samples, choice of a laboratory and finally, interpretation of results.

The general references given at the end provide a full account of the theory of the method.

THEORY

The carbon-14 (^{14}C) isotope (radiocarbon) is formed continuously in the upper atmosphere by the action of cosmic rays. The ^{14}C atoms combine with oxygen to form carbon dioxide which enters the Earth's carbon cycle. As ^{14}C is radioactive, there is a continual decay of ^{14}C which is balanced in a dynamic equilibrium by its production. If we make the assumption that the production rate is constant then the amount of ^{14}C in the atmosphere will remain constant. As the carbon dioxide is continually exchanged with the biosphere, this will also be in equilibrium. Thus all living things will contain the same proportion of ^{14}C while they remain alive. Once an organism dies, the equilibrium is lost as the radiocarbon will continue to decay while exchange with atmospheric carbon will cease. The rate of decay follows a negative exponential curve and the point at which the amount of remaining ^{14}C falls below the limits of measurement provides the upper limit of about 50 000 years BP for the dating method. Further details are given in Libby (1965) and more recently in Mook and Waterbolk (1985).

Radiocarbon dating depends on knowing:

1) how much radiocarbon would have been in the organism when alive,
2) the decay rate,
3) how much radiocarbon remains.

These will be examined in turn.

The Radiocarbon Activity of Living Things

This is assumed to be constant and in equilibrium with the atmosphere. Both these assumptions have only limited validity. As will be shown later, the radiocarbon activity in the atmosphere is not a constant. More serious for the palaeoecologist is the fact that not all living things are in equilibrium with atmospheric carbon dioxide. Aquatic plants, and organisms dependent on them, are capable of using dissolved carbon dioxide or bicarbonates in the water that are derived from old carbonate rock and thus not in equilibrium with the atmosphere. This is known as the "hard-water" effect. If the samples derive from a lake sediment, it is important to know the present, and if possible the past, carbonate input to the lake. The radiocarbon laboratory should be informed if a hard-water effect is suspected. In a limestone area, the hard-water effect typically may add between 200 and 1200 years to the apparent age of samples (Peglar et al., 1989). Series of core samples taken from bogs frequently extend down into lake muds from the pre-bog history of the area which may have been subject to a hard-water effect even though the peat itself will not be affected.

Marine organisms will have apparent ages some 400 years older than their true ages due to the fact that the ocean surface waters are mixed with "old" water from deep layers of the ocean which contain less radiocarbon. The ^{14}C activity of the surface waters is about 5% less than that of the atmosphere (for discussion of this "reservoir effect" see Stuiver and Polach, 1977 and Stuiver et al., 1986). Brackish water organisms will suffer from this effect to a variable extent (possibly combined with a hard-water effect) and are therefore best avoided. Certain plants such as *Cladium* that are rooted in organic sediments may take up a significant proportion of their carbon from the old sediments in which they are rooted, giving dates some centuries too old (Olsson, 1986). Land plants are free from these problems.

A further possible source of error arises from the fractionation of carbon isotopes by plants. Different groups of plants selectively absorb carbon isotopes in slightly different ratios from the environment, so they do not have exactly the same carbon isotope ratio as atmospheric carbon dioxide. Any fractionation that affects the amount of ^{14}C also affects the amount of the much more abundant carbon-13 (^{13}C) which can be measured by a mass spectrometer. The radiocarbon laboratory should routinely measure the ^{12}C/^{13}C ratio in each sample and apply a correction to the radiocarbon concentration to allow for fractionation. It would help the radiocarbon laboratory if the user were able to provide an identification of the major components of the sample, as typical fractionation ratios for different groups of plants are known. Because of the great variation in composition of peat and lake sediments it is important that a ^{13}C correction be applied to the radiocarbon dating of such materials, and the radiocarbon laboratory should be made aware that this correction is required.

The Decay Rate

The decay of a radioisotope is a nuclear process that is unaffected by normal physical conditions. The rate of decay is expressed in terms of a fixed constant, the half-life; the time taken for half of the isotope to decay. By international agreement at the Fifth Radiocarbon Dating Conference in 1962, the half-life of ^{14}C used for radiocarbon date calculation is 5570 ± 30 years, confirmed in 1986 (Mook, 1986).

That this is perhaps not the best estimate is normally of little importance for radiocarbon users because all dates are calculated using the same half-life and are therefore all comparable. It is only in the fields of archaeology and history, where the radiocarbon dates are directly compared with historically recorded dates, that a conflict might occur. However, for this recent time-span, calibration provides a correction that overrides all consideration of half-lives. The calibration provides a direct conversion from radiocarbon activity to calendrical date range. The difference between the officially accepted half-life (known as the Libby half-life) and the best estimate (5730 ± 40 years, Godwin, 1962) is 3%. For ages beyond the present calibration limit of about 10 000 years, the effect of a 3% change in half-life is normally insignificant compared with other sources of error. Until very recently other dating methods were not reaching this level of accuracy. However, the new Thermal Ionisation Mass Spectrometric (TIMS) uranium series dates promise an accuracy comparable to radiocarbon dating (Arnold et al., in press).

Measurement of the ^{14}C Activity in a Sample

There are two main reasons why radiocarbon measurement is difficult and hence expensive. The first is that ^{14}C radioactivity is low energy and inherently difficult to measure, and the second is that the amounts are incredibly small. The natural level of radioactive carbon in the atmosphere is about 1 part in 10^{12}. This explains the complexity of the measurement process and the high cost of an individual measurement.

There are a number of different ways in which the radiocarbon in a sample may be measured, the method used depending to a certain extent on the size of the sample. Two basic methods are used to detect the radioactivity of the ^{14}C; one handles the sample as a gas and the other as a liquid. The former is gas proportional counting and the latter is liquid scintillation counting. Both have advantages and disadvantages and they have changed in popularity over recent years. The recurrent costs of gas counting are perhaps slightly lower, but the equipment for scintillation counting is available ''off the shelf''. From the user's point of view, the method of radioactive measurement is not important. What is important is the size of sample that the system can handle and the potential accuracy that it can offer.

Routine Laboratories Most radiocarbon laboratories using either scintillation counting or gas counting work with an ideal sample size of 1 to 10 g of sample carbon. These laboratories can normally achieve a precision of ± 60 to ± 120 years on a sample of 5000 years, giving a 95% confidence band for the measurement of between about 250 and 500 years. These laboratories are now usually known as ''routine'' radiocarbon laboratories. Many have objected to this term as it might imply poor quality. However, the term was coined only to distinguish the main bulk of radiocarbon laboratories from the small sample laboratories, the ''high precision'' laboratories and the AMS laboratories discussed below.

Small Sample Laboratories There are at present about 9 institutions that have developed a facility for handling very small samples (10 to 100 mg of carbon) using radioactive measurement systems (Otlet et al., 1986). Most of these systems use a number of small gas counters that can operate continuously for very long periods of time. The smaller the sample, the longer the measurement time that is required in order to achieve measurement with the same precision. It is only in the last few years that electronics have been stable enough to allow the long measurement times required for milligram sized samples. As the AMS system described below becomes more widely available, it is likely that the small sample radioactive counting systems will be phased out.

High Precision Laboratories There are still very few laboratories that can offer high precision measurement. At the time of writing there are only five or six high precision laboratories in the world and these are basically those that have been involved in the International Radiocarbon Calibration Programme (see the special calibration volume of Radiocarbon, vol 28). High precision dating is possible only if the samples are relatively large — perhaps 5-20 g of carbon which can be a serious limitation to palaeoecological studies. Although the measurement theory is more or less the same in these laboratories as in normal laboratories, the quality control of the measurement system and the corrections applied to the samples are of a much higher order and this is reflected in the cost per sample. Each of the high precision laboratories has been involved in calibration studies and this has allowed the most stringent interlaboratory comparisons to be made (Pearson and Stuiver, 1986). For example, comparison of 214 duplicate analyses between the Seattle and Belfast laboratories showed a difference of 0.6 ± 1.6 years. Typical precisions from these laboratories are one standard deviation of less than 20 years. This gives a 95% confidence interval of 80 years and, in many cases, an age range after calibration of only about 100 years. Whether the extra cost of a high precision measurement is justified in particular cases will be examined later.

AMS Laboratories The third type of measurement system is totally different in concept. This is the Accelerator Mass Spectrometry method in which the ^{14}C atoms are separated by their difference in mass rather than by their radioactivity. The equipment is hugely complex and expensive (typically about £1 000 000, compared with a gas counting system for about £150 000). Although the capital cost of the AMS systems is very high, each sample can theoretically be measured in about 15 minutes, compared with between 1 and several days for radioactive counting methods. Further, the cost per sample is coming down to the same order as radioactive measurements. At the moment, the large number of replicates and known-age check samples that are needed, reduce the output of dates from a typical laboratory to 10 to 15 per week (Batten et al., 1986). The great virtue of this method is that it can measure very small samples — from as little as 0.2 mg. The ideal sample size is about 5 mg, to allow for convenience of preparation chemistry. At present there are about 30 AMS laboratories, although not all are measuring ^{14}C. These laboratories can typically quote reproducibility of 0.3%, but due to problems of bias, contamination and instability, their limit of accuracy is still about 1%. At present and for the foreseeable future, the AMS laboratories are not capable of high accuracy. The best reproducible accuracy is likely to remain about 1%. This is equivalent to a one standard deviation precision of ± 80 years on a one half-life sample. The combination of high accuracy and very small sample size is still not possible.

This level of accuracy from AMS may seem a limitation, but in some situations the advantages of small sample size override the loss of accuracy. For example, the problem of the hard-water effect mentioned above can sometimes be overcome in the dating of sediment cores by extracting land plant macrofossils from the sediment and dating these by AMS. Andree et al. (1986) describe the dating of birch seeds extracted from calcite-rich gyttga sediments and their dating by AMS. Another interesting approach is described by Brown et al. (1989) who have extracted *Picea* pollen from a sediment and dated it by AMS, thus dating directly the events in the pollen record. Thus AMS dating has opened up many new possibilities because of its small sample size capability.

SAMPLE SELECTION

There are several considerations in sample selection. Provided that the material contains biogenic carbon that was part of the natural carbon cycle within the last 50 ka, it is potentially amenable to carbon dating. The method will provide an estimate of the length of time since the material dated was alive. Whether this is what the submittor really wants to know must be determined before the sample is dated. Many potential samples such as sediments are heterogeneous and contain biological materials of different ages. The selection of a sample component from this mixture will depend on what questions are being asked. If the questions are concerned with time differences and rates of change then consideration must be given to the precision of measurement that would be needed to answer the questions. There is no point in expecting routine radiocarbon dates with a real age range of 500 years to answer questions relating to the migration of a plant species that may have taken only one or two centuries.

The greatest source of confusion in the interpretation of radiocarbon dates comes from poor sample selection. Many deposits are heterogeneous. Thus for example peats normally consist of a mixture of short lived components (mosses), remains of older components such as *Calluna* stems and the roots of younger plants that will have penetrated the sediment from above, together with mobile soluble materials. For example a whole sample of peat buried beneath the bank of an archaeological site at Pubble (Smith et al., 1972a) gave a date of 3220 ± 65 yr BP (UB-195A), intermediate between that of its fine particulate fraction (3835± 80 yr BP, UB-195F) and the alkali soluble humic fraction (2850 ± 60 yr BP, UB-195C). The humic acids from this sandy site were obviously very mobile with an apparent age about 1000 years later than the particulate material in the same matrix. If deposits are heterogeneous, there is little point in dating the material more accurately than the likely age range of the components, unless there is a clear association between a particular component and the event being dated. Thus in the case of a deposit upon which a pollen analysis has been performed, and which contained twigs, the twigs might seem to provide the ideal short-lived sample to date the events shown by pollen analysis. However, it is possible for the twigs to have been derived from an earlier deposit. In this case, AMS dating of the pollen fraction might provide the only reliable date. In a Late-glacial mud sample from Sluggan (Smith et al., 1972b) for instance, the fine particulate fraction was considered to give the best age estimate as this fraction contained the material of pollen size (Table 2.1). The coarse fraction was younger, as was the humic acid fraction, although in this case the whole sample age was similar to the fine fraction age.

Table 2.1 *Radiocarbon dating of a late-glacial mud sample from Sluggan, Northern Ireland (Smith et al., 1972b).*

Sample		Date (yr BP)
UB-229A	Whole sample	12 360 ± 165
UB-299C	Humic acids	11 225 ± 160
UB-299D	Particulate matter >250 μm	12 060 ± 125
UB-299F	Particulate matter <250 μm	12 470 ± 125

Archaeological sites may pose special problems because of the long persistence of charcoal, a favourite archaeological sample. At Goodland Neolithic site, for example, a sample of fine charcoal in a peaty matrix with roots gave an age of 4575 ± 135 yr BP (UB-320E), compared with 1710 ± 65 yr BP (UB-320C) for the humic acid and 885 ± 80 yr BP for rootlets.

At archaeological sites there is also the possibility of charcoal of many ages being incorporated in the same deposit. A classic example of this problem is provided by the dating of Ballymacdermot court cairn (Smith et al., 1974), from which numerous charcoal samples were taken for dating from what appeared to be sealed contexts (Table 2.2). It might be tempting to assume that Q-694 was the ''correct'' date because it fits most closely with preconceived ideas about the age of court cairns, but there is no way of knowing whether there was still some admixture of different age charcoal in this sample. Notice how UB-702 has a radiocarbon age nearly 2000 yrs before court cairn construction, indicating that at this site there is the possibility of admixtures of both older and younger charcoal. In fact it is not impossible that there was no Neolithic charcoal on the site; the ''Neolithic'' age of some samples being a mixture of Mesolithic and Viking charcoal! Also, consider the implications of the order in which the samples were submitted to the laboratory. The first sample gave a Bronze Age date, so three more samples were submitted. By chance the first two of these gave ''Neolithic'' dates. Had the measurements stopped there, the site might have been considered to be satisfactorily dated. Two of the results fitted with the preconceived ideas about court cairn dating and there was no reason to question them. However the third sample of the batch (UB-693) was dated and gave an AD result. This threw all the dating into question and a further 6 samples were submitted which only served to muddy the waters more.

Table 2.2 *Radiocarbon dates from charcoal samples from Ballymacdermot Court Cairn (Smith et al., 1974).*

Sample		Date (yr BP)
UB-207	below stones blocking forecourt	3660 ± 60
UB-693	brown earth with Neolithic pottery	1180 ± 75
UB-694	brown earth with Neolithic pottery	4830 ± 95
UB-695	brown earth layer in chamber 3	4295 ± 90
UB-697	sealed by large stone in chamber 3	940 ± 75
UB-698	below granite blocks in chamber 1	4715 ± 190
UB-700	charcoal on pre-cairn soil	1025 ± 40
UB-702	charcoal between lowest cairn stones	6925 ± 95
UB-703	charcoal between lowest cairn stones	975 ± 70
UB-705	below stones blocking forecourt	3515 ± 85

Another problem of relevance to both archaeological and palaeoecological dating relates to the age of the sample at the time of the event one wishes to date. The carbon in wood is fixed at the time each annual ring is formed, thus the centre of an old tree may already be several hundred years old when the tree dies. If wood from such a tree is burnt to charcoal and incorporated into a deposit its radiocarbon age will pre-date the event (the fire) one wishes to date. For a mixed charcoal sample the age range may be about 1-200 years, so that the resolution of the sample, even before measurement at the radiocarbon laboratory may be ± 100 years.

SELECTION OF A RADIOCARBON LABORATORY

Before a sample is submitted to a radiocarbon laboratory, a clear question must have been established, to which the sample is capable of providing an answer.

The first decision in laboratory selection involves a choice between the analytical methods outlined above. This decision depends on the expected sample age, available

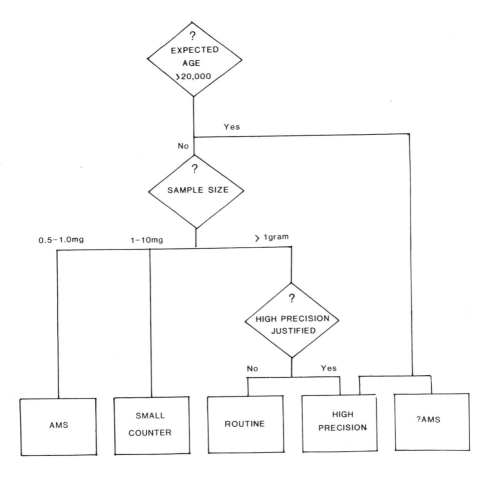

Figure 2.1 *Suggestions for decision-making stages in the selection of an appropriate laboratory for radiocarbon dating. (Age is given in years BP.)*

sample size and the precision required to answer the scientific questions posed (Figure 2.1). Older samples (> 20 ka) are suitable for high precision or possibly AMS laboratories as these are the only laboratories that are likely to be working to the necessary high standards of preparative chemistry as well as the necessary measurement precision to measure very small amounts of ^{14}C. For younger material, small samples require either AMS or small counter analysis, while for samples of more than 1 g carbon there is the option of high precision measurement, if the sample integrity justifies this.

The second consideration in laboratory selection is best summed up by *Caveat emptor*. Not all radiocarbon laboratories are equally good. Results of an interlaboratory intercomparison nearly ten years ago showed a serious underestimation of errors (International Study Group, 1982). Unfortunately a more extensive intercomparison completed in 1989, involving over 50 laboratories, showed that both serious biases and the underestimation of errors is still prevalent (a special issue of Radiocarbon in 1991 will be devoted to this). The results of such tests have so far been published without identifying the individual laboratories, although individual laboratories know their own results and should be willing to discuss them. More important for the future is that the recent poor results mentioned above have prompted the establishment of a quality assurance protocol for radiocarbon laboratories and the availability of known age test samples that will be provided by the International Atomic Energy Authority in Vienna. Beware laboratories that have not agreed to abide by the new protocol or will not discuss the results of the international intercomparisons. Radiocarbon dating is an expensive service and inaccurate dates are worse than no dates.

INTERPRETING AND USING RADIOCARBON DATES

The decision has been taken, the sample sent off, the forms filled in and in due course (a 6 month delay is not unusual) a date comes back. In the past the notion has been general that a date can be "accepted" or "rejected." To quote from Coope, 1986, "Acceptability of a radiocarbon date rests, to a large extent, on the expectations of the researcher who submitted the sample or one who wishes to make use of the information." This really is a most damning indictment of both radiocarbon laboratories and radiocarbon users. It implies that only those results that fit preconceived ideas would be accepted and that those that don't fit are "wrong," due to some error by the laboratory. This has been a widely held view. If the laboratory has been chosen wisely, then the result must be accepted as a reliable estimate of the mean age of the organic material dated. The date must be interpreted, but cannot be "rejected." To suppress (i.e. not publish) dates that don't fit preconceived ideas is scientific dishonesty.

What Does a Radiocarbon Date Mean?

Radiocarbon dates are quoted as x years $\pm$ y before present (BP), BP being defined as before 1950 AD. The $\pm$ y is a one standard deviation estimate of the error of measurement which may include two components; errors associated with radioactive measurement and an estimate of errors of reproducibility in the laboratory. If only the former is included, the International Study Group (1982) suggest the following error multipliers to estimate the total errors:

If the quoted error is < 20 multiply by 1.3
If the quoted error is 20-80 multiply by 2.0
If the quoted error is > 80 multiply by 1.0

This rule-of-thumb is unsatisfactory, particularly for dates with standard deviations in the 75-85 range. A number of authors have strongly criticised this approach, not because they believe the view is pessimistic but because they consider that the errors the International Study Group are attempting to allow for are non-random and not amenable to such a simplistic approach (Pearson and Stuiver, 1986). It is thus more satisfactory to obtain from the radiocarbon laboratory its best estimate of additional error, based on interlaboratory tests and on quality control replication, and add this value to each sample measurement.

It is important to remember that the precision of a radiocarbon date is only quoted to ± 1 standard deviation. In discussing and interpreting the results it is better to use two standard deviations which gives about 95% probability that the true value lies in the range. Thus if a measurement is given as 8000 ± 80 and the error is increased by 40 years to allow for possible laboratory bias to ± 120, and then doubled, then there is a 95% probability that the date lies between 7760 and 8240 yrs BP, a range of just under 500 years. To try to interpret the dating information closer than this is wishful thinking. A clear understanding of this is necessary at the project design stage. For example, Sutherland, (1986) states in the context of Late-glacial environments "further accurate dating is necessary to establish possible leads or lags between the terrestrial and marine environmental changes..." Unless these leads or lags were likely to be greater than about 500 years, a conventional radiocarbon dating approach would not solve the problem. In order to resolve either small time differences or short durations, high precision dating is essential.

What About Calibration, Won't this Make the Result More Accurate?

The short answer is no. The longer answer requires an explanation of the calibration of radiocarbon dates. Earlier, it was assumed that a dynamic equilibrium was maintained because a constant production of radiocarbon was balanced by a constant decay. The constancy of production is only an approximation. There have been fluctuations in ^{14}C production due to variations in cosmic rays reaching the Earth. There is no theoretical way of predicting these variations, so the only way of providing a correction factor for the variations in the past is to make an empirical calibration curve. This has been done by using the calendrical accuracy of dendrochronology to provide the standard against which the radiocarbon method can be corrected. Known-age samples of wood have been measured at very high accuracy by high

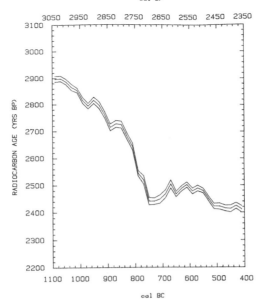

Figure 2.2 *A portion of the calibration curve approved by the International Calibration Committee covering 1100 to 400 Cal yr BC from Pearson and Stuiver (1986). The figure shows some of the serious radiocarbon fluctuations that occurred in the first millennium BC.*

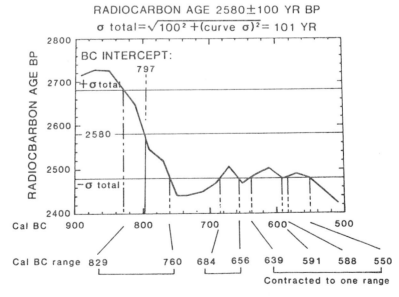

Figure 2.3 *A demonstration of the calibration of a radiocarbon date of 2580 ± 100 to give possible calendrical age ranges of 829-760, 684-656 and 639 to 550 Cal yr BC (Pearson and Stuiver, 1986).*

26

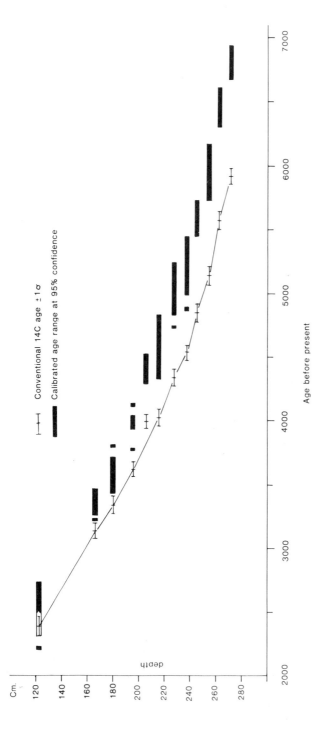

Figure 2.4 *Graph of dates against depth for a series of peat and lake mud samples for the mire at Ballynagilly in County Tyrone (Pilcher and Smith, 1979). The original radiocarbon dates with one standard deviation errors are plotted together with the deposition rate curve as published by Pilcher and Smith. The error on each radiocarbon measurement has been doubled to give the 95% confidence band, then this range calibrated using the tables of Stuiver and Pearson (1986), Pearson and Stuiver (1986) and before 2500 BC the curve of Pearson et al. (1986). Some dates show greatly increased band widths, and others show multiple band widths. The shape of the calibration curve is such that a single measurement may have a high probability of belonging to two separate parts of the calibration curve with a low probability of belonging to the part between these ranges. These multiple ranges make interpretation of deposition rates unreliable.*

precision radiocarbon laboratories to give a calibration curve with a one standard deviation error band. A continuous curve back to 2500 BC has been approved by the International Calibration Committee and has been published together with calibration tables and instructions for using them (Stuiver and Pearson, 1986, Pearson and Stuiver, 1986). For the period 2500 BC back to 5100 BC a single laboratory estimate of the calibration relationship is given by Pearson et al (1986). Some indication of the relationship back to 13 000 years is given by Stuiver et al. (1986). Measurements have been completed for a calibration back to 10 000 years (using German wood, Becker, 1986) and these should be published in Radiocarbon during 1991.

The calibration relationship is not a smooth one, as can be seen from the section reproduced in Figure 2.2. A consequence of this is that a single radiocarbon date may represent several true ages or a band of ages. Figure 2.3 shows how this increases the error associated with the age estimation, as discussed by Stuiver and Pearson (1986), Pearson and Stuiver (1986) and Baillie and Pilcher (1982). The effect of the calibration is more serious in some time periods than others. For example, all periods between about 400 BC and 800 BC have more or less the same radiocarbon age. The biggest limitation of the calibration curve for the Quaternary scientist is that many of the dating problems of interest fall outside the range of present calibrations. The dating of a post-glacial pollen sequence immediately produces the dilemma that early samples cannot be calibrated while later ones can.

To illustrate the effect of calibration, part of the time-depth curve from the mire at Ballynagilly (Pilcher and Smith, 1979) has been re-calculated (Figure 2.4). The radiocarbon dates have been accepted at face value as no re-evaluation of laboratory error was available. The one standard deviation error has been multiplied by two and the calibration tables of Stuiver and Pearson (1986) and Pearson and Stuiver(1986) have been applied back to 2500 BC, after which the dates have been read from the graphs of Pearson et al. (1986). The blocks gives the new estimated dates. As can be seen, several of the radiocarbon dates give ambiguous calendrical dates or very large ranges of dates. The line shows the time-depth curve drawn by Pilcher and Smith (1979) and used in the estimation of interpolated dates for the pollen analysis. The calibrated results show that the use of this line, reasonable though it appears, was probably not justifiable. The picture would have looked slightly worse if an additional error term for laboratory bias had been added.

What Should be Done with Samples Older Than 8000 Years?

By the time this volume appears, a calibration curve should be available covering almost 10 ka. Beyond that date, the safest thing is to do nothing. What happens to the calibration relationship before 8 ka is still not known, although the indications are that major fluctuations occurred (Stuiver et al., 1986). It is most likely that at the end of the last glaciation there were considerable perturbations of the global carbon cycle with the release of old carbon from ice, and an increase in biomass as temperatures rose. The lower ocean temperatures during the full glacial period would have allowed a greater solubility of carbon dioxide from the atmosphere, leaving the atmospheric carbon dioxide concentration at only about 60% of its present level. It is hard to believe that these changes would not have had dramatic effects on the radiocarbon levels of the atmosphere. A hint of the perturbations during the last glaciation is given in a statement by Rose (1986), discussing the dating of the Late Devensian glacial maximum, "Unfortunately each of the series of dates recorded for marine boreholes shows major reversals in the ages which need further investigation."

There is a possibility that one day there will be a calibration extending back into the last glaciation. Wood is known back to 40 ka in New Zealand (Ogden, 1982) and old wood is being investigated in Tasmania (Cook, personal communication). However, it has taken about 15 years to produce the last 7000 years of the tree-ring sequence, so even another 7000 years back to the start of the Late-glacial will not be an easy task. At present, calibration is only available for the last 10 000 years. Preliminary results from high precision, mass spectrometric uranium series dates on radiocarbon dated corals offer potential for extension of the calibration (Bard et al., 1990).

Guide-lines on the Quotation of Dates

These guide-lines are based largely on the recommendations of the 12th International Radiocarbon Conference in Trondheim, 1986 (Mook, 1986).

1) Always quote the laboratory number with the radiocarbon determination.

2) Quote original ^{14}C measurements in years BP with their 1 sigma errors.

3) Always quote the source of the calibration curve or table used for any calibrated date.

4) Quote calibrated dates as Cal AD or Cal BC.

CONTAMINATION

The discussion of contamination has been left to now because, unfortunately, it is often after the event rather than before that contamination is considered. Contamination is the presence in the sample of a carbon containing substance other than the one that it is intended to date. As illustrated above, the presence of younger humic acids in a peat sample could be considered as contamination even though they are an integral part of the sample. There are three types of contamination that need to be considered.

Old Carbon

The most common source of old carbon contamination is the presence of particles of coal or lignite in lake sediments. These may be a source of particular problems in sediments of low carbon content where coal or lignite particles could form a significant proportion of the sample (Olsson, 1972). Coals and most lignites are pre-Quaternary and contain no ^{14}C. The effect of contamination by old carbon is always that 1% contamination makes the date 80 years older (Mook and Waterbolk, 1985). As coal and lignite particles are relatively heavy, a small number may contribute a significant percentage of carbon to the sample. A further source of old carbon is eroding organic material that finds its way into lake and river bed samples. The series of radiocarbon dates from cores taken from Lough Neagh (O'Sullivan et al., 1973) shows clearly the effect of eroding blanket peat in the surrounding upland areas since the start of intensive farming in the area (Figure 2.5).

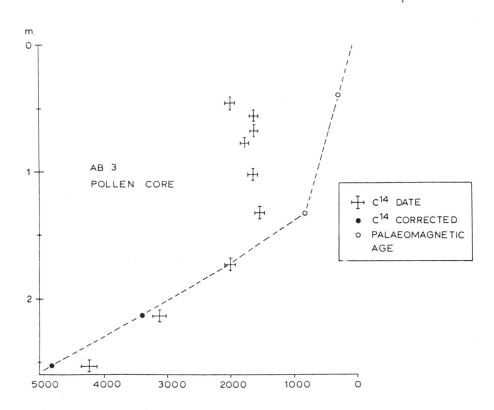

Figure 2.5 *Radiocarbon dated core AB3P from Lough Neagh, Antrim Bay. The crosses plot the vertical depth of each radiocarbon dated sample and one standard deviation of the quoted age in years BP. Corrected 'dates' are approximations derived from one of the early calibration curves (O'Sullivan et al., 1973).*

30

Modern Carbon

The effect of contamination by modern carbon varies with the age of the sample. For example, consider contamination by 1% of modern carbon (Table 2.3):

Table 2.3 *Effect of contamination on radiocarbon dates of different ages (years BP) by 1% of modern carbon. The error is the number of years by which the result will be too young (Mook and Waterbolk, 1985).*

Sample age	Error
1,500	15
3,000	35
6,000	90
12,000	270
24,000	1400
48,000	12000

The serious effect of even 0.1% modern carbon on a 48 000 year sample (an error of 2700 years) illustrates how carefully such samples have to be handled and processed.

Radioisotope Contamination

This is seldom mentioned in the radiocarbon literature and yet may be one of the most serious dating risks facing most Quaternary ecologists. Most palaeoecologists work in science departments of universities and polytechnics. In the same or closely related departments, often in the same building, research workers are using a variety of ^{14}C-labelled compounds as tracers in biological and chemical experiments. From the point of view of human safety, the activity of these isotopes is small. A typical batch of a labelled amino acid might be delivered in a vial containing 250 microcuries, whereas experiments requiring labelled carbon dioxide might require the use of 1 millicurie of barium carbonate. Let us suppose that an experiment calls for drops of about 10 microcuries to be applied to a number of plants. Suppose that one drop of 10 microcuries is dropped onto the bench. This drop has an activity of about 2 $\times$ 10^7 dpm (radioactive disintegrations per minute). Suppose that the plant physiologist wipes up the droplet on the bench, but without knowing it, transfers 1% to his hands (2×10^5 dpm). He leaves his laboratory and transfers 10% of the residue on his hand to a door handle (2×10^4 dpm on handle). A passing palaeoecologist opens the same door and picks up 10% of the residue from the handle (2000 dpm), then returns to his laboratory and starts to prepare radiocarbon samples from a sediment core. Suppose he is a careful scientist and washes his hands first, leaving only 1% of the activity on his hands (20 dpm). As he prepares his samples, 10% of the activity is transferred to each of several samples. This is only an addition of 2 dpm activity per sample, a totally insignificant amount, certainly not detectable by any normal radiation protection methods. However, if 2 dpm is added to a 10 000 year old sample the date will be between 2000 and 5000 years too young (depending on sample size). Such a result would probably stand out as anomalous, but add a few more transfer stages in the chain that leads to the palaeoecologist, and the contamination might represent only a few hundred years which would not be detected as contamination. Clearly this problem is even more serious with very old samples and may go some way to explain the large number of positive age determinations on coal, lignite and interglacial deposits that have appeared in the literature. The problem will not go away; with a half-life of 5500 years, any contamination of buildings is bound to be accumulative. Peat and sediment samples are the most vulnerable as the pre-treatment used on the samples is less likely to remove contamination. Preparation of such samples should be avoided in areas likely to be contaminated; if possible it should be carried out in the radiocarbon laboratory itself. Similarly, samples should not be stored in any building in which tracer experiments are carried out.

SPECIAL CASES

Very Old Samples

Both the AMS and the high precision laboratories are theoretically capable of going back to 60 000 or even 65 000 years BP but demonstrations of this capability have yet to appear in the literature. Even if the laboratories can demonstrate this capability its use will be strictly limited because of the exponential increase in the effect of contamination in older samples.

The radiocarbon laboratory has to expend a great deal of effort in the pre-treatment of very old samples and these should not be submitted unless there is good reason and a high probability of a useful result. Any sample that can reasonably be considered as interglacial — i.e. that is stratigraphically below glacial deposits and has a forest flora — should not be submitted for dating. Any true interglacial deposit will be beyond the range of radiocarbon dating, and yet because of the problems of minute proportions of contamination, may still give a positive date. Such samples just add to the detritus of useless radiocarbon determinations that silt up the literature. If a sample is really suspected of being in the age range of say 20 000 to 60 000 years BP — i.e. it has an interstadial flora or fauna — then the dating should be undertaken in the closest cooperation with the radiocarbon laboratory. Such samples require the greatest care, and ideally should involve the radiocarbon laboratory in the process of taking the samples which should be transported directly from the field to the radiocarbon laboratory. If sub-sampling for pollen analysis is required, this can be done in the clean environment of the radiocarbon laboratory.

Shells

The carbonates in shells are not bound as strongly as the carbon in organic molecules and can exchange with environmental carbonate or bicarbonate. Dates based on shell carbonate can be quite reliable if account of this exchange is taken. Many radiocarbon laboratories dissolve away one third from the outside of shell samples and then date two samples composed of the middle and inner thirds. Provided that these two samples give the same result, the date is acceptable as any contamination by carbonate exchange is progressive towards the centre of the shell. A more satisfactory approach to shell dating is described by Yates (1986). By careful light microscope and scanning electron microscope examination of shells it is possible to see and remove any portions that show diagenetic changes. The dating can then be carried out on uncontaminated shell. This approach is probably preferable to the "blind" chemical dissolution method more commonly used. An alternative approach is to use AMS dating of the protein in the shells (Gillespie et al., 1986). The very small proportion of protein, particularly in old shells, has made this impossible until the advent of AMS.

High Precision Wiggle Matching

Because of the detailed variations in the calibration curve (the wiggles) it is possible to pin down the age of certain materials very accurately — say to within 10 years. This has been demonstrated using the annual rings in wood (Pearson, 1986), but could also be applied to laminated sediments. Four or more samples are required whose spacing in time must be known by ring counting or sediment layer counting. Each is measured by a high precision laboratory, thus producing what is effectively a piece of floating calibration curve. This piece of curve can then be matched to the published calibration curves and the position of best fit determined with great accuracy. The method is obviously expensive, but could have valuable applications in studies of pollen influx and deposition rates.

CONCLUSIONS

When radiocarbon dating first became a realistic possibility for Quaternary studies, it seemed like the ideal answer to most dating problems. Gradually more and more limitations and qualifications have appeared and, most recently, the publication of the calibration curves have demonstrated the limitations on accuracy. In spite of this, it is still the only possible dating method for many types of material. There are now several possible measurement systems that are suitable for different types of sample. The user needs to understand the potential and limitations of these methods in order to choose where to send his samples. Because of the limitations described in this chapter, it is no longer acceptable for the radiocarbon user to treat the method as a black box. Enough understanding of the method is needed for the Quaternary scientist and the radiocarbon scientist to be able to communicate and work together. The introduction of both AMS and high precision dating open up exciting new possibilities for Quaternary research and we can look forward to a new generation of radiocarbon dating in which the dating of discrete macrofossils and fractions by AMS and the high precision dating of larger samples complement each other. For many studies there will be less justification for the use of routine radiocarbon measurements which provide neither the accuracy of high precision measurement nor the sample specificity of the AMS technique.

REFERENCES

Andree, M., Oeschger, H., Siegenthaler, U., Riesen, T., Moell, M., Ammann, B. and Tobolski, K. 1986. ^{14}C dating of plant macrofossils in lake sediment. *Radiocarbon*, **28**, **No 2A**, 411-416

Arnold, M., Bard, E. and Duplessey, J.C. (in press). AMS dating of climatic variations in the north Atlantic and adjacent areas. *Journal of Quaternary Science*, in press.

Baillie, M.G.L. and Pilcher, J.R. 1983. Some observations on the high-precision calibration of routine dates. In *Archaeology Dendrochronology and the Radiocarbon Calibration Curve*, (ed Ottaway, B.S.), University of Edinburgh, Department of Archaeology Occasional Paper, **9**, 51-63.

Bard, E., Hamelin, B., Fairbanks, R.G. and Zindler, A. 1990. Calibration of ^{14}C timescale over the past 30 ka using mass spectrometric U-Th ages from Barbodos corals. *Nature*, **345**, 405-409.

Batten, R.J., Bronk, C.R.,Gillespie, R., Gowlett, J.A.J., Hedges, R.E.M. and Perry, C. 1986. A review of the operation of the Oxford Radiocarbon Accelerator Unit. *Radiocarbon*, **28**, **No 2A**, 177-185.

Becker, B. 1986. Extension of the Holocene dendrochronology by the Pre-Boreal pine series, 8800 to 10 100 BP. *Radiocarbon*, **28**, **No 2B**, 961-967.

Brown, T.A., Nelson, E., Mathews, R.W., Vogel, J.S. and Southon, J.R. 1989. Radiocarbon dating of pollen by accelerator mass spectrometry. *Quaternary Research*, **32**, 205-212.

Coope, G.R. 1986. The Middle Devensian. In *NERC Radiocarbon Dating* (eds Bowen, D.Q. and Harkness, D.D.), Natural Environment Research Council, Swindon, 10-11.

Gillespie, R., Hedges, R.E.M. and Humm, M.J. 1986. Routine AMS dating of bone and shell proteins. *Radiocarbon*, **28**, **No 2A**, 451-456.

Godwin, H. 1962. Half-life of radiocarbon. *Nature*, **195**, 984.

International Study Group 1982. An interlaboratory comparison of radiocarbon measurements in tree rings. *Nature*, **298**, 619-623.

Libby, W. 1965. *Radiocarbon Dating*, University of Chicago Press, Chicago, pp. 175.

Mook, W.G. 1986. Recommendations/resolutions adopted by the Twelfth International Radiocarbon Conference. *Radiocarbon*, **28**, **No 2A**, 799.

Mook, W.G. and Waterbolk, H.T. 1985. *Handbooks for Archaeologists: No. 3 Radiocarbon Dating*, European Science Foundation, Strasbourg, pp. 65.

Ogden, J. 1982. Australasia. In *Climate from Tree Rings* (eds Hughes, M.K., Kelly, P.M., Pilcher, J.R. and LaMarche, V.C.), Cambridge University Press, Cambridge, 90-103.

Olsson, I.U. 1972. A critical analysis of ^{14}C datings of deposits containing little carbon. In *Proceedings of the. 8th International Conference on Radiocarbon Dating*, **2**, (eds Rafter, T.A. and Grant-Taylor, T.), Royal Society of New Zealand, Wellington, G12-G28.

Olsson, I.U. 1986. A study of errors in ^{14}C dates of peat and sediment. *Radiocarbon*, **28**, **No 2A**, 429-435.

O'Sullivan, P.E., Oldfield, F. and Batterbee, R.W. 1973. Preliminary studies of Lough Neagh sediments I. Stratigraphy, chronology and pollen analysis. In *Quaternary Plant Ecology* (eds Birks, H.J.B. and West, R.G.), Blackwell Scientific Publications, Oxford, 267-278.

Otlet, R.L., Huxtable, G. and Sanderson, D.C.W. 1986. The development of practical systems for ^{14}C measurement in small samples using miniature counters. *Radiocarbon*, **28**, **No 2A**, 603-614.

Pearson, G.W. 1986. Precise calendrical dating of known growth-period samples using a "curve fitting" technique. *Radiocarbon*, **28**, **No 2A**, 292-299.

Pearson, G.W. and Stuiver, M. 1968. High-precision calibration of the radiocarbon time scale, 500-2500 BC. *Radiocarbon*, **28**, **No 2B**, 839-862.

Pearson, G.W., Pilcher, J.R., Baillie, M.G.L., Corbett, D.M. and Qua, F. 1986. High-precision ^{14}C measurement of Irish oaks to show the natural ^{14}C variations from AD 1840 to 5210 BC. *Radiocarbon*, **28**, **No 2B**, 911-924.

Peglar, S.M., Fritz, S.C. and Birks, H.J.B. 1989. Vegetation and land-use history at Diss, Norfolk, U.K. *Journal of Ecology*, **77**, 203-222.

Pilcher, J.R. and Smith, A.G. 1979. Palaeoecological investigations at Ballynagilly, a Neolithic and Bronze Age settlement on Country Tyrone, Northern Ireland. *Philosophical Transactions of the Royal Society of London, Series B*, **286**, 345-369.

Rose, J. 1986. The late Devensian glacial maximum (the Dimlington stadial), In *NERC Radiocarbon Dating* (eds Bowen, D.Q. and Harkness, D.D.), Natural Environment Research Council, Swindon, 7-8.

Smith, A.G., Pearson, G.W. and Pilcher, J.R. 1972a. Belfast radiocarbon dates III. *Radiocarbon*, **13**, 103-125.

Smith, A.G., Pearson, G.W. and Pilcher, J.R. 1972b. Belfast radiocarbon dates IV. *Radiocarbon*, **13**, 450-467.

Smith, A.G., Pearson, G.W. and Pilcher, J.R. 1974. Belfast radiocarbon dates VII. *Radiocarbon*, **16**, 269-276.

Stuiver, M. and Pearson, G.W. 1986. High-precision calibration of the radiocarbon time scale, AD 1950-500BC. *Radiocarbon*, **28**, **No. 2B**, 805-838.

Stuiver, M. and Polach, H. 1977. Discussion: reporting of ¹⁴C data. *Radiocarbon*, **19**, 355-363.

Stuiver, M., Kromer, B., Becker, B. and Ferguson, C.W. 1986. Radiocarbon age calibration back to 13,000 years BP and the ¹⁴C age matching of the German oak and US bristlecone pine chronologies. *Radiocarbon*, **28**, **No 2B**, 969-979.

Stuiver, M., Pearson, G.W. and Braziunas, T. 1986. Radiocarbon age calibration of marine samples back to 9000 Cal Yr BC. *Radiocarbon*, **28**, 980-1021.

Sutherland, D.G. 1986. Late-glacial, In *NERC Radiocarbon Dating* (eds Bowen, D.Q. and Harkness, D.D.), Natural, Environment Research Council, Swindon, p9.

Yates, T. 1986. Studies of non-marine mollusks for the selection of shell samples for radiocarbon dating. *Radiocarbon*, **28**, **No 2A**, 457-463.

Chapter 3

POTASSIUM-ARGON AND ARGON-ARGON DATING

D.A. Richards and P.L. Smart

The K-Ar dating technique has been widely used for dating igneous rocks up to four billion years old, but has until recently, been restricted to older Quaternary deposits. The development of the $^{40}Ar/^{39}Ar$ technique in the mid 1960s and subsequent improvements in instrumentation now offer considerable potential for precisely dating Quaternary deposits younger than 30 ka (Gillot et al., 1982). Given the utility of tephras as distinctive and widely distributed chronostratigraphic marker horizons in both terrestrial and oceanic sediments, it is to be expected that the $^{40}Ar/^{39}Ar$ technique will be of increasing importance in Quaternary studies.

CONVENTIONAL K-AR DATING

Basic Principles

Potassium is one of the most abundant elements in the earth's crust and is found in minerals such as micas, feldspars, feldspathoids, clay minerals and evaporites. There are three naturally occurring isotopes of potassium; ^{39}K (93.23%) and ^{41}K (6.73%), which are both stable, and the radioisotope ^{40}K (0.00117%). The latter decays according to a branched decay scheme to the stable isotopes ^{40}Ar and ^{40}Ca. It is the ingrowth of the radiogenic gas ^{40}Ar that forms the basis for K-Ar dating. In fact, the majority of the ^{40}K (88.8%) decays to ^{40}Ca, but this isotope cannot be used for dating because it is the most common naturally occurring stable isotope of calcium, and thus decay of ^{40}K gives only a minimal increase in its abundance.

The principle application of the K-Ar technique in Quaternary studies is to the dating of volcanic rocks. On cooling below a critical closure temperature, ^{40}Ar from the decay of ^{40}K becomes trapped within the lattice. Its abundance then increases with time (t) according to the equation:

$$t = \frac{1}{\lambda} \ln \left(1 + \frac{\lambda}{\lambda_e} \cdot \frac{^{40}Ar}{^{40}K} \right) \qquad (3.1)$$

Here, λ is the total decay constant for ^{40}K, this having a value of 5.543×10^{-10} a^{-1} and a corresponding half-life of 1.250×10^9a; λ_e, the decay constant for decay to ^{40}Ar has a value of 5.81×10^{-9} a^{-1} (Steiger and Jäger, 1977).

Assumptions

It is a basic assumption of the technique that the system remains closed to both ^{40}Ar and ^{40}K after crystallisation. This may not be the case if the rocks become reheated, recrystalise or suffer appreciable weathering. Thus, it is important to sample fresh material, and to examine it petrographically to determine whether weathering or the development of secondary minerals, such as zeolites and xenocrysts in basalts, has occurred. Similarly, hydrated and devitrified glass samples should be avoided, as loss of ^{40}Ar will have occurred, leading to a low age estimate. Individual minerals may resist ^{40}Ar loss to different extents. Hart (1964), for instance, showed that hornblende separates resisted the effects of reheating in a contact metamorphic zone better than biotite or feldspar. A simple test for ^{40}Ar loss is to compare age estimates derived from whole rock and mineral fractions to determine whether they are concordant. This technique is also useful in determining whether detrital mineral fractions have been incorporated into the rocks, something which is common in volcanic material and gives rise to an over-estimation of sample age. For an example, see the discussion by McDougall et al. (1980) and McDougall (1981) of the K-Ar age of the KBS Tuff, northern Kenya, which is found in association with early hominid remains.

A second important assumption is that no non-radiogenic ^{40}Ar is present, or that the amount may be estimated. In practice, both whole rock and K-feldspar mineral separates have some ^{40}Ar from the atmosphere trapped within them. Argon accounts for only about 1% by volume of atmospheric air, but 99.6% of this is the isotope ^{40}Ar. Fortunately, this is accompanied by ^{36}Ar which can be used to determine the amount of non-radiogenic ^{40}Ar from the ^{40}Ar to ^{36}Ar ratio of 295.5 for atmospheric air. Thus, for samples less than 20 Ma, equation (3.1) can be approximated by;

$$ t = \frac{1}{\lambda} \cdot \frac{^{36}Ar}{^{40}Ar} \cdot (\frac{^{40}Ar}{^{36}Ar} - 295.5) \qquad (3.2) $$

where all values are measured abundances.

Measurement and Precision

Potassium concentrations are measured by means of atomic absorption spectrophotometry or flame photometry on a sub-sample of the cleaned, crushed and sieved whole rock or mineral separate. Argon is extracted from a second sub-sample, typically with a mass of a few grams, by fusion under high vacuum. A known quantity of ^{38}Ar enriched spike is then added and the abundance ratios of the three isotopes ^{36}Ar, ^{38}Ar and ^{40}Ar are determined in a gas isotope mass spectrometer.

Improvements in mass spectrometry systems have enabled ages as low as 1.2 ka to be obtained on samples rich in potassium, e.g. sanidines (Gillot et al., 1982). The precision of K-Ar ages on young samples or those with low potassium content is controlled by the error in measurement of ^{36}Ar whose abundance is always very low (Hall and York, 1984). The reproducible age estimates of 1.2 ka reported were for samples with 5 to 6% potassium, corresponding to 0.2% of radiogenic argon. The uncertainties, however, are relatively large ($\pm$ 100%). These reduce to better than $\pm$ 5% at 125 ka, but would be significantly greater with minerals of lower potassium concentration because the proportion of radiogenic argon would be smaller.

^{40}Ar / ^{39}Ar DATING

This technique was developed in the mid 1960s and offers a number of advantages over the conventional K-Ar technique (Hall and York, 1984). Measurement of both the K and Ar isotopes can be made on the same aliquot of sample, circumventing the problem of sample heterogeneity which can render the K-Ar age estimates of whole-rock basalts, for example, unreliable. Also, by adopting a step-heating technique, it is possible to determine whether 'closed-system' conditions have been maintained (see below).

Basic Principles

The sample, typically 1 to 10 g, is irradiated with fast neutrons in a nuclear reactor to produce ^{39}Ar, the relevant reaction being ^{39}K (n,p) ^{39}Ar. Because the ^{39}Ar abundance is proportional to that of ^{39}K in the samples, which is in turn proportional to ^{40}K, a single mass-spectrometric analysis may be used to determine the ^{40}Ar/^{40}K ratio. Because calibration of neutron flux density is difficult, the proportionality constant relating ^{39}Ar and ^{40}K is determined directly by simultaneously irradiating a standard of known K-Ar age. The sample and standard may not receive the same neutron dose, as the neutron flux will not be totally uniform in the reactor, thus giving rise to a potential source of uncertainty.

Unfortunately, this simple procedure is complicated by interference reactions involving the formation of ^{39}Ar and ^{36}Ar from calcium, and ^{40}Ar from ^{40}K. Of these, the production of ^{36}Ar is the most serious in Quaternary samples, but may be corrected for by measuring ^{37}Ar, a second non-naturally occurring isotope also produced from calcium.

Advantages of the ^{40}Ar/^{39}Ar Technique

Because mass specrometry enables high-precision analysis of very small samples, the ^{40}Ar/^{39}Ar technique offers the possibility of assessing the degree to which both the closed system and the initial ^{40}Ar/^{40}K ratio assumptions are valid. ^{40}Ar/^{39}Ar dating of mineral separates as small as 1 mg may now be achieved. An argon laser is used to fuse single grains of potassium-bearing minerals *in vacuo*. This enables the presence of mixed populations of detrital mineral grain of different ages to be identified and the major crystallisation event can therefore be unambiguously dated (e.g. Bogaard et al., 1989). This technique also allows more comprehensive application of the isochron technique, which expresses observed $^{40}Ar/^{36}Ar$ ratios in terms of non-radiogenic (initial) and radiogenic sources. Thus;

$$\frac{^{40}Ar}{^{36}Ar} = \left(\frac{^{40}Ar}{^{36}Ar} \right)_i + \left(\frac{\lambda}{\lambda_e} \right) \cdot \left(\frac{^{40}K}{^{36}Ar} \right) (\exp (\lambda t) - 1) \tag{3.3}$$

where i refers to the initial ratio, and all other notation is as used previously.

In some systems, the non-radiogenic component may not have a $^{40}Ar/^{36}Ar$ abundance ratio identical to that of the present atmosphere. Some samples are enriched in ^{40}Ar relative to ^{36}Ar on formation because they incorporate gases derived from outgassing of old crystalline rocks or the mantle. These yield conventional K-Ar ages which are too old. The isochron is derived by plotting the $^{40}Ar/^{36}Ar$ and $^{40}K/^{36}Ar$ abundance ratios for individual mineral grains (separates in earlier applications of the procedure) which have the same initial $^{40}Ar/^{36}Ar$ ratio and closure (crystallisation) time. The intercept of the resulting straight line plot is equal to the initial $^{40}Ar/^{36}Ar$ ratio and the gradient (m) is such that;

$$m = \left(\frac{\lambda_e}{\lambda} \right) (\exp (\lambda t) - 1) \tag{3.4}$$

thus enabling t to be calculated. An example of the isochron technique applied to age estimates of 33 individual K-feldspar grains is given in Figure 3.1a from Bogaard et al. (1989). These ages were obtained by laser fusion of grains, approximately 1 mm in diameter, from lapilli in a single tephra unit. The isochron defines a linear plot with $(^{40}Ar/^{36}Ar)_i$ equal to 293.4 $\pm$ 2.3, indicating a normal atmospheric source, and an age of 215 $\pm$ 4 ka. A second isochron plot (Figure 3.1b) shows the effect of the presence of older xenocrysts. Here many points plot below the isochron for non-contaminated samples defined in Figure 3.1a.

Single fusion, albeit on small individual grains, does not allow investigation of the degree of post-crystallisation disturbance of the system or loss of argon. This can, however, be undertaken by the continuous laser step-heating variant of the $^{40}Ar/^{39}Ar$ technique (York et al., 1981). Gas fractions evolved at progressively increased temperatures are isolated and analysed to enable estimation of sample age from the $^{40}Ar/^{39}Ar$ ratio of the evolved gas. An undisturbed mineral should give a similar ratio (age) over the entire gas release, giving rise to a "plateau" age. Loss or gain of ^{40}Ar at specific mineral sites will, however, disturb this pattern because each mineral degases at different temperatures (Hall and York, 1978). Furthermore, it is often observed that it is the low to intermediate temperature steps which release most radiogenic argon, while high temperature fractions contain appreciable amounts of atmospherically derived ^{40}Ar, as indicated by the $^{40}Ar/^{36}Ar$ ratio.

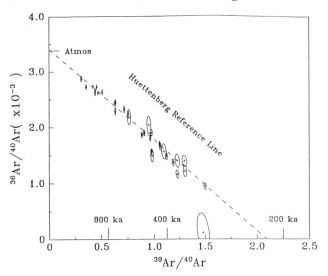

Mafic Huettenberg

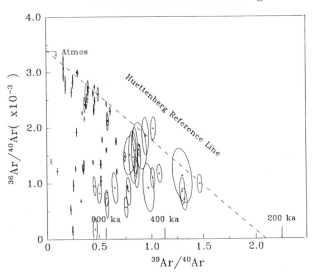

Differentiated Huettenberg

Figure 3.1 *Ar isotope correlation diagrams ($^{36}Ar/^{40}Ar$ plotted against $^{39}Ar/^{40}Ar$) with measured values marked by crosses and surrounded by their estimated 1σ uncertainty ellipses. Atmos is the composition of atmospheric Ar and the ages marked correspond to x-axis intercepts at various age values. All values are normalized to the same irradiation conditions. Dashed lines define the isochron for the Huettenberg tephra. Note the effect of older xenocrysts on samples from differentiated Huettenberg tephra, compared to mafic tephra (Bogaard et al., 1989).*

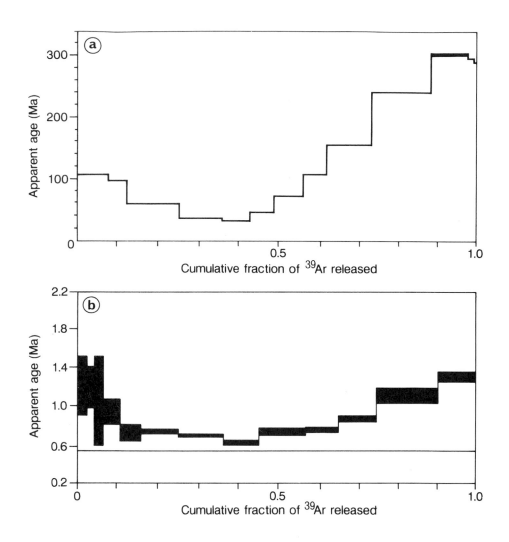

Figure 3.2 *⁴⁰Ar/³⁹Ar age spectra vs. cumulative fraction of ³⁹Ar released from K-feldspars separated from the Neschers pumic flow: (a) total feldspar component from top horizon, (b) clear grain K feldspar from separate only. The continuous line represents the weighted mean of the laser probe results on clear grains (Lo Bello et al., 1987).*

The analysis of a Quaternary pumice flow from Nescher, France by Lo Bello et al. (1987) illustrates the inherent problems of the $^{40}Ar/^{39}Ar$ method, and the measures taken to overcome them. The age spectra illustrated in Figure 3.2 show the disparity between results obtained from two different samples from the same stratigraphic unit. The original K-feldspar separates consisted of both clear (80%) and cloudy fractions; the former sanidine, the latter, orthoclase and plagioclase. For the sample in Figure 3.2a, the step-heating produces a saddle-shaped curve, whose age minima is well in excess of the expected age of the sample. In comparison, the second sample (Figure 3.2b) comprised only clear grains and yielded both a well defined plateau value and a reasonable age (the slight sag is attributed to contamination by as little as 0.0075% of older feldspars). In fact, laser fusion dating of individual grains demonstrated that the clear grains were 0.58 ± 0.02 Ma, while the cloudy grains probably derived from a Hercynian pluton through which the source vent for the eruption penetrated. These yielded an age of 330 Ma, with the lower ages for initial temperature steps representing loss of argon during heating in the subsequent volcanic phase.

Applications

A recent example of the application of the $^{40}Ar/^{39}Ar$ technique was presented by Bogaard et al. (1989) from which the isochron plots of Figure 3.1 were derived. They dated a widely distributed phonolite tephra (Huttenberg tephra) from the East Eifel volcanic area. Within an area south of Bonn, the Huttenberg tephra is found to be underlain by loess and overlain by an interglacial alfisol palaeosol. Eruption was interpreted as having occurred during a glacial to interglacial transition which was dated to 215 ± 4 ka and attributed either to the substage 7a/7b boundary or the stage 7/8 boundary (termination III). The former is in general agreement with several recent oceanic timescales, such as that of Martinson et al. (1987), while both interpretations are significantly younger than the recent uranium/thorium age estimates of Winograd et al. (1988). Had the conventional K-Ar technique been employed in dating the Huttenberg tephra, an age of about 445 ka would have been obtained. This is in error by more than 100% and indicates the care that is required in interpreting and applying the results from the K-Ar method to ensure that the samples used meet the assumptions of the method.

REFERENCES

Bogaard. P., Hall, C. M., Schmincke, H.-U. and York, D. 1989. Precise single-grain $^{40}Ar/^{39}Ar$ dating of a cold to warm climate transition in Central Europe. *Nature*, **342**, 523-525.

Gillot, P.Y., Chiesa, S., Pasquare, G. and Vezzoli, L. 1982. <30 000-yr K/Ar dating of the volcano-tectonic horst of the Isle of Ischia, Gulf of Naples. *Nature*, **299**, 242-244.

Hall, C. M. and York, D. 1978. K-Ar and $^{40}Ar/^{39}Ar$ age of the Laschamp geomagnetic polarity reversal. *Nature*, **274**, 462-464.

Hall, C. M. and York, D. 1984. The applicability of dating young volcanics. In *Quaternary Dating Methods* (ed. Mahaney, W.C.), Elsevier, Amsterdam pp. 67-74.

Hart, S. R. 1964. The petrology and isotopic mineral age relations of a contact zone in the Front range, Colorado. *Journal of Geology*, **72**, 493-525.

Layer, P. W., Hall, C. M. and York, D. 1987. The derivation of ^{40}Ar/^{39}Ar age spectra of single grains of hornblende and biotite by laser step heating. *Geophysical Research Letters*, **14**, 757-760.

Lo Bello, Ph., Feraud, G., Hall, C. M., York, D., Lavina, P. and Bernat, M. 1987. ^{40}Ar/^{39}Ar step-heating and laser fusion dating of a Quaternary pumice from Neschers, Massif Central, France: The defeat of xenocrystic contamination. *Chemical Geology (Isotope Geosciences Section)*, **66**, 61-71.

Martinson, D. G., Psias, N. G., Hays, J. D., Imbrie, J., Moore, T. C. and Shackleton, N. J. 1987. Age dating and the orbital theory of the Ice Ages: Development of a high resolution 0-300 ka chronostratigraphy. *Quaternary Research*, **27**, 1-29.

McDougall, I. 1981. ^{40}Ar/^{39}Ar age spectra from the KBS Tuff, Koobi Fora Formation. *Nature* **294**, 120-124.

McDougall, I., Maier, R., Sutherland-Hawkes, P. and Gleadow, A. J. 1980. K-Ar age estimate for the KBS tuff, East Turkana. Kenya. *Nature*, **284**, 230-234

Winograd, I. J., Szabo, B. J., Coplen, T. B. Riggs, A. C. 1985. A 250 ka climatic record from Great Basin vein calcite: Implications for Milankovitch theory. *Science*, **242**, 120-124.

Steiger, R. H. and Jäger, E. 1977. Subcommission on Geochronolgy: Convention on the use of decay constants in geo- and cosmochronology. *Earth and Planetary Science Letters*, **36**, 359-362.

York, D., Hall, C. M., Yanase, Y., Hanes, J. A. and Kenyon, W.J. 1981. ^{40}Ar/^{39}Ar dating of terrestrial minerals with a continuous laser. *Geophysical Research Letters*, **8**, 1136-1138.

Chapter 4

URANIUM SERIES DATING

P.L. Smart

Uranium series dating methods have been of great importance in Quaternary geology, providing a suite of techniques applicable to a wide range of geological materials up to 1 Ma in age. Because most of these techniques are isotopic, involving decay of a parent isotope to a daughter at a known rate, uranium series ages are numerical values which have stated uncertainties, and have thus proved particularly important in validating newer, more experimental techniques (for instance Smart et al., 1988) and providing calibration points for calibrated methods (for instance Bowen et al., 1989). An excellent recent review is provided by Schwarz (1989) while Ivanovich and Harmon (1982) provide a substantive but less recent account which includes details of chemical procedures and instrumental techniques. Here we first examine the general principles and assumptions involved in uranium series dating before considering the specific dating techniques most commonly used.

GENERAL PRINCIPLES

Disequilibrium - the Prerequisite for Dating

Uranium has two naturally occurring decay series, whose parent isotopes are long-lived, ^{238}U (half-life 4.49×10^9 years) and ^{235}U (half-life 7.13×10^8 years) (Figure 4.1). ^{235}U is less abundant than ^{238}U, comprising only 0.72 atom per cent of natural uranium. A further uranium isotope, ^{236}U, is no longer found in nature because its half-life is only 2.4×10^7 years. However, its daughter ^{232}Th has a half-life of 1.39×10^{10} years, three times longer than the probable age of the earth. It is thus the most abundant isotope of thorium in nature, and heads a third alpha emitting series (Figure 4.1).

The half-lives of the parent isotopes at the head of the three series are much longer than any of their daughters; for instance in the ^{238}U series the most persistent daughter is ^{234}U, the third most common isotope of uranium, with a half-life of 2.48×10^5 years. This disparity means that the number of parent atoms remains essentially constant for several half-lives of the daughter, the activity of which

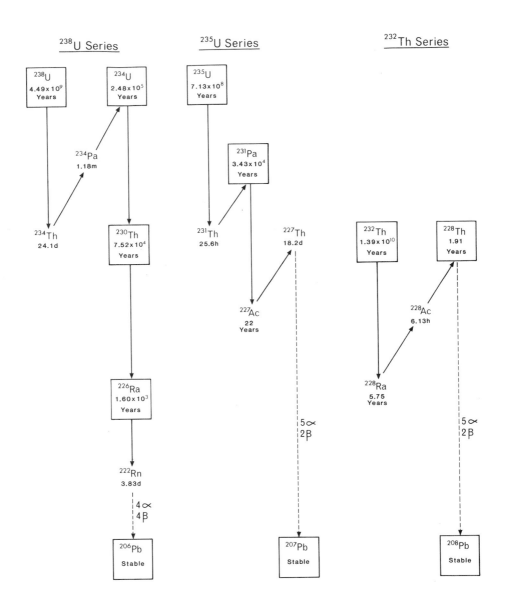

Figure 4.1 *The radioactive decay series and half lives for ^{238}U, ^{235}U and ^{232}Th. Of the longer lived isotopes outlined by boxes, only the $^{234}U/^{238}U$, $^{230}Th/^{234}U$ and $^{231}Pa/^{235}U$ daughter/parent combinations are used in Quaternary dating. Vertical arrows are alpha decays, diagonal arrows beta decays and dotted arrows are incomplete series.*

increases exponentially at a rate controlled only by its own decay constant:

$$N_2 \lambda_2 = N_1 \lambda_1 (1 - e^{-\lambda_2 t}) \qquad (4.1)$$

where:
N_1 = number of parent atoms,
λ_1 = decay constant of parent isotope,
N_2 = number of daughter atoms,
λ_2 = decay constant of daughter isotope,
t   = time,

and

$$\lambda = \frac{\ln 2}{T^{1/2}} \qquad (4.2)$$

where: $T_{1/2}$ = half-life

When t is greater than several half-lives of the daughter, the activity ratio of daughter to parent approaches 1, and secular equilibrium is established. In closed natural systems, equilibrium is established throughout the series, with the concentrations of the daughters being inversely proportional to their decay coefficient:

$$N_1 \lambda_1 = N_2 \lambda_2 = \ldots = N_n \lambda_n \qquad (4.3)$$

Only the concentration of the stable isotopes of lead formed at the end of the series (Figure 4.1) will increase through time, at a rate determined by the parent of the series.

If the system is not closed, however, and daughters can escape, there will be a break in the decay chain and a state of disequilibrium will exist between the nuclides above and below the break. Radon, for instance, is a gas which occurs in all three series and may be lost by gaseous diffusion from a porous rock matrix. More commonly, chemical differences between the various elements in the series give rise to separation during weathering, transport and deposition in the hydrosphere. Thus, thorium is strongly absorbed onto clay surfaces, while uranium may move as a complex ion in solution. In natural systems, it is therefore not unusual to find disequilibrium between the longer lived nuclides. Once isotope migration ceases and the system becomes closed, for instance upon precipitation of a mineral from solution, there is a slow return to equilibrium, as described by equation (4.1), and it is this that is employed to determine the sample age. In practice only three daughter/parent isotope pairs are routinely used in uranium series dating of Quaternary deposits (Figure 4.1):

1) $^{234}U/^{238}U$ with an effective age range of 1.5 Ma
2) $^{230}Th/^{234}U$ with an effective age range of 350 ka
3) $^{231}Pa/^{235}U$ with an effective age range of 150 ka

Two types of uranium series disequilibrium dating methods can be recognised, the daughter deficient (DD) and daughter excess (DE) types. In DD methods, the daughter nuclide is either absent on return to a closed system, or is at a concentration less than that at secular equilibrium. There is therefore an increase of the daughter to parent activity ratio through time until equilibrium is achieved. The most important DD method is based on the measurement of $^{230}Th/^{234}U$ ratios in a variety of deposits, including tufa, speleothem, shell, bone and phosphates, which are frequently deficient in thorium on deposition.

In Daughter Excess methods, the daughter isotope is present in excess of the concentration at secular equilibrium. There is therefore an exponential decrease in the activity of the unsupported daughter with time, until it is all consumed (no parent present) or reaches equilibrium (co-existing parent). Disequilibrium of the DE type may be caused either by preferential leaching of the parent isotope or by precipitation of the daughter. A number of DE methods have been employed in the dating of sediments in ocean cores, which have an excess of thorium compared to uranium due to the strong adsorption of thorium on the sediment surface.

General Assumptions of Uranium Series Dating Methods

Before examining in detail the various methods of uranium series disequilibrium dating, it is important to review the requirements implicit in all these dating methods:-

1) The decay coefficient(s) must be known accurately.
2) The activity ratio of daughter to parent nuclide must be measurable to a high level of precision.
3) The deposit to be dated has neither gained nor lost parent or daughter nuclides since deposition — i.e. the parent to daughter ratio is solely a function of radioactive decay.
4) The initial parent to daughter ratio is known or can be assumed.

Fortunately, considerable research has been carried out to determine precisely the decay coefficients of alpha emitting nuclides and develop methods for the determination of nuclides. The first two requirements can thus generally be satisfied, although with recent improvements in analytical techniques, new, more precise determinations of half-lives are needed and are becoming available (Goldstein et al., 1989b). Previously, most uranium series isotopes were determined by alpha spectrometry using silicon surface barrier detectors, a complex chemical preparation procedure being necessary to separate the nuclide of interest from the sample matrix and from other isotopes with overlapping spectra (see Ivanovich and Harmon, 1983 for details). More recently, thermal ionisation mass-spectrometry has been used to determine relative abundances of uranium and thorium isotopes (Edwards et al., 1986). With the more general advent of suitable thermal ionisation mass-spectrometers this technique will become the standard method.

It is important to understand the derivation of the error terms frequently quoted for isotopic dates. The precision of any determination is normally measured by the standard deviation (σ). As nuclear decay is a random process, the probability that a particular atom will decay is described by the Binomial Distribution. Because the probability is very small, and the number of events generally large, the Poisson Distribution provides a good approximation and the standard deviation can be estimated from the number of counts (m) using:

$$\sigma = m^{1/2} \qquad\qquad (4.4)$$

Expressing σ in terms of a percentage of the total number of counts:

$$\sigma = \frac{m^{1/2}}{m} \times 100\% \qquad\qquad (4.5)$$

Thus, ten thousand counts are needed to give a 1σ error of $\pm$ 1% (since $\sqrt{(10\,000)}/10\,000 = 1\%$) for each isotope. The standard deviation of all counts included in the determination of a particular nuclide ratio, including those for the counter background, are combined using the normal rules governing the propagation of errors (see Gascoyne, 1977 for example). Finally, the upper and lower bounds of the isotope ratio are substituted into the age calculation. The resulting 1σ age range is frequently asymmetric due to the exponential form of the radioactive decay law. The quoted errors therefore include only counting uncertainties. It is also important to remember that there is only a 68% probability that the actual age falls within the 1σ bounds. (There is a 95% probability that the actual age falls within the 2σ bounds, assuming of course that no systematic errors are present).

The major advantage of mass-spectrometric uranium series (MSU) analysis is that it permits determination of isotope ratios with precisions between 10 and 100 times better than alpha spectrometry because individual atoms (which are numerous) are counted, rather than infrequent alpha particles emitted by the slow radioactive decay process. This development has revolutionised both the potential for discrimination of events closely spaced in time by uranium series methods, and the effective age range of the $^{230}Th/^{234}U$ technique. It is now possible to determine ages as low as 50 years to a maximum of c 500 ka, with typical 2σ errors at 125 ka of $\pm$ 1 ka (Edwards et al., 1987, Edwards et al., 1988). Furthermore, MSU requires very much smaller sample sizes than alpha spectrometry (c 0.2 g), enabling careful selection of suitable material and better discrimination of the internal stratigraphy of samples such as speleothems (Li et al., 1989).

Many laboratories undertaking uranium series work have taken part in a series of intercomparison projects (USIP Phase I, II and III: see Harmon et al., 1979, Ivanovich and Warchal, 1981 and Ivanovich et al., 1984). During the course of the project there has been a reduction in the systematic errors associated with the determination of uranium concentration and $^{234}U/^{238}U$ and $^{230}Th/^{234}U$ ratios. In the most recent phase, using two speleothem samples, the interlaboratory variance (expressed as the standard deviation) was found to be very similar to the mean counting uncertainty for both isotopic ratios, suggesting a satisfactory degree of interlaboratory standardisation had been achieved. Other sources of error were, however, still significant in determination of the uranium concentration. In general, experienced laboratories obtained better quality results than those commencing work in the field. At present no intercomparisons between mass-spectrometric laboratories have been undertaken.

Returning to the remaining two assumptions commonly made in uranium series disequilibrium dating, assumption (3) of no loss or gain of nuclides is normally called the closed system assumption. Reliable age estimates are only obtained if this assumption is not violated, and it is therefore important in assessing materials for dating to identify criteria which adequately demonstrate that the system has remained closed. These may be based on physical or chemical examination of the sample material; lack of crystalised fabric or dissolutional voids in speleothems for instance, or on the isotopic ratios derived during analysis — $^{234}U/^{238}U$ ratios in excess of that of sea-water in marine molluscs which have taken up uranium for example. In practice, uranium series ages have been obtained for a range of materials (Table 4.1) some of which show minor departures from closed system behaviour, and others which are essentially open systems to isotope migration and provide age estimates with a low reliability. A variety of techniques have been employed to correct for open system conditions; these range from essentially arbitrary corrections, through statistical to modeling approaches (Rosholt, 1980).

Finally, an understanding of the geochemistry which gives rise to the isotope disequilibrium is essential in order to provide reliable estimates of the initial parent to daughter activity ratio (assumption 4). In materials ideal for uranium series dating this is exactly known, but frequently departures from this condition occur and again correction procedures are necessary which reduce the reliability of the age estimate (Table 4.1). For instance in $^{230}Th/^{234}U$ dating of speleothems the initial $^{230}Th/^{234}U$ ratio is assumed to be 0, but in some cases detritus may be present which contains ^{230}Th (and ^{234}U) which is leached during analysis, and a correction is therefore required (Schwarcz, 1980). All corrected age estimates should be viewed with considerable caution — they are only reliable if the assumptions made in the correction procedure are true.

Table 4.1 *Reliability of uranium series dates for terrestrial materials due to deviations from closed system behaviour and contamination by ^{230}Th and ^{234}U from detritus.*

Reliability	Material	Closed system?	Contaminated?
Reliable	Unaltered coral	Closed	Clean
	Clean speleothem		Clean
	Volcanic rocks		-
	Dirty speleothem		Contaminated
Possibly reliable	Ferruginous concretions	Possibly closed	Contaminated
	Tufa		Contaminated
	Mollusc shells		Contaminated
	Phosphates		Contaminated
Generally unreliable	Diagenetically altered corals	Open	Clean
	Bone		?
	Evaporites		Contaminated
	Caliche		Contaminated
	Stromatolites		Contaminated
	Peat and wood		?

THE $^{230}Th/^{232}Th$ METHOD FOR DATING VOLCANIC ROCKS

Application

This method have been used primarily for dating geologically young volcanic rocks but the same isotope ratio is also used in a variant of the ^{230}Th excess method for deep sea sediments. The maximum determinable age is about 300 ka.

Theory

During crystallization of magmas, uranium and thorium are segregated, so that the minerals in the resulting rock have different Th/U ratios. Adams et al. (1959) quote Th/U ratios for selected minerals in igneous rocks as follows: accessory zircon less than 1, accessory apatite about 1, epidote 2-6 and monzanite 25-50. On formation, the minerals therefore all have the same $^{230}Th/^{232}Th$ ratio (i.e. no fractionation occurs), but different $^{238}U/^{232}Th$ ratios, and plot on a line of slope 0 on a graph of these two ratios (Figure 4.2). For minerals deficient in thorium, the $^{230}Th/^{232}Th$ ratio will increase as radiogenic ^{230}Th is formed by decay of ^{234}U. Conversely, excess thorium will result in unsupported ^{230}Th, and a gradual decline in the $^{230}Th/^{232}Th$ ratio with time. At any particular time the isotope ratios of all minerals plot as straight lines or isochrons, whose gradient varies as a function of time according to the relationship:

$$(\frac{230\text{Th}}{232\text{Th}})_t = (\frac{230\text{Th}}{232\text{Th}})_0 \; e^{-\lambda_{230}t} + (\frac{238\text{U}}{232\text{Th}})_t \; (1 - e^{-\lambda_{230}t}) \qquad (4.6)$$

The initial [230]Th/[232]Th ratio is determined from the intersection of the isochron and equiline, the latter being a line passing through the origin with a gradient 1, representing the ratios at secular equilibrium.

Assumptions and Criteria for Application

1) Mineral phases with identical [230]Th/[232]Th ratios but different [238]U/[232]Th ratios must be separable from the rock matrix.
2) The magma must have a short transit time to the surface after crystallization compared with the half life of [230]Th.
3) The mineral phases must have been formed essentially simultaneously.
4) The system must have remained closed to isotopic migration. Fresh samples without extensive alteration or weathering are therefore required.

Example

Condomines and Allegre (1980) have reported uranium series determinations on lava samples from the Stromboli volcano, Italy. They separated magnetites of two different sizes, clinopyroxene and plagioclase from the crushed rock, for which they also reported a whole rock analysis (Figure 4.2). The isochrons defined form good straight lines, indicating phases formed essentially simultaneously. The Stb12 isochron cuts the equiline at a [230]Th/[232]Th ratio of 1.16, giving an age of 156 ka. This is in stratigraphic agreement with the younger age determined for the overlying intermediate lava complex (Sample Stb34). Considerable improvements in precision are now possible using MSU (Goldstein et al., 1989a).

THE [230]Th EXCESS, [231]Pa EXCESS, [230]Th/[232]Th and [230]Th/[231]Pa METHODS FOR THE DATING OF DEEP SEA SEDIMENTS

Application

These four interrelated methods have been widely employed in the determination of deep-sea sediment accumulation rates during the Brunhes epoch. They have also been used for the dating of oceanic manganese nodules (Ku and Broecker, 1969), an application not discussed further in this review. The age ranges are about 150 ka for the [231]Pa excess and [230]Th/[231]Pa methods, and 300 ka for the [230]Th excess method.

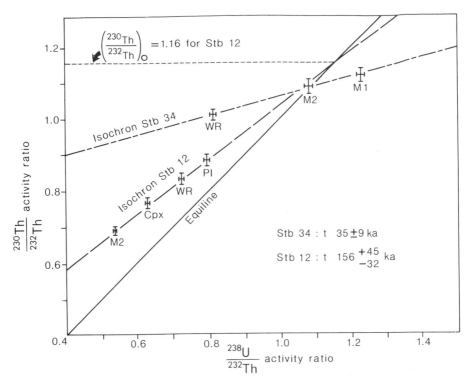

Figure 4.2 *Isochron diagram for two samples of andesite lava from the basal (Stb12) and intermediate (Stb34) complexes of Stromboli volcano (after Condomines and Allegre, 1980). Fractions analysed are: magnetite 20-80 µm (M1), magnetite 8-20 µm (M2), plagioclase (P1), clinopyroxene (Cpx) and whole rock (WR).*

Theory

Uranium has a remarkably uniform concentration of 3.3 ± 0.2 µg/L in deep ocean water, and there is therefore a continuous and uniform production of ^{230}Th and ^{231}Pa by decay of their respective parents ^{234}U and ^{235}U. The high insolubility of both thorium and protoactinium ensures, however, that once formed, the daughters adsorb rapidly onto sediment particles. Thus the thorium concentration of ocean water is very low, with an upper limit of 8 × 10^{-5} µg/L and a ^{230}Th/^{234}U activity ratio of about 6 × 10^{-4}. As the sediment particles fall to the ocean floor, they continue to accumulate ^{230}Th (and ^{231}Pa), giving a continuous increase in the ^{230}Th/^{232}Th ratio of the sediment, which can be used to calculate sedimentation rates. In contrast, uranium is not adsorbed from sea water and that present in the sediment is derived almost wholly from detrital sources, and is close to secular equilibrium. There is therefore a considerable ^{230}Th and ^{231}Pa excess in the sediments accumulating on the ocean floor, with values greater than 100 reported for the ^{230}Th/^{234}U ratio. The excess is directly proportional to ocean depth and inversely proportional to the sedimentation rate. On deposition, nuclide scavenging ceases, and the excess daughters decay until equilibrium is achieved. The age of the sediment can be calculated from the sedimentation rate (s), determined from a plot of the logarithm of the nuclide excess (C) against depth in the core (d), thus for ^{230}Th:

$$\ln C = \ln C_0 - (\lambda_{230}/s)d \tag{4.7}$$

The ^{230}Th/^{231}Pa method is a modification of the basic ^{230}Th and ^{231}Pa excess methods of dating described above. Because both the ^{231}Pa and ^{230}Th excess decay simultaneously from the time of deposition, but with different half lives, there is a change in the ^{230}Th/^{231}Pa ratio through time with an apparent half life of 6.2×10^4 years. The age can then be calculated using:

$$\left(\frac{^{230}\mathrm{Th_{xs}}}{^{231}\mathrm{Pa_{xs}}} \right)_t = \left(\frac{^{230}\mathrm{Th_{xs}}}{^{231}\mathrm{Pa_{xs}}} \right)_0 e^{(\lambda_{230} - \lambda_{231})t} \tag{4.8}$$

The initial ratio can either be taken from the top value in the core or assigned the theoretical value of 10.92 based on the relative abundance and decay rates of the parent nuclides.

Assumptions and Criteria for Application

1) There must have been no post-depositional migration of uranium, thorium or protactinium in the sediment, nor gross physical disturbance of the sediments. The former is unlikely given the insolubility of the daughters, and limited observations that core pore-waters contain a similar uranium concentration to sea water.

2) Production of ^{230}Th and ^{231}Pa in the water column has been constant through time. The uranium content of sea water is the major factor controlling production and has remained constant for at least the last 400 ka.

3) The sedimentation rate has remained constant through time. This assumption is often not satisfied, as is indicated by poor straight line fits to the log excess activity/depth plot. Fluctuations in sedimentation rate due to changes in the biogenic fraction can be corrected by taking carbonate free values, but other changes may be equally important. Normalisation to ^{232}Th has also been employed (the ^{230}Th/^{232}Th method), but this assumes that all thorium isotopes behave in an identical manner. As ^{232}Th is dominantly detrital in origin and ^{230}Th authigenic, this is not likely to be the case. The most satisfactory method of overcoming variations in sedimentation rates is the continuous strip sample method of Kominz et al. (1979) which avoids this assumption. The core is divided into adjacent sub-units (commonly the oxygen isotope stages) for analysis. The age (t_i) at the base of the ith section of the continuous strip is:

$$t_i = -\frac{1}{\lambda_{230}} \ln\ 1-(N_i/N_t) \tag{4.9}$$

where N_i is the cumulative ^{230}Th excess above the bottom of the ith strip sample and N_t is the total ^{230}Th excess of all strips in the core. The method is illustrated below.

4) For the ^{230}Th/^{231}Pa method it is necessary to assume (in addition to the above) that the ^{230}Th/^{231}Pa ratio of deposited sediment has remained constant through time. There is a substantial body of evidence to indicate that fractionation of ^{230}Th and ^{231}Pa occurs in the oceans, so that it is relatively rare for sediments to have the theoretical ratio on deposition. Furthermore, mixing of the sediments at the top of the core or loss on sampling may give a rather low initial value for the ^{230}Th/^{231}Pa ratio. The preferred method is therefore to obtain this ratio from a plot of its variation with depth, as in the excess dating methods.

Example

Kominz et al. (1979) used the ^{230}Th excess continuous strip sampling method to calibrate the aluminium deposition rate of Pacific deep sea core V28-238. The ^{230}Th excess and calculated ages are shown in Figure 4.3. It is apparent that by stage 13, all the excess ^{230}Th has decayed. If the stage 1 termination is assigned an age of 11.2 ka, 23.4 dpm/cm^3 of ^{232}Th are missing from the top of the core, equivalent to about 4 cm. The results of this analysis agree with the longer of two time scales proposed for Caribbean core P6304-9 by Rana and Emiliani (1969) and Broecker and Ku (1969) using the ^{230}Th/^{231}Pa method. The latter authors employed the plotting procedure (Figure 4.4) to obtain sedimentation rates, while the former used an initial ratio of 9.40. The main difference, however, arose from the uranium concentrations determined, which are needed to correct for the supported ^{230}Th and ^{231}Pa. Rana and Emiliani quote rather lower values than those obtained by Broecker and Ku, giving a lower gradient and higher sedimentation rate. The different dates obtained using slightly different methods on identical samples in these two studies are a good illustration of why isotopic dating methods do not yield 'absolute' ages.

THE HELIUM/URANIUM METHOD

Application

While not strictly a uranium series dating method, this technique is based on uranium decay, and is therefore included in this section. It has been used primarily for dating marine molluscs and corals. Attempts have also been made to date groundwaters (Andrews et al., 1982). The method is of limited precision for material less than 100 ka in age, but is theoretically capable of dating material 10 Ma in age.

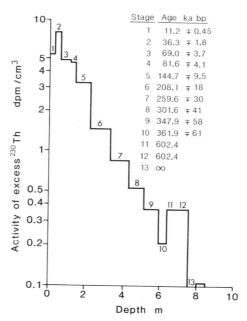

Figure 4.3 ^{230}Th *excess of composite strip samples of Pacific core V28-238. The figures are the* ^{18}O *stage numbers, the average age of which is given in the table, assuming the stage 1/2 boundary is 11.2 ka. (After Kominz et al., 1979.)*

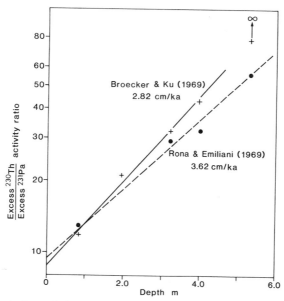

Figure 4.4 *Variation of the ratio excess* ^{230}Th*-excess/*^{231}Pa*-excess in Caribbean core P6304-9 using the uranium values reported by Rana and Emiliani (1969) and Broecker and Ku (1969).*

Theory

Alpha particles produced by decay of uranium series nuclides contained in aragonite are trapped within the crystal and accumulate with time. Given the present uranium concentration, the helium production rate at any time in the past may be calculated. For material in excess of 1 Ma in age, the helium increases linearly at a rate of 12.05×10^{-8} cm³ ^{4}He at STP/µg U/Ma; for younger material disequilibrium between the isotopes in the decay series gives a gradual increase of helium production with time (Figure 4.5). The ingrowth of ^{230}Th and its daughters is of particular significance because these dominate the helium production for samples in secular equilibrium.

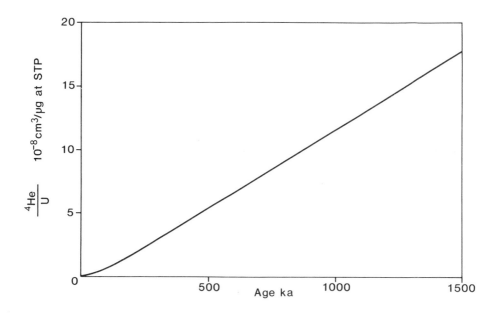

Figure 4.5 *Variation in helium — thorium ratio with time. (From data in Bender, 1973.)*

Assumptions and Criteria for Application

1) Non-radiogenic helium must be not present. That derived from atmospheric sources can be eliminated by chlorox treatment and grinding (Bender, 1973), but the presence of as little as 5×10^{-4} g per gram of helium bearing aluminosilicate detritus in the deposited aragonite can cause a significant error. Variable helium/uranium ratios for samples of the same age may indicate contamination.

2) The system must be closed with respect to uranium. This can be tested by comparing the uranium concentrations of fossil with modern material, and by the

constancy of the $^{234}U/^{238}U$ ratio, which is 1.15 ± 0.03 in modern biogenic marine aragonites. Samples which have recrystallized should not be employed. Bender et al. (1979) employed a correction for uptake of uranium and thorium.

3) The system must be closed with respect to helium and radon. Radon loss can be tested experimentally by emanation experiments in the laboratory. Helium loss is minimised in material with high electron density such as aragonite. It may be indicated for individual samples of the same age by deviations in the helium/uranium plot. For samples of the order 10^7 years old significant diffusive loss of helium is expected, but a limited comparison of ESR and He/U ages for Barbados corals suggests it is probably significant in younger samples (Radtke et al., 1988).

4) No ^{230}Th must be present on precipitation of the aragonite as this causes an enhanced initial helium production compared to theory. The ^{230}Th is predominantly found bound to particles of detritus, and can be detected by the presence of the long-lived isotope ^{232}Th.

5) A correction must be made for the stopping of alpha particles by interstitial water if the samples have been preserved below the water table. The method is discussed in Bender (1973).

Example

In developing the method, Fanale and Schaeffer (1965) sampled mollusc cells from two raised beaches in California for which $^{230}Th/^{234}U$ ages of >300 ka (6 analyses) and 120 to 140 ka (20 analyses) were available. The helium-uranium ages were 360 ± 60 ka (3 samples) and 115 ± 20 ka (6 samples) respectively. A wide range of uranium concentrations was found but all samples yielded concordant ages (Figure 4.6). This indicated that uranium uptake had occurred relatively early in the history of shells, and since that time the system had remained closed. The concordant ages between different samples and the good agreement with $^{230}Th/^{234}U$ ages suggests that only radiogenic helium was present. No analyses for ^{232}Th were presented.

THE $^{234}U/^{238}U$ METHOD

Application

This method is potentially one of the most useful for dating Pleistocene events, with an effective age range of 1.5 Ma. In practice, however, there are considerable difficulties in establishing the initial $^{234}U/^{238}U$ ratio with any confidence. The method has therefore only been used for marine corals and molluscs, where the activity ratio of sea-water can be assumed constant, and in secondary carbonates where stability of the initial $^{234}U/^{238}U$ ratio can be demonstrated.

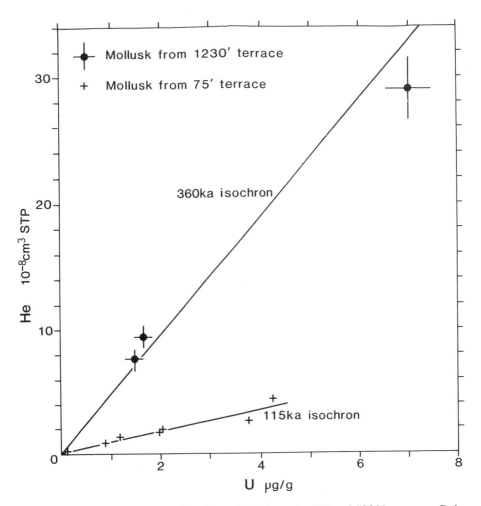

Figure 4.6 *Helium content of mollusc shells from the 75' and 1230' terraces, Palos Verdes Hill, California. (After Fanale and Schaeffer, 1965).*

Theory

In most natural waters there is disequilibrium between ^{238}U and ^{234}U due to the preferential release of ^{234}U into solution from mineral surfaces. $^{234}U/^{238}U$ activity ratios in natural waters may be as high as 20, although normally the value is closer to 1. Occasionally waters with a ^{238}U excess are also found. On incorporation into a closed solid phase, there may thus be an excess of ^{234}U, which will decline at a rate controlled by the half life of ^{234}U. Thus:

$$\left[\left(\frac{^{234}U}{^{238}U} \right)_t - 1 \right] = \left[\left(\frac{^{234}U}{^{238}U} \right)_0 - 1 \right] e^{-\lambda_{234}t} \qquad (4.10)$$

59

where $(^{234}/^{238}U)_t$ and $(^{234}U/^{238}U)_0$ are the present and initial activity ratios and λ_{234} is the half life of ^{234}U. Where the deviation from equilibrium is relatively small, as is the case for corals and molluscs deposited from sea water, the full age range of the method cannot be realised due to limitations in analytical precision.

Assumptions and Criteria for Application

1) The system must remain closed to migration of uranium isotopes. Criteria for assessing this are discussed below for the $^{230}Th/^{234}U$ method.

2) The initial $^{234}U/^{238}U$ ratio must be known, as is the case for sea-water, or estimated from present day analyses, as was the case for vein calcite deposited from long residence time groundwaters in a Nevada spring (Winograd et al., 1988). In the case of speleothems, field sampling of cave percolation waters has demonstrated that there are seasonal and long term changes in the $^{234}U/^{238}U$ ratio for individual inflows (Thompson et al., 1975). Furthermore, there may be large spatial variations in the ratio. For instance Gascoyne (1981) quotes dripwater values ranging from 0.77 to 1.6 along 1 km of passage in Ingleborough Cave, Yorkshire. There is also considerable evidence that individual speleothems show sudden variations in the initial $^{234}U/^{238}U$ ratio calculated from the present ratio and the $^{230}Th/^{234}U$ age (Figure 4.7 sample 76503). Only where it is possible to demonstrate constancy of the initial $^{234}U/^{238}U$ ratio from sequential $^{230}Th/^{234}U$ dated samples (Figure 4.7 sample 76501) can estimation of $^{234}U/^{238}U$ ages be justified.

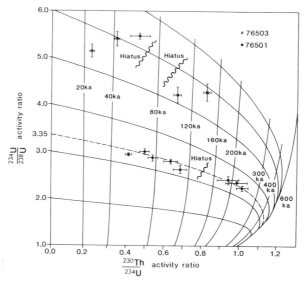

Figure 4.7 *Variation of $^{234}U/^{238}U$ and $^{230}Th/^{234}U$ ratios in two stalagmites from Tumbling Creek Cave, Ozark Mountains, Missouri. The initial $^{234}U/^{238}U$ ratio remained constant in sample 76501 but not 76503. (After Gascoyne and Schwarcz, 1982).*

Example

In Victoria Cave (Yorkshire) Gascoyne et al. (1983a) calculated the initial $^{234}U/^{238}U$ ratio for 18 uncontaminated samples which have not yet obtained equilibrium for ^{230}Th and therefore yield finite ages. Using this mean value of 1.098 ± 0.015 and permitting the ratio to vary by $\pm$ three standard deviations, four uncontaminated, older speleothems yielded ages ranging from 350 to 740 ka, and a fifth, 1.5 Ma. Sequential analyses of single flowstones do not, however, demonstrate constancy of the initial ratio through time, and Gascoyne et al. (1983a) stress that the $^{234}U/^{238}U$ ages are mere statistical guesses.

THE $^{230}Th/^{234}U$ METHOD

Application

The $^{230}Th/^{234}U$ method has proved to be the most versatile and useful of all the uranium series methods, and has been applied to a wide range of materials including speleothems, travertines, caliches, molluscs, corals, bone, teeth, lacustrine sediments, evaporites, phosphorites and peat. The effective range of the method is 350 ka for alpha spectrometry (although reduced precision is often a problem beyond 200 ka) and 500 ka for MSU.

Theory

Uranium is readily oxidised from the 4+ state, in which it is present in igneous rocks, to the 6+ state to form the soluble uranyl ion $(UO_2)^{2+}$. (The oxidised 6+ state is the usual form in carbonate rocks). This ion is readily soluble, and frequently forms anion complexes in natural waters with carbonate and phosphate. In contrast, thorium is rapidly hydrolysed on dissolution and is strongly adsorbed onto clay minerals, hydroxides and other solid surfaces. The thorium content of natural waters is therefore negligible, while some groundwaters may contain in excess of 100 μg/L of uranium. On formation of a solid phase from solution by biogenic or chemical precipitation, uranium is coprecipitated and trapped in the crystal lattice. No thorium is present on deposition. There is thus a deficiency of ^{230}Th compared to the parent isotope ^{234}U. Through time there is a progressive increase in the $^{230}Th/^{234}U$ ratio until equilibrium is achieved. As discussed above, however, there is also disequilibrium between ^{234}U and ^{238}U, and the decay of excess ^{234}U increases the $^{230}Th/^{234}U$ ratio slightly for any given time (Figure 4.8). The graphical isochron plot illustrates the relationship between $^{230}Th/^{234}U$ and $^{234}U/^{238}U$ ratios through time for a closed system with varying initial $^{234}U/^{238}U$ ratio and an initial $^{230}Th/^{234}U$ ratio of zero. It is derived from the equation:

$$\frac{^{230}Th}{^{234}U} = \left(\frac{1 - e^{-\lambda_{230}t}}{^{234}U/^{238}U} \right) + \left(1 - \frac{1}{^{234}U/^{238}U} \right) \left(\frac{\lambda_{230}}{\lambda_{230} - \lambda_{234}} \right) (1 - e^{-(\lambda_{230} - \lambda_{234})t})$$

$$(4.11)$$

Given the $^{234}U/^{238}U$ and $^{230}Th/^{234}U$ ratios for a suitable sample, the equation may be solved for t using an iterative procedure (see appendix C in Ivanovich and Harmon, 1982).

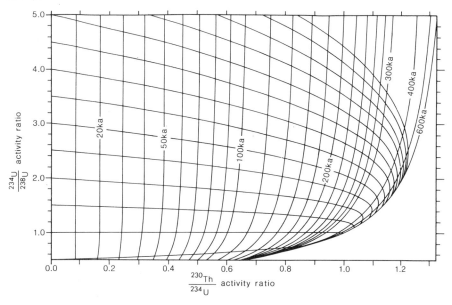

Figure 4.8 *Relation between $^{234}U/^{238}U$ and $^{230}Th/^{234}U$ ratios for closed systems initially free of ^{230}Th. The sub-horizontal curves are decay paths for systems of initial $^{234}U/^{238}U$ equal to values of 0.5,1.0,1.5 etc. The steep curves are isochrons. (After Gascoyne, 1977.)*

Assumptions and Criteria for Application

1) There should be no ^{230}Th incorporated in the crystal lattice on deposition. Most non-authigenic ^{230}Th is introduced bound to the surface of detrital mineral grains, and is accompanied by ^{232}Th. This long lived isotope can therefore be used to monitor the degree of non-authigenic (or detrital) thorium contamination. Correction for non-authigenic ^{230}Th is generally needed if the $^{230}Th/^{232}U$ ratio is less than 20. Release of uranium from detrital grains may also occur, but is not readily monitored. Samples rich in detritus are therefore best avoided.

2) The system should remain closed to the migration of uranium and thorium after deposition. This may be indicated by an anomalous $^{230}Th/^{234}U$ ratio (>1), by a positive correlation between the uranium concentration and $^{234}U/^{238}U$ for coeval samples, and by lack of agreement with $^{231}Pa/^{235}U$ ages on the same samples. There may also be gross physical evidence of recrystallisation, solution, secondary precipitation or high porosity. All such samples should be avoided. The selection of suitable samples and appropriate test criteria are discussed in turn below for the most important types of samples used for the $^{230}Th/^{234}U$ and $^{231}Pa/^{235}U$ methods.

THE ^{231}Pa/^{235}U AND ^{231}Pa/^{230}Th METHODS

Application

The ^{231}Pa/^{235}U method is based on principles similar to those of the ^{230}Th/^{234}U method and can be used in the same wide range of materials, providing that the uranium concentration is sufficient to yield analysable amounts of ^{235}U. Concordance of ^{231}Pa/^{235}U and ^{230}Th/^{234}U is frequently employed as a test for closed system behaviour. The ^{231}Pa/^{235}U method has a range of 200 ka, but if the ^{231}Pa/^{230}Th ratio is considered, this can be extended to about 250 ka.

Theory

^{231}Pa is the grand-daughter of ^{235}U (Figure 4.1), but the intervening daughter ^{231}Th is very short-lived and can be considered as always in secular equilibrium with its parent. Like thorium, protactinium is of limited solubility in natural waters and is therefore absent from solids formed from solution. The ^{231}Pa/^{235}U method uses the ingrowth of ^{231}Pa with the parent ^{235}U, which is described by:

$$\frac{^{231}\text{Pa}}{^{235}\text{U}} = 1 - e^{-\lambda_{231}t} \qquad (4.12)$$

Note that there are significant differences in the published half life of ^{231}Pa which may cause a 5 ka age discrepancy at 100 ka (Gascoyne, 1985). As ^{230}Th and ^{231}Pa are both absent on initial deposition, the change of ^{231}Pa/^{230}Th with time can be described by combining equations (4.11) and (4.12) and allowing for the greater abundance of ^{238}U compared to ^{235}U.
Thus:

^{231}Pa/^{230}Th = . . .

$$= 21.7 \left[\frac{1 - e^{-\lambda_{231}t}}{(1 - e^{-\lambda_{230}t}) + (\frac{^{234}\text{U}}{^{238}\text{U}} - 1)\frac{\lambda_{230}}{\lambda_{230} - \lambda_{234}}(1 - e^{-(\lambda_{230} - \lambda_{234})t})} \right] (4.13)$$

An isochron plot for this equation is given in Figure 4.9.

The ^{231}Pa/^{230}Th method has the advantage of a greater age range than the ^{231}Pa/^{235}U method. ^{231}Pa is usually measured by determination of ^{227}Th or ^{227}Ac and the method may sometimes be described by referral to these isotopes (e.g. ^{227}Th/^{230}Th Method). For carbonates a minimum of 1 µg/g of uranium must be present to yield a satisfactory analysis (Gascoyne, 1985).

Assumptions and Criteria for Application

1) There should be secular equilibrium between ^{231}Pa and the daughters commonly determined (^{227}Th or ^{227}Ac). This will generally not be a problem but care is needed in the design of the radiochemical and counting procedures (Gascoyne, 1977).

2) No ^{231}Pa (or ^{230}Th) should be present on initial deposition. Gascoyne (1985) has suggested that ^{231}Pa (or ^{227}Ac) is present in some samples, but will not affect ages in excess of 50 ka.

3) The system should remain closed to the migration of radionuclides after deposition.

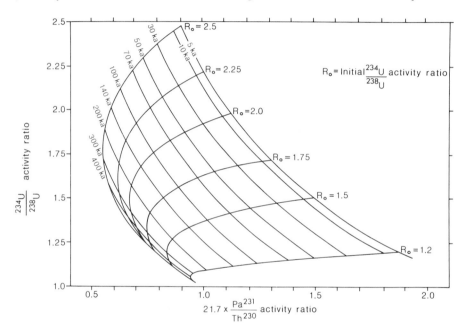

Figure 4.9 *Relation between $^{234}U/^{238}U$ and $^{231}Pa/^{230}Th$ ratios in a closed system initially free of ^{231}Pa and ^{230}Th. The sub-horizontal curves are decay paths for systems of initial $^{234}U/^{238}U$ (Ro) equal to values of 1.2, 1.5, 1.75, 2.0 etc. The steep curves are isochrons. (After Gascoyne 1977.)*

SAMPLE SELECTION AND TEST CRITERIA FOR APPLICATION OF THE ^{230}Th/^{234}U, ^{231}Pa/^{235}U AND ^{231}Pa/^{230}Th METHODS TO GEOLOGICAL MATERIALS

Corals

Unrecrystallised fossil corals have proved to be one of the most useful and reliable materials for uranium series age determination. Their most important application is in the dating of past high sea-levels, and particularly of high sea stands recorded in raised reef complexes, found where tectonic uplift occurs (Mesolella et al., 1989, Bloom et al., 1974, Edwards et al., 1987, Fairbanks, 1989). This work has been augmented by palaeoclimate studies employing [18]O in coralline aragonite (Ahron, 1983), and most recently by use of high precision mass spectrometric uranium series on corals from cores through the raised reefs of Barbados (Bard et al., 1990), to permit calibration of the radiocarbon timescale for the past 30 ka.

Broecker and Thurber (1965) have demonstrated that recent corals contain little or no [230]Th and are therefore suitable for the [230]Th/[234]U method. They also contain sufficient uranium for application of both the [230]Th/[234]U and [231]Pa/[235]U methods. When carefully cleaned by scraping and ultrasonic treatment in water, most fossil samples yield low [232]Th activities; detrital contamination is therefore not a problem. Early studies yielded geologically consistent ages, and also close agreement between the [230]Th/[234]U and [231]Pa/[235]U methods indicating closed system conditions, providing that non-recrystallised samples were selected. This is clearly demonstrated in Figure 4.10a after Veeh and Burnett (1982), which shows the evolutionary trend expected for closed system evolution with initial [230]Th/[234]U of zero and [234]U/[238]U of 1.15. Very few samples differ from this model by more than 2σ. More recently, evidence of both [234]U and [230]Th uptake has been demonstrated in fossil corals (Bender et al., 1979, Szabo, 1979). It is therefore prudent to demonstrate concordant dates from at least two methods before uncritically accepting uranium series dates.

Bloom et al. (1974) provide an excellent summary of the criteria employed in field and laboratory for sample selection. Both these authors and Bender et al. (1979) stress the importance of detailed geological study prior to sample collection in order to identify the reef crest facies. Non-recrystallised samples are most frequently recovered from bare rock rather than beneath a soil cover. Many different species have been dated, but the robust and distinctive reef-crest species *Acropora palmata* and *Porites asteroides* are preferred, because their relation to the contemporaneous sea level is known. When broken in the field, recrystallised samples show calcite cleavage or sparry overgrowths. In the laboratory, samples should be inspected under a binocular microscope for detrital sediment or void infilling by sparry calcite. Sub-samples may also be submitted for X-ray diffraction; the presence of low-Mg calcite indicates recrystallisation while high-Mg calcite suggests the presence of detrital infilling (reject if detectable). Although, strontium and magnesium determinations may assist in this selection process, Ku and Ivanovich (1990) indicate that neither elemental nor mineralogical criteria are adequate to distinguish samples with only partial recrystallisation. Samples of 5-20 g are normally adequate for alpha spectrometric analysis, while only milligrams are required for mass-spectrometric determination. On analysis, the uranium concentration should be close to that of modern corals at the site (about 2.7 $\pm$ 0.5 µg/g), the [234]U/[238]U ratio corrected for decay should be 1.15 $\pm$ 0.02 (that of modern sea-water), and there should be good agreement between duplicate analyses.

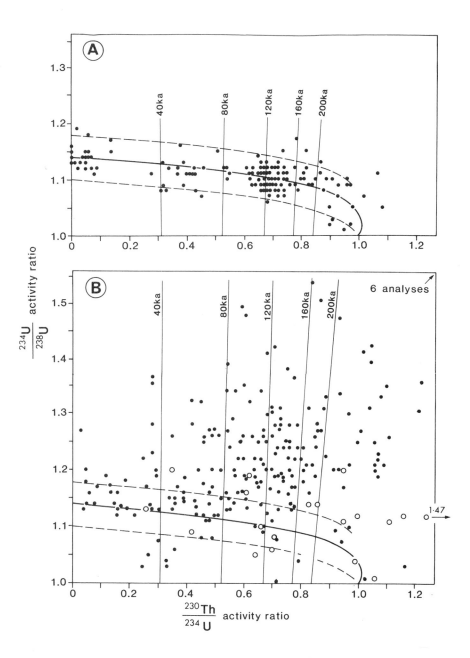

Figure 4.10 *Comparison of $^{234}U/^{238}U$ and $^{230}Th/^{234}U$ ratios for (A) non-recrystallised corals with $^{234}U/^{238}U$ counting uncertainties less than ± 0.02, and (B) fossil molluscs. Open circles denote calcitic molluscs. The heavy sub-horizontal curve is the decay path for a sample with a $^{234}U/^{238}U$ ratio of 1.14 (that of present sea-water) and initially free of ^{230}Th. The parallel curves denote ± 2σ. The steep curves are isochrons. (After Veeh and Burnett, 1982).*

Speleothems

Speleothems are secondary mineral deposits found in caves. They comprise predominantly stalactites, stalagmites and flowstones of the calcium carbonate mineral calcite, although aragonite and sulphate minerals are also found. Most calcite speleothems (this mineral form will be assumed below) are deposited as a result of either degassing of carbon dioxide from percolation waters on entering the cave atmosphere (White, 1976) or, more rarely, by evaporative concentration or complex inorganic reactions (Atkinson, 1983). In all cases, supersaturation with respect to calcite causes precipitation from solution with incorporation of uranium but no thorium into the crystal lattice. This has been confirmed by analysis of recently deposited speleothems. The resulting deposits are built up in layers which can often be differentiated by colour, opacity or crystal size. Stalagmites and flowstones are preferred to stalactites for dating because the latter have a complex structure comprising conical layers around a central void from which it is more difficult to cut samples of limited age range. The central core may also permit leaching of uranium by percolating water. Crystal growth is usually normal to the contemporary surface, giving pallisade structure in stalagmites, and when it is slow, crystals are often continuous across growth layers (Kendall and Broughton, 1978). The presence of this distinctive internal structure indicates lack of recrystallisation. Sugary, porous crystal structures, frequently found in tropical speleothems with high growth rates, may permit leaching. They may also indicate a phase of recrystallisation, giving open system conditions. Conversion of aragonite forms to calcite or vice versa is also strong evidence of recrystallisation and such samples should be discarded.

Geological and geomorphic criteria are usually the first considered in selection of speleothems for dating. Figure 4.11 illustrates some of the many ways that speleothems may be incorporated into Quaternary deposits and yield useful information. Where possible, within the bounds of good conservation practice, *in situ* samples are preferred to previously broken material, unless the exact source is clear. It is very important to record the detailed context of the samples collected. It is often difficult to determine the internal condition of speleothem material in the field, but samples containing detritus (sand, clay, or limestone fragments) which are often brown coloured, should be rejected, as should porous, vuggy material with a sugary texture. Further details of sample selection are given in Schwarcz (1980).

A second important application of speleothem age determinations is in palaeoclimate studies. In areas lacking gypsiferous, dolomitic and pyritic interbeds, speleothems in deep caves (where evaporation is zero) are deposited by the carbon dioxide degassing mechanism described above. The carbon dioxide partial pressure of cave percolation waters is controlled primarily by that of the soil atmosphere. Thus, where soil is absent, or more significantly where biological activity in the soil does not occur (i.e. there is no root respiration or aerobic bacterial decomposition), speleothems cannot be deposited. This will also be the case where no groundwater recharge occurs. Both these situations are associated with cold climates, and the frequency of speleothem growth may therefore be interpreted directly in terms of palaeoclimate (Gascoyne et al., 1983b, Gordon et al., 1989, Figure 4.12). Palaeoclimate studies have also been conducted using the oxygen isotope composition of speleothem calcite, and the deuterium content of fluid inclusions (see review by Schwarcz, 1986). Milky white speleothems have been found to have a higher density of fluid inclusion than transparent macrocrystalline forms. Sample selection in these specialised studies will depend primarily on the age range of the speleothems; of particular interest are continuous flowstone sequences which may span long periods of time, and slow growing stalagmites deposited under conditions of isotopic equilibrium.

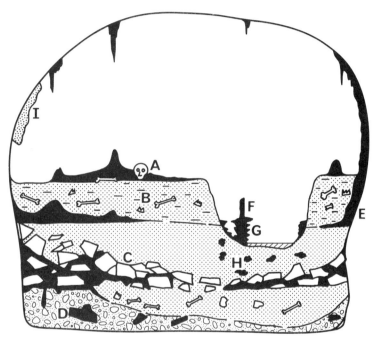

Figure 4.11 *Cross-section through a hypothetical cave showing inter-relations between speleothem (black) and associated cave sediments (stippled). Speleothem A incorporates and thus postdates archaeological material, which also postdates sediment unit B. This unit is pre-dated by wall flowstone C, which caps the underlying archaeologically barren unit D. Older wall-derived flowstones (E) are contemporaneous with the breccia unit, while speleothem clasts in the gravel (F) predate deposition of this unit. An invading stream has cut a trench in the archeological unit B and a subaqueous rimstone pool, G marks a ponding level developed once the stream has abandoned this route. There was associated cementation of unit D by percolating waters, giving crystalline cements H, but these are of limited value in defining the chronology. Finally, high on the wall are the remains of an earlier fill sequence (I), cemented by calcite which predates all the other deposits.*

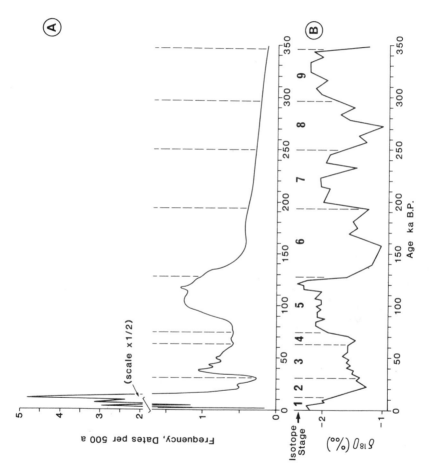

Figure 4.12 *Comparison of the frequency of 341 reported* $^{230}Th/^{234}U$ *for UK speleothems from former glacial and periglacial areas (A) with the oxygen isotope record of core V28-238. (B) (Modified after Gordon and Smart, 1984).*

It is important to section, photograph and sketch the specimen prior to analysis. Note should be made of the growth pattern, the presence of hiatuses, dissolution phases, porous zones, areas of later crystal infill and sediment rich layers. Such an examination will assist in the selection of the best material for analysis, and may also yield useful palaeoclimatic information. Because the analysis is destructive, it is also wise to reserve some material for future use. The amount of sample required for analysis depends on the uranium concentration. Typically, 25 to 200 g are used for alpha-spectrometric determination, compared to less than a gram for mass-spectrometric analysis.

There are numerous and diverse examples of the applications of uranium series dating of speleothems including archeological (Schwarcz, 1980, Green et al., 1981), palaeontological (Gascoyne et al., 1981), geomorphological (Gascoyne et al., 1983a, Williams et al., 1982) sea level change (Li et al., 1989), and palaeoclimatic studies, (Harmon et al., 1978 and Gordon and Smart, 1989).

Table 4.2 *Uranium concentrations in marine molluscs of various ages. (After Kaufman et al., 1971.)*

Age of sample ka	No. of samples	Percentage with µg/g U				
		<0.12	0.12-0.50	0.50-2.0	2.0-8.0	>8.0
Living	78	69	26	5	0	0
Fossil<20	101	4	29	59	9	0
Fossil 200-500	259	2	21	43	29	5
Fossil>500	30	0	23	37	30	10

Molluscs

Because of their widespread occurrence in both marine and terrestrial Quaternary deposits, a reliable uranium series method for the dating of molluscs would be of considerable utility. However, as conclusively demonstrated by Kaufman et al. (1971) the prospects are poor because mollusc shells cannot be considered as closed geochemical systems. The uranium concentration of modern molluscs does not exceed 0.5 µg/g, and is often much less. Fossil specimens show very much higher values, indicating uptake of uranium (Table 4.2) (Kaufman et al., 1971). Analyses for non-recrystallised molluscs plot well above the closed system line for the initial sea-water $^{234}U/^{238}U$ ratio on the $^{234}U/^{238}U$ and $^{230}Th/^{234}U$ plot (Figure 4.10a), indicating that isotopic exchange is occurring with meteoric freshwaters with a high $^{234}U/^{238}U$ ratio. The exchange is continuous with time, such that older samples show an increasing rather than decreasing $^{234}U/^{238}U$ ratio. There is also poor agreement between uranium series and ^{14}C ages, and between $^{230}Th/^{234}U$ and $^{231}Pa/^{235}U$ ages.

Calcitic molluscs appear to show less isotopic exchange during diagenesis, but unlike aragonitic molluscs (which generally have negligible ^{230}Th/^{232}Th ratios), calcitic species have ^{230}Th/^{232}Th ratios of less than 20. A correction for non-authigenic ^{230}Th is therefore needed. Thus, even though statistical compilations of uranium series analyses on molluscs may appear to yield a coherent chronology (Figure 4.13, Hillaire-Marcel et al., 1986 and Causse et al., 1989), there remains considerable uncertainty as to its reliability.

Several attempts have been made to apply open system models to the dating of molluscs, the best known being the SR model of Szabo and Rosholt (1969). However, Kaufman et al. (1971) criticize this as being unrealistic, based on unproved assumptions and conflicting with known geochemical behaviour. Until some understanding of the uptake and exchange mechanisms occurring in molluscs can be gained, the validity of the assumptions employed in the various models cannot be demonstrated, and their results must therefore be treated with caution.

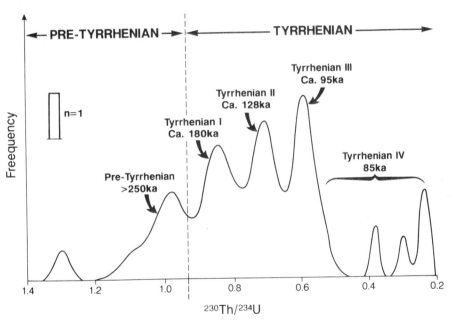

Figure 4.13 *Frequency histogram of ^{230}Th/^{234}U activity ratios in Almeria samples. Each isotopic ratio is compiled in classes of 0.1 according to its $\pm$ 3σ Gaussian distribution.*

Carbonate and Evaporite Deposits

A major disadvantage of cave deposits is that they may not be readily related to the surficial sediments used in the construction of classical Quaternary chronostratigraphic sequences. Many other terrestrial deposits have, however, been dated using the ^{230}Th/^{234}U method, including travertines (Schwarcz and Latham 1984, Kronfield et al., 1988, Lao and Benson, 1988), caliches and calcretes (Ku et al., 1979 and Szabo et al., 1981, Hillaire-Marcel and Causse 1989), carbonate lacustrine marls (Kaufman 1971 and Szabo and Butzer 1979), stromatolites (Hillaire-Marcel, et al., 1986), phosphates (Roe et al., 1983), and evaporitic salt deposits (Peng et al., 1978 and Hendy et al., 1979) and, most recently, ferruginous soil nodules (Short et al., 1989). All these materials contain uranium coprecipitated from solution at the time of deposition, but in many there is also a major detrital ^{230}Th component, for which correction procedures are required. This component is normally associated with acid insoluble sediment included at the time of deposition but in some pure travertines, non-authigenic thorium appears to be incorporated, bound on organic matter. Schwarcz and Latham (1984) have, for example, demonstrated that ^{228}Th in excess of that in equilibrium with ^{232}Th is present in some travertines due to uptake of ^{228}Ra from groundwater. This caused interference with the ^{228}Th spike used and a correction was therefore made using the ^{228}Th/^{232}Th ratio of an unspiked sample.

The simplest correction procedure is to assume the ratio of ^{230}Th/^{232}Th present in the detritus, and to subtract ^{230}Th equivalent to the product of this ratio and the sample ^{232}Th activity.

$$\frac{^{230}Th_{au}}{^{234}U_{au}} = \frac{^{230}Th_s}{^{234}U_s} - \frac{^{230}Th_d}{^{232}Th_d} \times \frac{^{232}Th_s}{^{234}U_s} \qquad (4.14)$$

where:

au = ratio in authigenic carbonate.
s = ratio in acid soluble component.
d = ratio in acid insoluble (detritus) component.

This method is frequently used in correcting dates from material with minor contamination, but as the ^{230}Th/^{232}Th ratio of detritus commonly varies between 1.0 and 2.0, it is somewhat unreliable, particularly for older samples. The ratio may be determined for carbonate free sediment inclusions from samples of sediments thought to be causing the contaminations, by hydrofluoric acid dissolution of the acid insoluble residues, or from young samples of known age (Kaufman and Broecker 1965, Kronfield et al., 1988). Usually, however, more complex experimental procedures are adopted, involving the acid leaching of the readily soluble component of the sample (primarily carbonate). The acid insoluble component (primarily silicate) may then be treated with hydrofluoric and perchloric acids to enable analysis of its isotopic composition. In all cases, ^{232}Th is used as a tracer for the detrital component. Differential release of thorium and uranium from the detritus, however, limits the linearity of the tracer response in estimating uranium release. For single samples, the authigenic isotope ratios (carbonate only) can be obtained from isochron plots of the respective acid soluble and acid insoluble residue pairs (Szabo et al.,

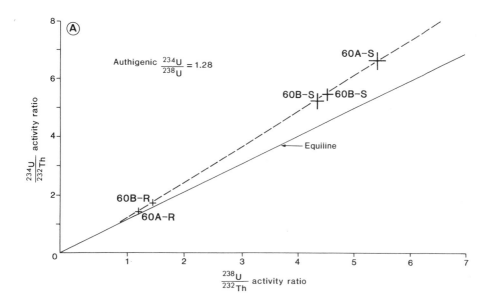

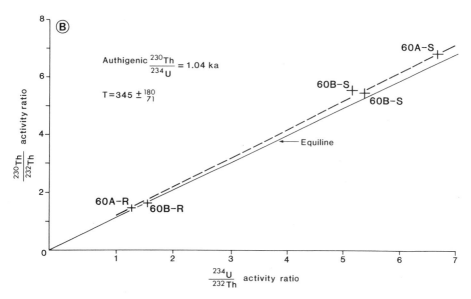

Figure 4.14 *Isochron plots for the acid soluble (S) and acid insoluble (R) components of coeval calcretes 60-A and 60-B from the Lathrop Wells area, Nevada. (After Szabo et al., 1981).*

1981). The slope of the $^{230}Th/^{232}Th$ and $^{234}U/^{232}Th$ plot yields the $^{230}Th/^{234}U$ ratio for pure carbonate, while the slope of the $^{234}U/^{232}Th$ versus $^{238}U/^{232}Th$ plot yields the corresponding $^{234}U/^{238}U$ ratio (Figure 4.14). Similar plots can also be compiled for coeval samples containing different degrees of detrital contamination (Schwarz and Latham, 1989), or from progressive leaching of one sample with acids of different strength (Ku and Liang, 1984). Detrital carbonate grains, for instance limestone fragments of infinite age, also occur in impure carbonates. These may be difficult to identify because they are soluble in the acids used for sample preparation, and do not yield a clear isotopic signature. Careful sample selection after use of conventional petrographic techniques offers the only possibility for overriding this problem. In all cases, however, adequate validation of the assumptions made is lacking and corrected dates should be treated with considerable caution.

Many terrestrial secondary carbonates and evaporites are porous, and may not constitute closed systems. Lao and Benson (1988) demonstrate that thorium is deposited in the primary carbonates of arid lake basins, and that uranium may be subsequently lost during recrystallisation and by leaching. A second problem is that further carbonate may be precipitated, for example in the pores and vugs of tufas after initial deposition. This is also a problem with carbonate soil concretions which may be multiphase (Hillaire-Marcel and Cause, 1989) and deposited considerably later than the sediments in which they are found. These effects give a considerable range of uranium concentrations, $^{234}U/^{238}U$ and $^{230}Th/^{234}U$ ratios for multiple analyses of coeval deposits. Various attempts have been made to overcome these effects, including use of isochrons, elimination of suspect leached results and statistical averaging of large numbers of analyses. Despite the apparently satisfactory agreement with other dating methods (notably ^{14}C which is not without difficulties in such deposits), and demonstration of stratigraphically correct age sequences, uranium series dates on these materials should not be treated as reliable without very careful examination.

Peat and Wood

Relatively little uranium series dating work has been carried out on these materials. Vogel and Kronfield (1980) argued that peat may constitute a closed system in which absorption of migrating uranium and thorium occurs at the margins of the deposit. Material from the interior may thus remain a closed system. In practice, the uranium isotope ratios of most samples indicate significant uranium uptake from groundwaters (Kafri et al., 1982, Vogel and Kronfield, 1980). Correction for the presence of non-authigenic ^{230}Th introduced on detritus must also be made, introducing further uncertainty into the derived ages (Kafri et al., 1982 employ a value for $^{230}Th/^{232}Th$ of 0.805, Vogel and Kronfield, 1980, 1.0 and Kaufman, 1971, 2.84 $\pm$ 0.86). Thus the reliability of ages calculated for peats is poor although in some cases they agree well with ^{14}C estimates and increase systematically with stratigraphic position, in others this is not the case. Similar results have also been reported for wood (de Vernal et al., 1986). Further work is needed.

74

Bone

Rae and Ivanovich (1986) have completed a detailed systematic study of $^{230}Th/^{234}U$ dating of bone. They recommend the use of the outer layers, comprising surface lamellar bone from the cortical surfaces for dating, as these are the sites for primary post-mortem uranium fixation. However, these surfaces may also be subject to leaching by percolating groundwaters (indicated by uranium depletion compared to bulk sample) and it is thus necessary to avoid sites where there is evidence of water movement in the deposits. Because of uranium uptake, age estimates from bones tend to be younger than the associated ^{14}C ages and uranium series ages from adjacent speleothems (Figure 4.15). Furthermore there is often only limited agreement between $^{230}Th/^{234}U$ and $^{231}Pa/^{235}U$ ages on the same sample. It seems that ages from bones, even those selected and prepared using the Rae and Ivanovich (1986) recommendations, cannot be treated as reliable.

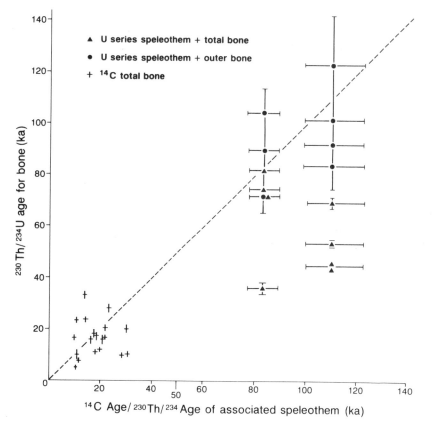

Figure 4.15 *Comparison of $^{230}Th/^{234}U$ age estimates on bone associated ^{14}C and $^{230}Th/^{234}U$ ages on speleothem. Note that whole bone analyses give lower estimates than the cortical surfaces, even for the latter analyses there is a wide range of ages between different samples. (Analyses from Rae and Ivanovich 1986, Szabo et al., 1969, Szabo 1980, and Cherdyntsev, 1971.)*

75

THE URANIUM-TREND METHOD

Application

This method, developed by Rosholt (1980), has been applied to a wide variety of surficial sediments including volcanic ash, alluvium, loess, morraine, till and soil. The time range covered is between 5 and 900 ka, with an uncertainty of about $\pm$ 10 ka increasing at the lower (<100 ka) and upper (>600 ka) ends of the range.

Theory

The technique attempts to model the open system behaviour of uranium series isotopes in the weathering zone. Uranium is considered to occur in a resistate or fixed state in the minerals of the surficial material, and as a water dominated, mobile phase moving through the deposit. Fractionation of the parent and daughter isotopes occurs during movement of the mobile phase through the soil, and also by preferential leaching of ^{234}U from the fixed mineral phase with continuing passage of the mobile phase. The mobile phase is characterised in the model by the uranium flux variable, F(O), whose precise physical significance is not known, although it includes both the concentration difference between solute and solid phases, and the quantity of water passing through the deposits. The decay coefficient of the uranium flux cannot be derived theoretically, and is instead calibrated empirically using deposits of known age. It is important to recognise that the method dates the onset of leaching of sediments; in an arid climate this may not be the same as the date of deposition.

In practice, between 3 and 10 samples, which might be expected to have evolved to different extents from the same initial isotopic composition (for instance, vertically in a soil profile), are sampled from a single deposit. The total activity of ^{234}U, ^{238}U, ^{230}Th and ^{232}Th are determined and plotted on two isochron plots (Figure 4.16), the first normalised with respect to ^{238}U, and the second with respect to ^{232}Th. The latter performs an identical function to the similar plot in the $^{230}Th/^{232}Th$ method. If all sub-samples lie on the straight line, then the deposit is homogeneous and coeval. The slope of the ^{238}U plot is proportional to age, whilst the intercept (a in Figure 4.16) and the slope of the $^{230}Th/^{238}U$ line from the ^{232}Th plot are used to obtain the time calibration for the half-period of F(O). Finally, the age is derived by application of a multi-function age equation (see Rosholt 1980).

Assumptions and Criteria for Application

1) The isotopic composition of the material must be homogeneous on deposition. This will generally be the case for well travelled, fine grained deposits.

2) A range of evolutionary states is needed to adequately define the isochrons. In many of the isochrons presented by Roshholt (1980) this is not the case, as differences in the extent of leaching have been small. There is then considerable uncertainty in the age.

76

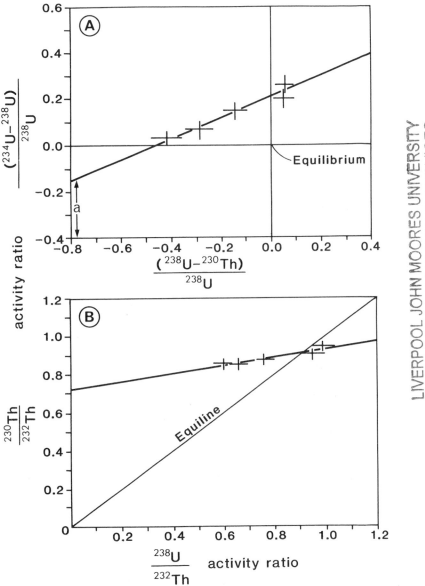

Figure 4.16 *Uranium trend dating of samples from alluvium in the Shirley Mountains, Wyoming. A: Uranium trend isochron, B: Thorium index plot. (After Rosholt, 1980.)*

3) Uniformity of texture is necessary to ensure that water flux is constant throughout the materials. This may represent a considerable problem if pedogenic processes, such as clay translocation or podzolisation, have been operating. Rosholt (1980) excluded such deviant points from the isochron plots.

Example

Rosholt (1980) has demonstrated the potential of the method by dating 18 time depositional units, from a wide range of environments ranging from desert soils, temperate podzols and volcanic ash. Four of the deposits (all loess) proved to be near equilibrium, but dates were assigned to the remaining deposits using time calibrations for F(O) at 5, 12, 140, 600 and 730 ka. Figure 4.16 presents isochron plots for samples from an alluvium in the Shirley Mountains, Wyoming, one of the better samples studied, which yielded an age of 16 ± 2 ka. There appears to be good agreement for samples collected from stratigraphically related sections, but no independent radiometric controls were tested. Further work is needed to demonstrate the generality of the F(O) curve through time in very different areas, the use of thorium plot to correct for site specific variation in F(O), and the reproducibility of the method for different sites in the same deposit.

CONCLUSIONS

The ^{230}Th/^{234}U and ^{231}Pa/^{235}U methods are undoubtedly the most useful of those described above, and can now be considered to yield reliable ages in good quality material such as coral and speleothem. For instance, Gascoyne (1977) has demonstrated a high degree of reproducibility for replicate measurements on the same sample (standard deviation ± 2.2 ka for a homogenised speleothem of age 47.8 ka, n = 12), the limiting factor being the counting uncertainty (± 1.7 ka). The advent of mass spectrometric uranium series techniques has allowed substantial reduction in counting uncertainties, offering the potential for a major improvement in the precision of age determinations. This will permit investigation of the leads and lags between different palaeoclimate series, and achievement of a much finer event resolution. We can expect exciting developments in our understanding of the nature and timing of Quaternary climatic change.

REFERENCES

Adams, J.A.S., Osmond, J.K. and Rogers, J.W. 1959. The geochemistry of thorium and uranium. *Physical Chemistry of the Earth*, **3**, 298-348.

Aharon, P. 1983. 140,000 year isotope climatic record from raised coral reefs in New Guinea. *Nature*, **304**, 720-723.

Andrews, J.N., Giles, J.S., Kay, R.L.F., Lee, D.J., Osmond, J.K., Cowart, J.B., Fritz, P., Barker, J.F. and Gale, J. 1982. Radio elements, radiogenic helium and age relationships for groundwater from granites at Stripa, Sweden. *Geochemica Cosmochimica Acta*, **46**, 1533-1543.

Atkinson, T.C. 1983. Growth mechanisms of speleothems in Castleguard Cave, Columbia Icefields, Alberta, Canada. *Arctic and Alpine Research*, **15**, 523-536.

Bard, E., Hamelin, B., Fairbanks, R.G., Zindler, A., 1990. Calibration of the ^{14}C timescale over the past 30 ka using mass spectrometric U-Th ages from Barbados Corals. *Nature*, **33**, 129-147.

Bender, M.L. 1973. Helium-uranium dating of corals. *Geochimica Cosmochimica Acta*, **37**, 1229-1247.

Bender, M.L., Fairbanks, R.G., Taylor, P.W., Matthews, R.K., Goddard, J.G. and Broecker, W.S. 1979. Uranium-series dating of the Pleistocene reef tracts of Barbados, West Indies. *Bulletin of the Geological Society of America*, **90**, 577-594.

Bloom, A.L., Broecker, W.S., Chappell, J.M.A., Matthews, R.K. and Mesolella, K.J. 1974. Quaternary sea level fluctuations on a tectonic coast. New [230]Th/[234]U dates from the Huon Peninsula, New Guinea. *Quaternary Research*, **4**, 185-205.

Broecker, W.S. and Ku, T.L. 1969. Caribbean cores P6304-8 and P6304-9: new analysis of absolute chronology. *Science*, **66**, 404-406.

Broecker, W.S. and Thurber, D.L. 1965. Uranium series dating of corals and oolites from Bahaman and Florida Cay limestones. *Science*, **149**, 58-60.

Cause, C., Coque, R., Fentos, J. Ch., Gasre, F., Gibert, E., Ben Ouezdou, H., Kouari, K. 1989. Two high levels of continental waters in the southern Tunisian chotts at about 90 and 150 ka. *Geology*, **17**, 922-925.

Cherdyntsev, V.V. 1971. *Uranium-234*, Israeli Program for Scientific Translations, Jerusalem, pp. 263.

Condomines, M. and Allegre. 1980. Age and magmatic evolution of Stromboli volcano [230]Th - [238]U disequilibrium data. *Nature*, **288**, 354-357.

de Vernal, A., Causse, C., Hillaire Marcel, C., Mott, R.J. and Occhietti, S. 1986. Palynostratigraphy and Th/U ages of upper Pleistocene interglacial and interstadial deposits on Cape Breton Island, eastern Canada. *Geology*, **14**, 554-557.

Edwards, L.R., Chen, J.H. and Wasserburg, G.J. 1986. [238]U-[234]U-[230]Th-[232]Th systematics and the precise measurement of time over the past 500,000 years. *Earth and Planetary Science Letters*, **18**, 175-192.

Edwards, L.R., Chen, J.H., Ku, T.L. and Wasserburg, G.J. 1987. Precise timing of the last interglacial period from mass-spectrometric determination of thorium — 230 in corals. *Science*, **236**, 1547-1553.

Edwards, R.L., Taylor, F.W. and Wasserburg, G.J. 1988. Dating earthquakes with high precision thorium — 230 ages of very young corals. *Earth and Planetary Science Letters*, **90**, 371-381.

Fairbanks, R.G., A 17,000 yr glacio-eustatic sea level record: influence of glacial melting rates on the Younger Dryas event and deep ocean circulation. *Nature*, **342**, 637-642.

Fanale, F.P. and Schaeffer, O.A. 1965. Helium-uranium ratios for Pleistocene and Tertiary fossil aragonites. *Science*, **149**, 312-317.

Gascoyne, M. 1977. Uranium series dating of speleothems: an investigation of technique, data processing and precision. *Department of Geology, McMaster University Technical Memo*, 77-4.

Gascoyne, M. 1981. A simple method of uranium extraction from carbonate groundwater and its applications to $^{234}U/^{238}U$ disequilibrium studies. *Journal of Geochemical Exploration*, **14**, 199-207.

Gascoyne, M. 1985. Application of the $^{227}Th/^{230}Th$ method to dating Pleistocene carbonates and comparison with other dating methods. *Geochimica Cosmochimica Acta*, **49**, 1165-1171.

Gascoyne, M. and Schwarcz, H.P. 1982. Carbonate and sulphate precipitates. In *Uranium Series Disequilibrium — Applications to Environmental Problems*, (eds Ivanovich, M. and Harmon, R.S.), Oxford University Press, Oxford, 268-301.

Gascoyne, M., Currant, A.P. and Lord, T.C. 1981. Age of Ipswichian fauna of Victoria Cave and its correlation to the marine palaeoclimate record. *Nature*, **294**, 17-23.

Gascoyne, M., Ford, D.C. and Schwarcz, H.P. 1983a. Rates of cave and landform development in the Yorkshire Dales from speleothem age data. *Earth Surface Processes and Landforms*, **8**, 557-568.

Gascoyne, M., Schwarcz, H.P. and Ford, D.C. 1983b. Uranium-series ages of speleothem from northwest England: correlation with Quaternary climate. *Philosophical Transactions of the Royal Society of London*, **B301**, 143-164.

Goldstein, S.J., Murrel, M.T. and Janecky, D.R. 1989a. Th and U systematics of basalts from the Juan de Fuca and Gorda Ridges by mass spectrometry. *Earth and Planetary Science Letters*, **96**, 134-146.

Goldstein, S.J., Murrel, M.T. and Williams, R.W. 1989b. Half-life of ^{229}Th. *Physical Review C*, **40**, 2793-2796.

Gordon, D. and Smart, P.L. 1984. Comments on "Speleothems, travertines and palaeoclimates" by Henning, G.J., Grun, R. and Brunnacker, K. *Quaternary Research*, **22**, 144-147.

Gordon, D., Smart, P.L., Ford, D.C., Andrews, J.N., Atkinson, T.C., Rowe, P.J. and Christopher N.S.T. 1989. Dating of Late Pleistocene interglacial and interstadial periods in the United Kingdom from speleothem growth frequency. *Quaternary Research*, **31**, 14-26.

Green, H.S., Stringer, C.B., Colcutt, S.N., Currant, A.P., Huxtable, J., Schwarz, H.P., Debenham, N., Embleton, C., Bull, P., Molleson, T.I. and Beuins, R.E. 1981. Pontnewydd Cave in Wales. A new middle Pleistocene Hominid Site. *Nature*, **294**, 707-713.

Harmon, R.S., Ku, T.L., Matthews, R.K. and Smart, P.L. 1979. Limits of U-series analysis: Phase I results of the uranium series intercomparison project. *Geology*, **7**, 405-409.

Harmon, R.S., Thompson, P., Schwarcz, H.P. and Ford, D.C. 1978. Late Pleistocene climates of North America as inferred from stable isotope studies of speleothems. *Quaternary Research*, **9**, 54-70.

Hendy, C.H., Healy, T.R., Rayner, E.M., Shaw, J. and Wilson, A.T. 1979. Pleistocene glacial chronology of the Taylor Valley, Antarctica, and the global climate. *Quaternary Research*, **11**, 172-184.

Hillaire-Marcel, C. and Causse, C. 1989. The late Pleistocene Laurentide glacier: Th/U dating of its major fluctuations and $\delta^{18}O$ range of the ice. *Quaternary Research*, **32**, 125-138.

Hillaire-Marcel, C., Carro, O., Causse, C., Goy J-L, Zazo, C. 1986. Th/U dating of *Strombus bubonis*-bearing marine terraces in southeastern Spain. *Geology*, **14**, 613-616.

Hiller, P. 1979. An open system model for uranium series dating. *Earth and Planetary Science Letters*, **42**, 138-142.

Ivanovich, M. and Harmon, R.S. 1982. *Uranium Series Disequilibrium — Application to Environmental Problems*, Oxford University Press, Oxford.

Ivanovich, M. and Warchal, R.M. 1981. Report on the second uranium series intercomparison project workshop, Harwell, 23-24 June 1980. *U.K. Atomic Energy Authority Report, AERE-R, 10044*.

Ivanovich, M., Ku, T.L., Harmon, R.S. and Smart, P.L. 1984. Uranium series intercomparison project (USIP). *Nuclear Instruments and Methods in Physics Research*, **223**, 466-471.

Kafri, U., Kaufman, A., Margaritz, M. 1982. Rate of Pleistocene subsidence and sedimentation in the Hula Basin as compared with those of other time spans in other Israeli tectonic regions. *Earth and Planetary Science Letters*, **65**, 126-132.

Kaufman, A. and Broecker, W.S. 1965. Comparison of [230]Th and ^{14}C ages on carbonate materials from Lakes Lahontan and Bonneville. *Journal of Geophysical Research*, **70**, 4039-4054.

Kaufman, A. 1971. U-series dating of Dead Sea Basin carbonates. *Geochimica Cosmochimica Acta*, **35**, 1269-1281.

Kaufman, A., Broecker, W.S., Ku, T.L. and Thurber, D.L. 1971. The status of U-series methods of mollusc dating. *Geochimica Cosmochimica Acta*, **35**, 1155-1183.

Keen, D.H., Harmon, R.S. and Andrews, J.T. 1981. U-series and amino acid dates from Jersey. *Nature*, **289**, 162-164.

Kendall, A.C. and Broughton, P.L. 1978. Origin of fabrics in speleothems composed of columnar calcite crystals. *Journal of Sedimentary Petrology*, **48**, 519-538.

Kominz, M.A., Heath, G.R., Ku, T.L. and Pisias, N.G. 1979. Brunhes time scales and the interpretation of climatic change. *Earth and Planetary Science Letters*, **45**, 394-410.

Kronfield, J., Vogel, J.C., Rosenthal, E. and Weinstein-Evron, M. 1988. Age and Palaeoclimatic implications of the Bet Shean travertines. *Quaternary Research*, **30**, 298-303.

Ku, T.L. and Broecker, W.S. 1969. Radiochemical studies on manganese nodules of deep-sea origin. *Deep Sea Research*, **16**, 625-637.

Ku, T.L., Bull, W.B., Freeman, S.T. and Knaus, K.G. 1979. $^{230}Th/^{234}U$ dating of pedogenic carbonates in gravelly desert soils of Vida Valley, south-east California. *Bulletin of the Geological Society of America*, **90**, 1063-1073.

Ku, T.L., Ivanovich, M. and Luo, S. 1990. U series dating of Last interglacial high sea stands: Barbados revisited. *Quaternary Research*, **33**, 129-147.

Ku, T.L. and Liang, Z.C. 1984. Dating of impure carbonates with decay series isotopes. *Nuclear Instrumental Methods in Physics Research*, **233**, 563-571.

Lao, Y. and Benson, L. 1988. Uranium series age estimates and paleoclimatic significance of Pleistocene tufas from the Lahontan Basin, California and Nevada. *Quaternary Research*, **30**, 165-176.

Li, W.X., Lundberg, J., Dickin, A.P., Ford, D.C., Schwarcz, H.P., McNutt, R. and Williams, D. 1989. High-precision mass-spectrometric uranium series dating of cave deposits and implications for palaeoclimate studies. *Nature*, **339**, 534-536.

Mesolella, K.J., Matthews, R.K., Broecker, W.S. and Thurber, D.L. 1969. The astronomical theory of climatic change: Barbados data. *Journal of Geology*, **77**, 250-274.

Mixon, R.B., Szabo, B.J. and Owens, J.P. 1982. Uranium series dating of molluscs and corals, and the age of the Pleistocene deposits, Chesapeak Bay area, Virginia and Maryland. *United States Geological Survey Professional Paper*, **1067-E**.

Peng, T.H., Goddard, J.G. and Broecker, W.S. 1978. A direct comparison of ^{14}C and ^{230}Th ages at Searles Lake, California. *Quaternary Research*, **9**, 319-329.

Radtke, U., Grun, R. and Schwarcz, H.P. 1988. Electron spin resonance dating of the Pleistocene coral reef tracks of Barbados. *Quaternary Research*, **29**, 197-215.

Rae, A.M. and Ivanovich, M. 1986. Succesful application of uranium series dating of fossil bone. *Applied Geochemistry*, **1**, 419-426.

Roe, K.K., Burnett, W.C. and Lees, A.I.N. 1983. Uranium disequilibrium dating of phosphate deposit from the Lau Group, Fiji. *Nature*, **302**, 603-606.

Rana, E. and Emillani, C. 1969. Absolute dating of Caribbean cores P6304-8 and P6304-9. *Science*, **163**, 66-68.

Rosholt, J.N. 1980. Uranium-trend dating of Quaternary sediments. *United States Geological Survey Open File Report*, 80-1087.

Short, S.A., Lowson, R.T., Ellis, J. and Price, D.M. 1989. Thorium-uranium disequilibrium dating of Late Quaternary feruginous concretions and rinds. *Geochimica Cosmochimica Acta*, **53**, 1379-1389.

Schwarcz, H.P. 1980. Absolute age determination of archaeological sites by uranium dating of travertines. *Archaeometry*, **22**, 3-24.

Schwarcz, H.P. 1986. Geochronology and isotopic geochemistry of speleothems. In Fritz, P. and Fontes, J. (eds) *Handbook of Environmental Isotope Geochemistry*, **2**, Elsevier, Amsterdam, 271-303.

Schwarcz, H.P. 1989. Uranium series dating of Quaternary deposits. *Quaternary International*, **1**, 7-17.

Schwarcz, H.P. and Latham, A.G. 1984. Uranium-series age determinations of travertines from the site of Vetresszollos, Hungary. *Journal of Archaeolgical Science*, **11**, 327-336.

Schwarcz, H.P. and Latham, A.G. 1989. Dirty calcites I. Uranium series dating of contaminated calcites using leachates alone. *Chemical Geology (Isotope Geosciences Section)*, **80**, 35-43.

Szabo, B.J. 1979. ^{230}Th/^{231}Pa and open system dating of fossil corals and shells. *Journal of Geophysical Research*, **84**, 4927-4930.

Szabo, B.J. 1980. Results and assessment of uranium-series dating of vertebrate fossils from Quaternary alluviums in Colorado. *Arctic and Alpine Research*, **12**, 95-100.

Szabo, B.J. and Butzer, K.W. 1979. Uranium series dating of lacustrine limestones from pan deposits and final Acheulian assemblage at Rooidan, Kimberley District, South Africa. *Quaternary Research*, **11**, 257-260.

Szabo, B.J. and Rosholt, J.N. 1969. Uranium series dating of Pleistocene molluscan shells from southern California — an open system model. *Journal of Geophysical Research*, **74**, 3253-3259.

Szabo, B.J., Carr, W.J. and Gottschall, W.C. 1981. Uranium-thorium dating of Quaternary carbonate accumulations in the Nevada test site region, southern Nevada. *United States Geological Survey Open File Report*, 81-199.

Szabo, B.J., Malde, H.E. and Irwin-Williams, C. 1969. Dilemma posed by uranium-series dates on archaeologically significant bones from Valsequillo, Puebla, Mexico. *Earth and Planetary Science Letters*, **6**, 237-244.

Thompson, P., Ford., D.C. and Schwarcz, H.P. 1975. ^{234}U/^{238}U ratios in limestone cave seepage waters and speleothem from West Virginia. *Geochimica Cosmochimica Acta*, **39**, 661-669.

Veeh, H.H. and Burnett, W.C. 1982. Carbonate and phosphate sediments. In *Uranium Series Disequilibrium - Applications to Environmental Problems*, (eds Ivanovich, M. and Harmon, R.S.), Oxford University Press, Oxford, 459-480.

Vogel, J.C. and Kronfield, J. 1980. A new method of dating peat. *South African Journal of Science*, **76**, 557-558.

White, W.B. 1976. Cave minerals and speleothems. In *The Science of Speleology*, (eds Ford, T.D. and Cullingford, C.H.D.), Academic Press, London, 267-327.

Williams, P.W. 1982. Speleothem dates, Quaternary terraces and uplift rates in New Zealand. *Nature*, **298**, 257-260.

Winograd, I.J., Szabo, B.J., Coplen, T.B. and Riggs, A.C. 1988. A 250,000 year climatic record from Great Basin vein calcite: Implications for Milankovitch theory. *Science*, **242**, 1275-1280.

Chapter 5

FISSION TRACK DATING

A.J. Hurford

PRINCIPLES

Fission track (FT) dating depends upon the spontaneous radioactive decay of the most abundant isotope of uranium, ^{238}U, by the explosive process of nuclear fission. In each fission event, the two fission fragments fly apart at 180° to create a single fission damage track in the enclosing atomic lattice. Under suitable conditions, these accumulated spontaneous fission tracks may be seen and counted, providing a measure of the fraction of total uranium atoms which have fissioned within a sample. Using the rate of spontaneous radioactive fission decay of ^{238}U, λ_f, the length of time during which fission tracks have been accumulating in the host material may be determined.

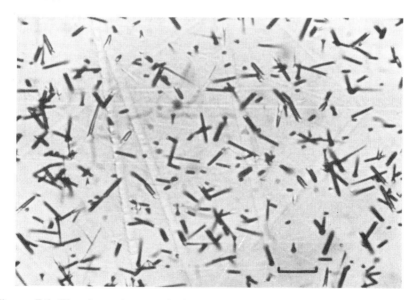

Figure 5.1 *The photomicrograph shows a polished section through an apatite crystal which has been etched for 20 seconds in 5M nitric acid at 20°C. The fission tracks are randomly oriented with respect to the plane of the section so that they are intersected at various angles, producing variation in shape from circular cross section to tracks almost parallel to the planar surface. The scale bar represents 10 μm.*

Tracks are revealed by chemical attack to give etch pits, readily visible and countable under an optical microscope (Figure 5.1). The number of fission tracks depends not only on the time during which they have been accumulating but also on the uranium content of the material, determined empirically by irradiating the sample with a monitored fluence of thermal neutrons, that is neutrons with a mean energy value of around 0.025 eV. Thermal neutrons induce fission in a fraction of the atoms of the less abundant uranium isotope, [235]U, to produce a second set of fission tracks which can be similarly etched and counted. This induced fission track count provides a measure of [235]U abundance, which is related to the [238]U concentration using the known [235]U/[238]U isotope abundance ratio of natural uranium (Fleischer et al., 1975). A standard glass containing a known amount of uranium is included in each irradiation as a monitor, alongside the samples.

Fission tracks may also be produced by the natural, spontaneous fission of the isotopes [235]U and [232]Th. Because of their considerably longer half-lives and lesser abundances, however, all observed fission tracks in terrestrial samples may be considered as effectively resulting from the decay of [238]U.

Although the exact mechanism of track formation is incompletely understood, the ion explosion spike mechanism (Fleischer et al., 1965a) is a widely accepted model. The two positively charged fission fragments are driven apart with great force, stripping electrons from the atoms of the host lattice which lie in their path in an attempt to restore their charge balance (Figure 5.2a). After the passage of the fission fragment, a zone of positively charged ions remain which mutually repel each other, forcing themselves into the lattice interstices. The resulting damage zone or fission track is typically between 10 and 20 µm long and a few angstrom units in width (Figure 5.2b). Such tracks are stable in insulating solids, but because of the movement of electrons in conducting and semi-conducting solids, the cations are quickly neutralized and thus fission tracks in such materials are unstable.

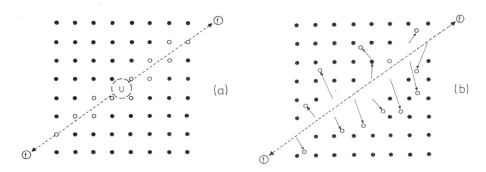

Figure 5.2 *Ion explosion spike mechanism: a model for track formation (redrawn after Fleischer et al., 1965). Solid circles are atoms in crystal lattice, which are stripped of electrons by positively charged fission fragments (f) derived from uranium atom U, leaving a zone of positively charged ions (open circles) in b).*

Essentially, FT dating requires the determination of the ratio of densities per unit area of spontaneous to induced fission tracks, directly analogous to measuring the ratio of daughter to parent isotopic abundances in other radiometric dating methods. Thus the fission track age equation centres on the ratio of the number of parent ^{238}U atoms still remaining to the number which have undergone radioactive decay, in this case by spontaneous fission (after Price and Walker, 1963 and Naeser, 1967):

$$t = \frac{1}{\lambda_d} \ln \left[1 + \frac{\lambda_d \, \varphi \, \sigma \, I \, \rho_s}{\lambda_f \, \rho_i} \right] \qquad (5.1)$$

where:

t = fission track age in years

λ_d = total decay constant for ^{238}U, 1.55125×10^{-10} a^{-1} (Jaffey et al., 1971)

λ_f = spontaneous fission decay constant for ^{238}U

I = ^{235}U / ^{238}U isotope abundance ratio, 7.2527×10^{-3} (Cowan & Adler, 1976)

σ = thermal neutron fission cross section for ^{235}U 580.2×10^{-24} cm^2 (Hannah et al., 1969)

φ = thermal neutron fluence

ρ_s/ρ_i = spontaneous/induced fission track density ratio in the sample.

In principle, since values for the constants λ_d, σ and I are well established, it remains only to determine the track density ratio, ρ_s/ρ_i, to measure the neutron fluence and to insert a value for the fission decay constant, λ_f in order to determine a FT age. Unfortunately, there is a wide disparity in the determined values of the fundamental spontaneous fission decay constant, λ_f (Thiel and Herr, 1976 and Bigazzi, 1981), with results obtained in most post-1960 experiments grouping around either 8.46×10^{-17} a^{-1} or 7.00×10^{-17} a^{-1}. The lower value is supported by track accumulation experiments and the dating of minerals and natural glasses of independently known age, the higher value by measurements made using rotating bubble chambers, ionisation chambers, radiochemical measurements and by the dating of man-made glasses of known date of manufacture. These two values of λ_f which are commonly used differ by 20%. In addition, the determination of absolute values for the neutron fluence, used to induce fission of ^{235}U in the sample, can be very complex. As stated above, for FT dating a fluence is usually monitored by counting the track density in an external detector against a uranium dosimeter glass, since this monitoring technique is identical to the neutron-^{235}U fission reaction in the dating sample. The track density in the monitor, ρ_d is related to the neutron fluence φ by:

$$\varphi = B \, \rho_d \qquad (5.2)$$

where B is a fluence calibration factor which may be evaluated from an independent measurement of the fluence using neutron induced gamma activity in a metal activation foil of gold, copper or cobalt.

Table 5.1 *An example of the multiplicity of FT ages calculated from the same count data obtained on 44 zircon crystals, given under (a), and calculated with different dosimetry schemes and different values of λ_f. See Hurford and Green (1982) for further explanation.*

(a) Count Data

Sample ref.	Number of crystals	Spontaneous ρ_i/No.	Induced ρ_i/No.	ρ_s/ρ_i	Dosimeter ρ_d/No.
72 N8 Z Fish Canyon Tuff zircon	44	46.97/4629	182.6/8998	0.2572	3.151/2420

(b) Calculated ages

Sample ref.	ρ_s/ρ_i	Dosimetry system	Fluence ($\times 10^{15}$ n/ cm^2)	Age (Ma) calculated with $\lambda_f = (\times 10^{-17}a^{-1})$		
				6.85 ± 0.20	7.03 ± 0.11	8.46 ± 0.06
72 N8 Z		cobalt wire	1.75	27.6 ± 0.5	26.9 ± 0.5	22.4 ± 0.4
Fish Canyon	0.2572	SRM 612 + Au	20.7 ± 0.14	32.6 ± 2.4	31.8 ± 2.3	26.4 ± 1.9
Tuff zircon		SRM 612 + Cu	1.85 ± 0.14	29.1 ± 2.2	28.4 ± 2.2	23.6 ± 1.8

Note: Track densities $\times 10^5$ tr/cm^2.

Several lines of evidence indicate that there is poor consistency between different methods of dosimetry which arises fundamentally from the different effective neutron capture cross sections of different isotopes ([235]U, [59]Co, [197]Au and [63]Cu) at each energy level in the neutron spectrum. This problem is accentuated when the neutron flux is less well thermalised (see Hurford and Green, 1982 and Green and Hurford, 1984 for further discussion). With such diverse values for both the fundamental decay constant, λ_f, and neutron fluence measurement systems, great variation in the calculated age can be obtained from the ρ_s/ρ_i track density ratio counted for a sample. Users of fission track data must therefore be critically aware of which system calibration parameters have been used and exactly how an age has been calculated. Hurford and Green (1982) have shown that FT ages consistent with the well-established K-Ar age of a volcanic sample may be obtained using different combinations of λ_f values and neutron fluence values (Table 5.1), which underlines that it is the ratio φ/λ_f that is effective in giving "correct" FT ages. Since there is no agreed single value for λ_f and, for practical purposes, neutron fluences cannot be measured absolutely, true values of these two parameters are not known independently of each other. Thus the ratio of φ/λ_f (or B/λ_f — see equation (5.2) above) must be evaluated by reference to some standard material whose age is independently known or can be reasonably inferred. This ratio has often been split into its component parts, although this reasoning is rarely explained to the reader. Man-made glasses whose date of manufacture is known (Wagner et al., 1975 and Thiel and Herr, 1976) and minerals from horizons which have cooled rapidly and whose age is known from K-Ar, ^{40}Ar-^{39}Ar or Rb-Sr dating (Fleischer and Price, 1964, Hurford and Gleadow, 1977 and Naeser et al., 1977) have provided such reference materials for evaluating B/λ_f (e.g. Figure 5.3).

An alternative empirical calibration suggested by Fleischer and Hart (1972) circumvents the need to select a λ_f value and for absolute neutron dosimetry. If equation (5.2) is substituted into equation (5.1), we obtain:

$$ t = \frac{1}{\lambda_d} \ln \left[1 + (\rho_s/\rho_i) \, \sigma \, I \, \lambda_d \, (B \, \rho_d/\lambda_f) \right] \qquad (5.3) $$

All of the constants, except λ_d, may be treated together as a single calibration constant zeta (ζ):

$$ t = \frac{1}{\lambda_f} \ln \left[1 + \lambda_d \, \zeta \, (\rho_s/\rho_i) \, \rho_d \right] \qquad (5.4) $$

Zeta is a proportionality constant which represents a calibration base-line for the specific uranium dosimeter glass in which ρ_d is counted, and can be evaluated from a series of age standards by:

$$ \zeta = \frac{\left[\exp (\lambda_d \, t_{std}) - 1 \right]}{\lambda_d \, (\rho_s/\rho_i)_{std} \, \rho_d} \qquad (5.5) $$

where the subscript std refers to the age and track density ratio measured in the standard.

In each of equations (5.1), (5.2), (5.3), (5.4) and (5.5), ρ_s and ρ_i are assumed to be counted on surfaces of similar registration geometry factor (see below). Such a system calibration should be based on a series of age standards (Figure 5.4), not on a single measurement which is far from precise.

88

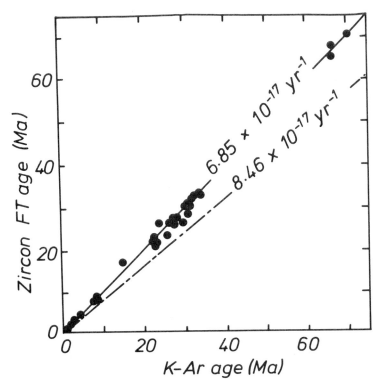

Figure 5.3 *Use of material of known age to substantiate preferred calibration parameters. K-Ar mineral ages plotted against zircon FT ages for the same volcanic and sub-volcanic rocks, FT ages being calculated with λ_f of $6.85 \times 10^{-17}a^{-1}$ and a specific neutron dosimetry. (Redrawn from Naeser et al., 1977.)*

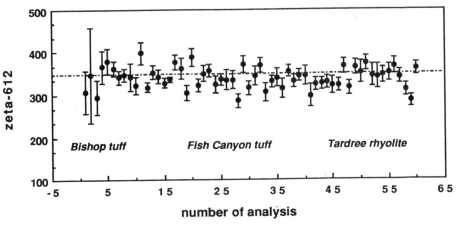

Figure 5.4 *Evaluation of zeta proportionality factor using multiple determinations on several putative age standards. Error bars are 2σ mean value shown by horizontal line. (From Hurford and Green, 1983).*

Proper selection of horizons suitable for use as age standards is crucial to the success of the entire FT system calibration and the following points should be considered (Wagner in Hurford and Green, 1981 and Hurford and Green, 1983):

1) the standard should come from a geologically well documented horizon, which contains reasonable quantities of the prospective standard and which is accessible.

2) the standard should be homogeneous in age. If a mineral concentrate, it should consist of a single generation and be free from crystals derived from older rocks.

3) the independent calibrating ages should be unambiguous and compatible with known stratigraphy.

4) the FT age must relate to the independent age and not to the age of an inherited component, or to a post-formational slow-cooling or over printing event.

The most widely used standards have been zircon and apatite from the Fish Canyon Tuff of southern Colorado (see Hurford and Hammerschmidt, 1985 and references therein). Comparison of zetas measured by different workers on the same material reveals a spread of values of 20-25%, possibly resulting from personal counting bias and different microscope conditions. Variation may also be introduced into zeta by both the reactor used and specific irradiation conditions. Recent results from Green (1985) suggest that different minerals yield different zeta values. Zeta therefore includes not only physical constants but also personal and experimental calibration factors, underlining the necessity for each worker to calibrate their FT dating parameters by reference to standard material.

In an attempt to resolve this ambiguity of calibration schemes in FT dating, the subcommission on Geochronology of the International Union of Geosciences, in consultation with the FT community, has recommended a unified approach to system calibration (Hurford, 1990) which should simplify calibration in future years.

WHAT CAN BE DATED?

Although early reviews of FT dating listed almost 100 minerals as being suitable for dating, the method has, in practice, been applied to comparatively few materials. A survey of fission track literature carried out in mid-1986 revealed that of 4200 published ages, 70% were carried out on just two minerals, apatite and zircon, with a further 26% resulting from determinations on glasses, micas and sphene.

Five factors control which phases can be dated by the FT method: uranium content, grain size, abundance, degree of crystallinity and the ability of the phase to preserve tracks, the latter being considered later.

The FT method can be applied to materials which have uranium contents ranging between a few ppm and several percent, the limiting factor being the ability to find and count spontaneous fission tracks. Figure 5.5 (after Wagner, 1978) provides a guide to the usefulness of material in terms of its age and uranium content.

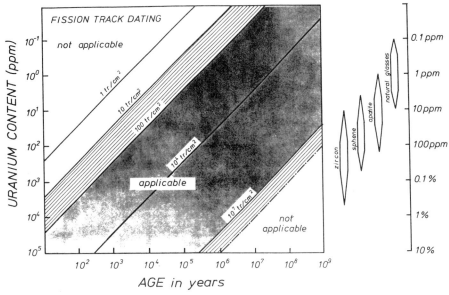

Figure 5.5 *Schematic representation of the relationship between sample age, uranium content and fission track density. Suitability of a sample for FT dating is essentially determined by the spontaneous track density, the accepted range being indicated by the central, finely ruled area. The more widely ruled marginal areas may be counted with difficulty. (Modified by Gleadow after Wagner, 1978).*

A density of 2×10^7 tracks/cm² represents an absolute upper limit, individual tracks no longer being distinguishable at higher densities. Glasses may be countable down to 10 tracks/cm² because larger surface areas are often available for scanning, although such analyses are excessively time-consuming. In addition, because track densities are low, analytical errors will be high. Routine practical counting requires a track density between 10^4 and 10^7 tracks/cm², which for a 1 Ma sample necessitates a uranium content of between 50 ppm and 1%; while many zircons and a few apatites have such uranium concentrations, those of most glasses are orders of magnitude lower, and thus glasses are generally unsuited to Quaternary FT analysis.

A lower limit to grain size is provided by the length of a fission track since the crystal should be significantly larger than the track itself in order that tracks may be satisfactorily observed. Tracks in zircon are about 1 μm and in apatite about 16 μm in length, and this imposes a minimum grain size of about 50 μm. In addition, counting areas should not be sited within one track length of the crystal boundary to preclude the counting of tracks originating from uranium outside the crystal.

The frequent use of apatite and zircon for FT analysis reflects their ubiquitous occurrence in many crystalline and sedimentary rocks. Other more exotic minerals may be readily datable, but the experimental time involved in locating them, in developing appropriate etching techniques and in understanding their annealing characteristics (see below) is usually unwarranted.

To be useful for FT dating, a phase must be well-crystalised or wholly glassy. Amorphous or cryptocrystalline material such as dental apatite, glauconite, amber and fossilised bone, although proposed as candidates for FT analysis, are totally unsatisfactory in track etching, probably as a consequence of the small effective grain size relative to the track dimensions. In addition, such phases rarely contain adequate uranium.

PRACTICAL CONSIDERATIONS

Sample Preparation

For most samples, standard mineral separation techniques (Wilfley table, heavy liquids and electromagnets) are used to prepare a relatively pure concentrate of the accessory minerals apatite, zircon and sphene. For larger crystals or glasses, sections may be cut using a very fine diamond saw. Fission tracks are etched and counted on an internal surface polished through the sample, to ensure that the tracks have not resulted from possible external contamination, perhaps from uranium deposited on an outer surface by circulating groundwater. Crystals are mounted in either FEP-Teflon (Zircon or sphene — Gleadow et al., 1976) or in epoxy-resin on a glass microscope slide (apatite or sphene — Naeser, 1967) and polished to produce a flat, strain-free internal surface at least 25 μm below the exterior. Chemical etching attacks the weakened, disordered structure of the track at a faster rate, V_T than the general rate of etching of the mineral surface, V_G. The difference between the two rates of etching determines the shape of the etch pit: if V_T is not much greater than V_G then the pit is broad and shallow, as in glass. A small number of fission tracks lying at shallow angles to the surface will be completely lost as general etching of the crystal surface progresses. The fraction of the total tracks crossing a surface which are actually revealed by etching is termed the etching efficiency of that surface: etching efficiencies of minerals are generally high, but for glass, efficiencies may be 0.5 or less (Fleischer et al., 1975).

In most minerals, the general etch rate, V_G is anisotropic and dependent upon crystallographic orientation. Thus the shape of the track etch pit will vary according to both the orientation of the track and variation of V_G in the plane of the etched surface, which may result in an apparent preferred orientation of the etched tracks and possible undercounting (Gleadow, 1981). Etching must be continued until the tracks appear both well-etched and isotropically oriented. It follows that some crystallographic planes will possess a higher V_G (and thus a lower etching efficiency) than other planes and in zircon, etching efficiency varies from about 100% on prismatic sections parallel to the c-crystallographic axis, to zero on basal sections (Naeser et al., 1980). Clearly, to ensure complete revelation of tracks it is imperative to count only those surfaces where the etching efficiency is high. These may be identified by the presence of sharply etched polishing scratches, less than 1.5 μm in width (Gleadow, 1978 and 1981).

Accumulation in a mineral of alpha particle recoil damage from the decay of uranium and thorium to lead, results in a modification of the etching properties of some minerals — particularly zircon and sphene: there is an acceleration in the etch rate and a progressive decrease in the anisotropy of etching. Virtual isotropic etching is reached when the structure is nearly metamict and comparable to a glass. Young zircons and sphenes contain little alpha-recoil damage and thus anisotropic etching can present a severe problem, with the distinct possibility that weakly etched tracks in some orientations may be overlooked. It is thus important to ensure that a sample is adequately etched; progressive etching (Figure 5.6) of minerals eventually produces a plateau value for the track density which does not vary with further etching. Optimum etching times are around twice the minimum etch time, E_{min}. Apatite has never been reported as metamict and appears not to retain alpha-recoil damage; thus problems of modification of etching properties do not apply to apatite. Fleischer et al. (1975) detail etching reagents and conditions for many minerals; Table 5.2 offers recommended recipes for etching commonly used materials.

Table 5.2 *Etching conditions for common minerals (where concentrations are not given strengths of acids are as supplied in concentrated form).*

Mineral	Etchant	Temperature	Time
Apatite	5M HNO$_3$	20°C	20 sec
Zircon	*KOH:NaOH eutectic	220°C	4-100 hr
	HF: H$_2$SO$_4$	165°C	1-10 hr
Sphene	*50M NaOH	120°C	30 min-5 hr
	1HF:2HCl:3HNO$_3$:6H$_2$O	20°C	1-25 min
Muscovite	HF (40%)	20°C	20 min

*Recommended

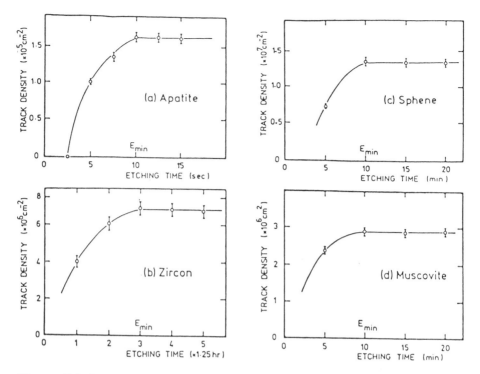

Figure 5.6 *Progressive etching in apatite, sphene, zircon and muscovite. With increasing etching, a stable track density is reached after a time E_{min}. To ensure complete revelation of tracks, samples should be etched for around 2E using conditions given in Table 5.2. (From Gleadow, 1974).*

Counting Fission Tracks

Counting fission tracks in a sample requires a high quality microscope capable of a magnification of at least 1000× with high intensity transmitted illumination and a calibrated counting grid inserted in the eyepiece. Sphene and zircon, having high refractive indices, are best counted using oil immersion objectives, the oil-filled tracks showing good contrast. Apatite and mica have lower refractive indices, similar to immersion oil, and are better observed with dry objectives. A strict discipline of counting must be established to ensure that all tracks seen within the eyepiece grid are counted. The characteristics of tracks, their linearity, random orientation and limited length (up to 16-17 μm in apatite, and 12 μm in zircon) are used in track identification.

Fission Track Dating Strategies

Many alternative strategies exist for obtaining the all-important spontaneous to induced track density ratio from which the age is derived. These procedures are not universally applicable to all dating samples: factors such as registration geometry of the etching surfaces, accumulated radiation damage, anisotropic etching and uranium inhomogeneity must be considered when matching a dating procedure to a sample. Figure 5.7 shows a schematic representation of different FT dating procedures. In practice, greatest use is made of the population and external detector methods: further description of the other procedures can be found in Gleadow (1981) and Hurford and Green (1982).

Population method With the population method spontaneous and induced track densities are determined on separate aliquots of the same sample. Induced tracks are revealed in irradiated crystals from which the spontaneous tracks have been removed by laboratory annealing prior to neutron irradiation. This procedure has the advantage of using identical etching conditions to reveal spontaneous and induced tracks on internal surfaces with identical registration geometries and similar track registration efficiencies (Fleischer et al., 1964). The method assumes that the two aliquots possess statistically equivalent uranium concentrations, an assumption which may be invalid if there is appreciable variation of uranium content within and between crystals. In such cases, the precision of the population method is less than that obtained from the external detector method. The population method is useful only for apatite and glass; it is inappropriate for sphene, zircon and other minerals because uranium concentration is highly variable between crystals, and laboratory annealing of spontaneous tracks also removes the accumulated radiation damage, thus producing extremely anisotropic conditions for etching the induced tracks, as described above. The main advantage of the population method, identical etching, is lost and the induced track density may well be underestimated (Gleadow, 1978) with the age seriously overestimated.

External detector method In the external detector method, spontaneous tracks are counted in the etched mineral, while the induced tracks are counted in an external detector of low uranium muscovite, held against the mineral during irradiation and subsequently etched. Spontaneous and induced tracks are measured in exactly matching areas from the same planar surface of an individual crystal, and thus uranium inhomogeneity, both within and between crystals, is of negligible consequence. The method also permits careful selection of crystals, avoiding those badly etched, wrongly orientated or containing dislocations. Between 10 and 25 crystals are counted in each analysis and the data combined to calculate an age for the sample. In this method spontaneous tracks result from the passage of fission fragments across the internal surface, from both above and below, producing a 4π geometry. Induced tracks result from a one way passage of fission fragments from the mineral into the external mica detector, giving a 2π geometry. The assumption of a correction factor of 0.5 to correct for the difference in geometry of the two surfaces has been shown to be valid only when the etching efficiencies of the two surfaces are virtually identical (i.e. 100%) and both spontaneous and induced tracks have been fully revealed (Gleadow, 1978 and Naeser et al., 1980). Great care is therefore required in both the control of etching and selection of appropriate crystals. For further reading, consult Gleadow and Lovering (1977), Green and Durrani (1978) and Gleadow (1978 and 1981).

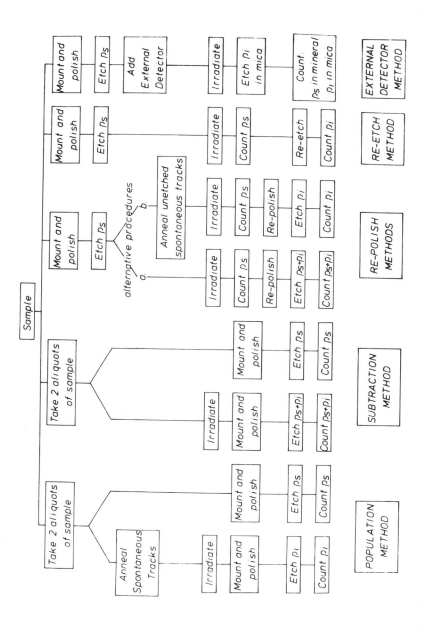

Figure 5.7 Schematic representation of different FT dating strategies. The population and external detector method are used almost exclusively. In the re-etch and external detector methods, external surfaces are used and a geometry correction factor is required. (From Hurford and Green, 1982.)

UNCERTAINTIES IN FISSION TRACK DATING

In quantifying the reliability of a FT age determination, three components must be considered: the precision of the analysis, the accuracy of the analysis and geological accuracy of the determined age. The uncertainty attached to a measured age is commonly only an assessment of the analytical precision of the determination. Some measure of the accuracy of a determination may also be included in the quoted error if the uncertainties on the physical constants used or on the measurement of standards are incorporated. Measured ages should always be considered within the limits of uncertainty set by the analyst.

Analytical Precision

Analytical precision provides a measure of the probable reproducibility of a determination which, on optimum samples, may be better than implied by the calculated estimate. Conversely a difficult sample may result in an underestimate of analytical uncertainty. FT dating is also heavily dependent upon personal technique and expertise and thus the reproducibility of a new student is likely to be less than that of an experienced worker. The calculation of the analytical precision of a fission track measurement has been much debated in recent years (see Green, 1981 and references therein). The now generally accepted statistical analysis makes the fundamental assumption that fission track counts follow a Poisson distribution. The Poisson distribution is a limiting case of the binomial distribution of a large number of events, in which the probability that a single event will occur is proportional to the length of time since the last event; each event is independent and has the same probability of occurring, with no two events occurring simultaneously. Radioactive decay is a random process; if a certain number, N_0, of radioactive atoms are allowed to decay for a series of time intervals, t, then the number of decays, m, observed in each interval will not be that same, but will be described by a Poisson distribution. The mean value of m is given by:

$$m = N_0 \lambda \Delta t \qquad (5.6)$$

for samples where ($\lambda \Delta t \ll 1$) and where λ is the decay constant (Friedlander et al., 1964, Green, 1981).

The standard deviation σ of the distribution is given by:

$$\sigma = m^{1/2} \qquad (5.7)$$

again for the case ($\lambda \Delta t \ll 1$).

In fission track dating, this Poisson distribution applies to the formation of tracks within a crystal with a given uniform uranium distribution and will account for the variations in the track density in different parts of such a crystal. Strictly, this distribution is for tracks originating in a homogeneous source, a situation different from a natural sample. For external detector analysis this is of no consequence since each crystal and its detector are considered as separate paired data sets and only in-grain variation of uranium contributes to the error. For practical purposes the standard deviation, $\sigma(t)$ of a FT age, determined by the external detector method, is calculated by summing the uncertainties on each track density:

$$\sigma(t) = t \left[(1/N_s) + (1/N_i) + (1/N_d) \right]^{1/2} \tag{5.8}$$

where N_s, N_i and N_d are, respectively, the total numbers of spontaneous, induced and dosimeter tracks counted. Non-Poissonian sources of variation may be introduced into an analysis, for example by careless technique, the presence of track-like defects, incomplete etching or the presence of crystals of more than one age (Green, 1981). Thus the conventional error assessment given in equation (5.8) represents a best limiting case. A χ^2 test has been proposed by Galbraith (1982) to discern whether the variation in a given data set exceeds that predicted by Poisson statistics. Most external detector method analyses pass the χ^2 test, suggesting that the conventional error assessment is a reasonable model.

For the population method, where data from different crystals possessing a variety of uranium contents are pooled to obtain a track density, intergrain inhomogeneity of uranium may contribute a major extra-Poissonian error. No rigourous treatment of error estimation has yet been made for the population method; in practice errors are calculated from the standard deviations of the individual spontaneous and induced track counts, assuming them to be normally distributed. The combined error is calculated from:

$$\sigma(t) = t \left[(\sigma/\bar{x})_s^2 + (\sigma/\bar{x})_i^2 + 1/N_d \right]^{1/2} \tag{5.9}$$

where σ is the standard error of the mean (that is $\sigma/N^{1/2}$) of the individual crystal counts and $\bar{x}$ is the mean count. The subscripts s and i indicate spontaneous and induced tracks respectively. As before, the contribution of uncertainty from the dosimeter glass count, N_d, is taken to be the Poisson error.

Analytical Accuracy

The analytical accuracy of a determined age demands absolute and accurate values for each physical constant used in its derivation. We have already considered the uncertainty of the decay constant value λ_f in FT dating, and the complexities of measuring absolute neutron fluences, necessary if a value of the decay constant is to be considered absolute. Both the credible alternatives (the zeta approach and the evaluation of the fluence calibration to decay constant ratio against age standards) mean that the FT method is not independent but relies upon samples whose ages are known from alternative sources, principally the K-Ar method. The accuracy of this independent dating method is thus inherent in the calibrating age and is passed on to the FT method.

Geological Accuracy

The geological accuracy of a determined age is the degree to which that age represents the true age of a geologic event such as volcanism, intrusion, uplift or metamorphism. Clearly there is a fundamental need for appropriate sampling; zircons occur as detrital grains in many clastic sediments and ages measured on such crystals probably will relate not to the sediment itself, but to some stage in the history of the rock from which the sediment was derived. Dating of a sedimentary sequence is thus dependent upon the presence of volcanic-derived rocks such as tuffs or bentonites within the sedimentary pile.

Deviation of a measured age from a geological age may result from the loss of fission tracks through annealing, leading to a complete or partial resetting of the FT clock. Again, the exact mechanism of annealing is incompletely understood, but in principle, the application of energy to a damaged lattice promotes the diffusion of the displaced ions back to their original positions. The ends of a fission track, where the fission fragment damage is less, may anneal first, either progressively from both ends towards the middle, or by the rebuilding of "walls" across the track which impede the passage of etchant. This suggests a correlation between the size of a fission track and the amount of annealing which that sample has undergone and in certain cases, specifically in glass, the degree of reduction of track size (in glass the track diameter) can be used to correct the age for partial annealing, to obtain the initial cooling age (Storzer and Wagner, 1969 and Storzer and Poupeau, 1973). Reductions in the length of confined tracks in apatite may also serve as an approximate correction to a measured age.

Fleischer et al. (1965b) have shown that temperature rather than pressure is the all important factor in annealing, the effect of any particular temperature being very time dependent: if an apatite sample is heated in the laboratory at 350°C for one hour, it will lose all its tracks; in nature, the same effect will occur if the sample is held at only 100°C for over 10^6 years. Laboratory experiments (Wagner, 1968, Naeser and Faul, 1969, Krishnaswami et al., 1974, Laslett et al., 1987) have defined the degree of track loss in various minerals at different times and temperatures, extrapolating the results by many orders of magnitude to geological time (Figure 5.8). Fleischer et al. (1975) offer a useful summary of laboratory annealing data. The extrapolated closure temperature for apatite of 100-120°C (Figure 5.8) has been confirmed by deep drill-hole measurements, where apatite at increasing depth (and thus increasing temperature) gives zero ages at temperatures of around 120°C (Naeser, 1979 and Gleadow and Duddy, 1981). For zircon, a number of geological studies indicate that a closure temperature of 200-250° is more reasonable than extrapolated laboratory values (Gleadow and Brooks, 1979 and Hurford, 1986).

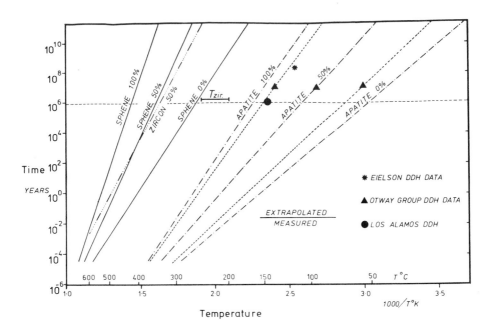

Figure 5.8 *Annealing data for apatite, sphene and zircon. Measured laboratory curves are extrapolated to geological time as indicated with the percentage track-loss shown on each curve. The annealing fan suggested for apatite is narrowed by inclusion of 100, 50 and 0% track-loss points found in the Otway Group drill holes (Gleadow and Duddy, 1981) and 100% track-loss points from Eielso and Los Alamos deep drill-holes (Naeser, 1979). The probable closure temperature range for zircon, as given by geological evidence, is denoted T_{zir}. (Updated from Naeser, 1979).*

QUATERNARY APPLICATIONS — A SYNOPSIS

Tephrochronology

Tephrochronology represents the most useful contribution FT dating can offer to Quaternary studies, helping in that difficult time area between the upper limits of ^{14}C dating, 40 to 50 ka BP and the lower age range of K-Ar dating, typically 500 ka BP. In addition, the FT external detector method permits analysis of single crystals which is of value in tephras where detrital contaminants are common. Zircon, with its higher uranium content and higher track stability temperature, is best suited for tephrochronological work (e.g. Naeser et al., 1973 and Gleadow, 1980). Volcanic glass shards have also been used (e.g. Seward, 1974 and Briggs and Westgate, 1978) although low uranium contents make counting tedious and low annealing thresholds mean that measured ages should be considered minima.

100

Archaeometry

Archaeometric applications include dating of stratigraphic layers associated with archaeological and hominid remains (e.g. Fleischer et al., 1965c, Aronson et al., 1977 and Gleadow, 1980) and dating material used in the manufacture of artefacts, and thereby deducing source areas and tracing trade routes (e.g. Durrani et al., 1971, Bigazzi and Bonadonna, 1973 and Miller and Wagner, 1981). Such archaeological ages constitute a minority application of the FT method and, since such samples are very young and often formed from low-uranium material, resultant ages possess high analytical errors and may not warrant the extended analytical times. See Fleischer et al. (1975) and Wagner (1978) for further examples.

Thermal History Studies

Although annealing (particularly in apatite) may hinder absolute dating of a formation, measurement of the pattern of apatite age decrease within a borehole sequence, and the reduction in length of confined fission tracks in apatite provide very powerful tools for modelling low-temperature thermal histories, particularly in sedimentary basins. It is highly significant that the temperature range of the track annealing zone in apatite, 60-125°C, is virtually identical with the temperature required for formation of liquid hydrocarbons and thus apatites contain a record of the heating of the parent rock in the oil generation window. This application although of great importance, is not specifically of Quaternary interest and is not considered further here. Green et al. (1986) and references therein provide a thorough introduction to the subject.

ASSESSING FISSION TRACK DATA

Presentation of a fission track age without data or details of its derivation denies critical assessment of the analysis, greatly reducing its value since it cannot be used or compared with other age data with any degree of confidence. Regrettably, many fission track ages have been published with inadequate, or in some cases without any analytical data. Naeser et al. (1979) first recommended a comprehensive reporting format for data with additional requirements being proposed by Hurford and Green (1982) and Miller et al. (1985). The following list represents a synopsis of the information which should be given either in a data table or in the accompanying text:

1) Sample details and identification number.

2) Type of material being dated (e.g. apatite, glass, zircon).

3) The sampling handling procedures appropriate to each sample type (e.g. EDM or population method).

4) The size of the sample counted; for the EDM, the number of crystals; for the population method the number of fields (or crystals).

5) ρ_s the spontaneous track density (tr cm^{-2}) and N_s the actual number of spontaneous tracks counted. If annealing corrections using the plateau, diameter or length measurement methods were made, the count data after annealing as well as the original values should appear.

6) ρ_i the induced track density (tr cm^{-2}) and N_i, the actual number of induced tracks counted. Naeser et al. (1979) recommend that for external detectors, the induced track density be corrected to that on an equivalent internal surface, normally dividing the measured and induced density by a correction factor of 0.5; some workers prefer to quote directly the measured induced track density. These alternatives emphasise the need to specify exactly what p_i means and what correction factor has been applied.

7) To estimate the spread of individual crystal results in the EDM, it is useful to include the relative χ^2-value. Where an analysis fails the χ^2-test and the age is calculated using the mean individual crystal track ratio and its uncertainty, the mean ρ_s/ρ_i ratio should be included in the table.

8) For population method analyses, some estimate of the dispersion of uranium between crystals should be reported.

9) Is there a quantitative assessment of the thermalisation of the irradiation facility used?

10) Where the neutron fluence has been monitored by a uranium dosimeter glass, the glass should be identified and the track density ρ_d (tr cm^{-2}), together with the number of tracks counted, N_d, stated.

11) In calculating the sample's age, what values of the fission decay constant λ_f, the uranium isotope abundance ratio I, and the ^{235}U thermal neutron fission cross section, σ, were used or what zeta value was used?

12) Have the calibration parameters, zeta or the neutron fluence/λ_f ratio been tested against age standards? Are the data included or referenced? Has the author demonstrated a consistency of analysis of age standards?

13) The method of error propagation should be included together with a note as to whether the errors are 1σ or 2σ.

14) Were any track length or diameter measurements made and/or corrections made for natural partial annealing? If so, details should be given.

Although this seems a lengthy and very demanding list, the requirements may be easily contained in a table (e.g. Table 5.3) and a single paragraph, so giving the reader greater confidence in using the data.

Table 5.3 *Sample table containing analytical data for a series of fission track age determinations.*

Sample and Locality	Mineral and No. crystals	Spontaneous ρ_s	(N_s)	Induced ρ_i	(N_i)	$P\chi^2\%$ or $s'\%$	ρ_s/ρ_i $\pm1\sigma$	Irrad. No.	Glass	Dosimeter ρ_d	(N_d)	Age Ma
KAW 2471 Gran Paradiso	zircon 20	70.86	(1466)	42.05	(870)	58%	—	Be-32	CN-1	3.203	(3835)	30.4±1.6
KAW 2464 Gran Paradiso	zircon 20	86.52	(2033)	52.99	(1245)	<2%	1.671 ±0.086	Be-32	CN-1	3.227	(3835)	30.4±1.8
Fish Canyon Tuff Standard	zircon 20	66.36	(3220)	45.50	(2232)	21%	—	Be-32	CN-1	3.395	(3835)	27.6±1.1
KAW 2461 Gran Paradiso	apatite 250/200	2.655	(472)	18.75	(2667)	5%	—	Be-30	612	5.008	(5950)	23.9±2.4

Notes:

(i)   track densities (ρ) are as measured and ($\times 10^5$ tr cm^{-2});

(ii) all ages calculated with zeta-612 = 339 and zeta-CN-1 = 112;

(iii) $P(\chi^2)$ is probability of obtaining χ^2 value for v degrees of freedom where v = no. crystals -1); mean ρ_s/ρ_i ratio used to calculate age and uncertainty where $P(\chi^2)$ <5%

(iv) for population method analyses, relative standard error of mean track count (s') is shown.

SUMMARY

FT dating is a reliable method of radiometric dating that is highly dependent upon experience in preparation technique and in counting. The method is applicable to those materials which possess a reasonable trace quantity of uranium; in practice this effectively limits the method to the minerals zircon, apatite and sphene, and certain glasses.

To derive credible and meaningful results on samples, extreme care must be taken in system calibration, employing multiple determinations on age standards of international repute in order to establish calibration parameters for each worker. Full details of analytical data should be presented to permit comparison with ages measured by other workers.

Great attention must be paid to problems of anisotropic etching in zircon and sphene, and etch times must be sufficient to reveal tracks in all orientations. Only surfaces of high etching efficiency must be analysed; such surfaces are prismatic, orientated parallel to the crystallographic axis and possess well-etched polishing scratches, less than 1.5 µm in width.

Quaternary applications consist principally of tephrochronology and, to a much lesser extent, archaeometry. FT analysis of detrital apatites in borehole samples from sedimentary basins provides a means of determining past thermal histories.

REFERENCES

Aronson, J.L., Scmitt, T.J., Walter, R.C., Taieb, M., Tiercelin, J.J., Johanson, D.C., Naeser, C.W. and Nairn, A.E.M. 1977. New geochronologic and paleomagnetic data for the hominid-bearing Hadar Formation of Ethiopia. *Nature*, **267**, 323-327.

Bigazzi, G. 1981. The problem of the decay constant λ of ^{238}U. *Nuclear Tracks*, **5**, 35-44.

Bigazzi, G. and Bonadonna, F. 1973. Fission track dating of the obsidian of Lipari Island (Italy). *Nature*, **242**, 322-323.

Briggs, N.D. and Westgate, J.A. 1978. A contribution to the Pleistocene geochronology of Alaska and the Yukon Territory: fission track age of distal tehpra units. In *Short papers of the 4th International Conference on Geochronology, Cosmochronology and Isotope Geology*, (ed Zartman, R.E.), U.S. Geol. Survey Open File Rep. **78-701**, 49-52.

Cowan, G.A. and Adler, H.H. 1976. The variability of the natural abundance of ^{235}U. *Geochimica et Cosmochimica Acta*, **40**, 1487-1490.

Durrani, S.A., Khan, H.A., Taj, M. and Renfrew, C. 1971. Obsidian source identification by fission track analysis. *Nautre*, **233**, 242-245.

Fleischer, R.L. and Hart, H.R. 1972. Fission track dating: techniques and problems. In

Calibration of Hominid Evolution, (eds Bishop, W.W., Miller, J.A. and Cole, S.), Scottish Academic Press, Edinburgh, 135-170.

Fleischer, R.L. and Price, P.B. 1964. Decay constant for spontaneous fission of [238]U. *Physics Review*, **133**, B63-B64.

Fleischer, R.L., Price, P.B., Walker, R.M. and Hubbard, E.L. 1964. Track registration in various solid-state nuclear track detectors. *Physics Review*, **133**, A1443-1449.

Fleischer, R.L., Price, P.B. and Walker, R.M. 1965a. Ion explosion spike mechanism for formation of charged particle tracks in solids. *Journal of Applied Physics*, **36**, 3645-3652.

Fleischer, R.L., Price, P.B. and Walker, R.M. 1965b. Effects of temperature, pressure and ionization on the formation and stability of fission tracks in minerals and glasses. *Journal of Geophysical Research*, **70**, 1497-1502.

Fleischer, R.L., Price, P.B., Walker, R.M. and Leakey, L.S.B. 1965c. Fission track dating of Bed I, Olduvai Gorge. *Science*, **148**, 72-74.

Fleischer, R.L., Price, P.B. and Walker, R.M. 1975. *Nuclear Tracks in Solids: Principles and Applications*, University of California Press, Berkeley, California. pp. 430.

Friedlander, G., Kennedy, J.W. and Miller, J.M. 1964. *Nuclear and Radiochemistry*, John Wiley, New York. pp. 320.

Galbraith, R.F. 1982. Statistical analysis of some fission track counts and neutron fluence measurements. *Nuclear Tracks*, **6**, 99-107.

Gleadow, A.J.W. 1974. *Geological Interpretation of Fission Track Data*. Unpublished doctoral thesis, University of Melbourne.

Gleadow, A.J.W. 1978. Anisotropic and variable track etching characteristics in natural sphenes. *Nuclear Track Detection*, **2**, 105-117.

Gleadow, A.J.W. 1980. Fission track age of the KBS tuff and associated hominid remains in northern Kenya. *Nature*, **284**, 225-230.

Gleadow, A.J.W. 1981. Fission track dating: what are the real alternatives? *Nuclear Tracks*, **5**, 3-14.

Gleadow, A.J.W. and Brooks, C.K. 1979. Fission track dating, thermal histories and tectonics of igneous intrusions in East Greenland. *Contributions in Minerology and Petrology*, **71**, 45-60.

Gleadow, A.J.W. and Duddy, I.R. 1981. A natural long-term annealing experiment for apatite. *Nuclear Tracks*, **5**, 169-174.

Gleadow, A.J.W. and Lovering, J.F. 1977. Geometry factor for external detectors in fission track dating. *Nuclear Track Detection*, **1**, 99-106.

Gleadow, J.W., Hurford, A.J. and Quaife, R.D. 1976. Fission track dating of zircon: improved etching techniques. *Earth and Planetary Science Letters*, **33**, 273-276.

Green, P.F. 1981. A new look at statistics in fission track dating. *Nuclear Tracks*, **5**, 77-86.

Green, P.F. 1985. Comparison of zeta calibration baselines for fission track dating of apatite, zircon and sphene. *Chemical Geology (Isotope Geoscience Section)*, **58**, 1-22.

Green, P.F. and Durrani, S.A. 1978. A quantitative assessment of geometry factors for use in fission track studies. *Nuclear Track Detection*, **2**, 207-213.

Green, P.F. and Hurford, A.J. 1984. Thermal neutron dosimetry for fission track dating. *Nuclear Tracks*, **9**, 231-241.

Green, P.F., Duddy, I.R., Gleadow, A.J.W. and Lovering, J.F. 1986. Apatite fission track analysis as a paleotemperature indicator for hydrocarbon exploration. In: *Thermal History of Sedimentary Basins: Methods and Case Histories* (eds Naeser, N.D. and McCulloh, T.H.), Springer-Verlag, New York, 181-195.

Hannah, G.C., Wescott, C.H., Lemmel, H.D., Leonard, B.R., Story, J.S. and Attree, P.M. 1969. Revision of values for the 2200 m/s neutron constants for four fissile nuclides. *General Electric Corporation: Atomic Energy Review*, **7**, 3-92.

Hurford, A.J. 1990. Standardisation of fission track dating calibration: recommendation by the Fission Track Working Group of the I.U.G.S. Subcommission on Geochronology. *Chemical Geology (Isotope Geoscience Section)*, **80**, 85-94.

Hurford, A.J. 1986. Cooling and uplift patterns in the Leopontine Alps, South Central Switzerland and an age of vertical movement on the Insubric Fault Line. *Contributions in Mineralogy and Petrology*, **92**, 413-427.

Hurford, A.J. and Gleadow, A.J.W. 1977. Calibration of fission track dating parameters. *Nuclear Track Detection*, **1**, 41-48.

Hurford, A.J. and Green, P.F. 1981. Standards, dosimetry and the uranium-238 λ decay constant: a discussion. *Nuclear Tracks*, **5**, 53-61.

Hurford, A.J. and Green, P.F. 1982. A user's guide to fission track dating calibration. *Earth and Planetary Science Letters*, **59**, 343-354.

Hurford, A.J. and Green, P.F. 1983. The zeta age calibration of fission track dating. *Chemical Geology (Isotope Geoscience Section)*, **1**, 285-317.

Hurford, A.J. and Hammerschmidt, K. 1985. ^{40}Ar-^{39}Ar and K-Ar dating of the Bishop and Fish Canyon Tuffs: calibration ages for fission track dating standards. *Chemical Geology (Isotope Geoscience Section)*, **58**, 23-32.

Jaffey, A.H., Flynn, K.F., Glendenin, L.E., Bentley, W.C. and Essling, A.M. 1971. Precision measurements of the half-lives and specific activities of ^{235}U and ^{238}U. *Physics Review*, **4**, 1889-1906.

Krishnaswami, S., Lal, D., Prabhu, N. and Macdougall, D. 1974. Characteristics of fission tracks in zircon applications to geochronology and cosmology. *Earth and Planetary Science Letters*, **22**, 51-59.

Laslett, G.M., Green, P.F., Duddy, I.R. and Gleadow, A.J.W. 1987. Thermal annealing of fission tracks in apatite II: a quantitative analysis. *Chemical Geology (Isotope Geoscience Section)*, **65**, 1-13.

Miller, D.S. and Wagner, G.A. 1981. Fission track ages applied to obsidian artifacts from South America using the plateau-annealing and track size correction techniques. *Nuclear Tracks*, **5**, 147-155.

Miller, D.S., Duddy, I.R., Green, P.F., Hurford, A.J. and Naeser, C.W. 1985. Results of interlaboratory comparison of fission track age standards, Fission Track Workshop, 1984. *Nuclear Tracks*, **10**, 383-391.

Naeser, C.W. 1967. The use of apatite and sphene for fission track age determinations. *Bulletin of the Geological Society of America*, **78**, 1523-1526.

Naeser, C.W. 1979. Fission track dating and geologic annealing of fission tracks. In *Lectures in Isotope Geology*, (eds Jager, E. and Hunziker, J.C.), Springer-Verlag, Heidelberg, 154-169.

Naeser, C.W. and Faul, H. 1969. Fission track annealing in apatite and sphene. *Journal of Geophysical Research*, **74**, 705-710.

Naeser, C.W., Gleadow, A.J.W. and Wagner, G.A. 1979. Standardisation of fission track data reports. *Nuclear Tracks*, **3**, 133-136.

Naeser, C.W., Hurford, A.J. and Gleadow, A.J.W. 1977. Fission track dating of pumice from the KBS tuff, East Rudolf, Kenya - discussion. *Nature*, **267**, 649.

Naeser, C.W., Izett, G.A. and Obradovich, J.D. 1980. Fission track and K-Ar ages of natural glasses. *United States Geological Survey Bulletin*, **1489**.

Naeser, C.W., Izett, G.A. and Wilcox, R.E. 1973. Zircon fission track ages of Pearlette family ash beds in Meade County, Kansas. *Geology*, **1**, 187-189.

Price, P.B. and Walker, R.M. 1963. Fossil tracks of charged-particles in mica and the age of minerals. *Journal of Geophysical Research*, **68**, 4847-4862.

Seward, D. 1974. Age of New Zealand Pleistocene substages by fission track dating of glass shards from tephra horizons. *Earth and Planetary Science Letters*, **24**, 242-248.

Storzer, D. and Poupeau, G. 1973. Ages-plateaux de mineraux de verres par la methode des traces de fission. *Comptes Rendus Acadamie de Science de Paris Series D*, **276**, 137-139.

Storzer, D. and Wagner, G.A. 1969. Correction of thermally lowered fission track ages of tektites. *Earth and Planetary Science Letters*, **5**, 463-368.

Thiel, K. and Herr, W. 1976. The ^{238}U spontaneous fission decay constant redetermined by fission tracks. *Earth and Planetary Science Letters*, **30**, 50-56.

Wagner, G.A. 1968. Fission track dating of apatites. *Earth and Planetary Science Letters*, **4**, 411-415.

Wagner, G.A. 1978. Archaeological applications of fission track dating. *Nuclear Track Detection*, **2**, 51-63.

Wagner, G.A., Reimer, G.M., Carpenter, B.S., Faul, H., Van der Linden, R. and Gijbels, R. 1975. The spontaneous fission rate of ^{238}U and fission track dating. *Geochimica et Cosmochimica Acta*, **39**, 1279-1286.

Chapter 6

LUMINESCENCE DATING

A.G. Wintle

Thermoluminescence (TL) dating was the first method to use the luminescence signal from mineral grains as a means of determining the age of a particular event. The method was initially used for dating heated archaeological material (see review by Aitken, 1990), such as pottery or burnt flint. More recently it has been applied to unfired material such as stalagmites, for which the event being dated is the formation of the calcite crystals, and sediments, for which the event is the last exposure to sunlight. The equipment used for these different applications is the same, although minor modifications to procedure are made depending upon the mineral type and the nature of the event being dated.

Within the last six years a new technique has been developed — optical dating. Instead of the luminescence signal being stimulated by the application of heat, an optically stimulated luminescence (OSL) signal is measured while the mineral is exposed to photons of visible or infra-red electromagnetic radiation. This procedure allows the study of the most light-sensitive luminescence signal and is particularly useful for sediments which may have received a relatively short light exposure at deposition.

WHAT IS TL?

Some minerals, such as quartz and feldspars, calcite and clays, are thermoluminescent. This means that when they are heated after they have been exposed to alpha, beta, or gamma radiation, they emit light. The amount of light obtained depends upon the TL sensitivity (the amount of TL produced per unit radiation dose) of the individual minerals and upon the amount of radiation to which they have been exposed. If they are immediately reheated, no more light is obtained; another exposure to radiation is required to produce another TL signal.

In the natural environment, the alpha, beta and gamma radiation is produced by the decay of naturally-occurring radioactive elements. The radiation is dominated by the decay of elements in the uranium and thorium decay chains and ^{40}K, an isotope of potassium which makes up 0.012% of the naturally occurring potassium isotopes. ^{40}K produces only beta and gamma radiation, but the uranium and thorium decay chains also produce short range alpha radiation. The TL in silt-sized minerals from pottery or sediments is produced by these three types of nuclear radiation in approximately equal proportions.

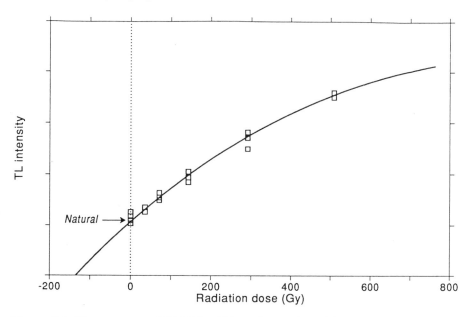

Figure 6.1 *TL response at 300 °C for Chinese loess (QTL120B) showing exponential growth with increasing radiation dose up to 500 Gy. Intercept on dose axis is 138 ± 5 Gy. Expected age for QTL120B is 25 ka.*

When a mineral is formed by crystallization from molten rock, the crystals will contain impurity atoms, i.e. atoms which do not belong in the main crystal structure, or other lattice defects. Some of these defects are attractive to free electrons which are produced in large numbers by nuclear radiation removing electrons from other atoms. Some of these electrons will get caught at the defects which are known as electron traps. When heat is subsequently applied to the crystal, these electrons are ejected from the traps and some recombine at another type of defect in the crystal which is termed a luminescence centre. Recombination of an electron at such a centre results in the emission of a photon. The emission of a large number of photons results in a measurable light signal. Hence the TL signal is proportional to the number of trapped electrons, which in turn is proportional to the amount of radiation exposure. Further details on the TL properties of minerals and the underlying mechanisms can be obtained elsewhere (see McKeever, 1985). Information relating to the TL dating of a variety of materials has been given by Aitken (1985).

Ideally the TL signal grows linearly with the radiation exposure, which is usually expressed in units of absorbed radiation dose, known as grays (Gy). After a long radiation exposure, the number of electron traps remaining empty, and therefore capable of trapping an electron produced nearby, is relatively small. This causes a reduction of the effective TL sensitivity and saturation of the TL response. This is shown in Figure 6.1, where the response is drawn as an exponential, representing the simplest physical model for saturation.

ZEROING OF EARLIER GEOLOGICAL SIGNALS

For TL to be used as a dating method, some event must have taken place at an appropriate time in the past which effectively emptied out the electrons which would have accumulated in the traps up to that point in time. In his recent review, Berger (1988) has defined two classes of event or process:

1) that which reduces the TL to zero at the time of interest. Obvious examples are pottery and other fired materials which have experienced application of heat (at least 300 °C for several hours), resulting in the emptying out of all the electrons. Other examples of this type of material are volcanic quartz and glass (Berger, 1985a) and precipitated carbonates, such as speleothems (Wintle, 1978, Debenham and Aitken, 1984). Calcite formed either by inorganic processes (e.g. speleothems) or by biological processes (e.g. foraminifera) contains empty electron traps, as confirmed by the study of very young samples (Debenham et al., 1982a).

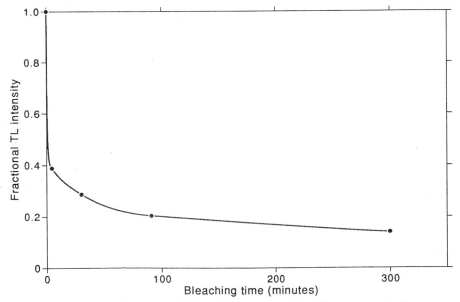

Figure 6.2 *Decay of natural TL for QTL120B at 300 °C as a result of exposure to a light source (6 times stronger than sunlight).*

2) that which reduces the signal to some non-zero level, which is unknown in advance. The main examples are sediments for which optical energy is responsible for the removal of electrons. Prolonged exposure to sunlight is capable of emptying out most, though not all, of the trapped electrons in feldspar and quartz (Wintle and Huntley, 1980, 1982). A typical bleaching curve is given in Figure 6.2.

Chemical effects and pressure (such as might be experienced beneath a glacier) have also been proposed as zeroing mechanisms and dates have been published for tills (Drozdowski and Fedorowicz, 1987). Little direct evidence has been presented to support these claims. Lamothe (1988) has suggested that TL signal growth may be seen for fine grains produced from large crystals as the result of subglacial abrasion.

FIRED MATERIALS

Before discussing the basic principles of the technique when used as a tool for dating sediments, mention should be made of the earlier application to heated materials and its recent use in providing a timescale for the arrival of modern man in the Near East.

TL dating of pottery and burnt stones was developed in the late 1960s and 1970s (Aitken, 1974 and 1985, Fleming, 1979, Wintle, 1980). TL dating of material older than 10 ka is mainly restricted to forms of heated silica, e.g. quartz, sandstone and flint. These materials are very low in radioactivity and, provided that their minimum thickness is greater than 0.5 cm, their radiation dose is derived almost entirely from the decay of radioactive elements in the soil surrounding them.

The most exciting applications have been to burnt flint in France (Valladas et al., 1986) and in Israel. A combined date of 92 ± 5 ka was obtained for 20 burnt flints from Qazfeh Cave in Israel (Valladas et al., 1988); the Mousterian deposits containing these flints are considered to be the forerunners of modern man — *Homo sapiens sapiens*. On the other hand, 38 dated flints from the nearby Kebara Cave containing remains of Neanderthal man ranged from about 48 to 60 ka (Valladas et al., 1987). These dates have overturned the widely-held views of hominid evolution in the Near East.

Quartz pebbles baked by natural heating (e.g. caused by incorporation in a lava flow) have been studied as well as quartz grains extracted from heated inclusions associated with explosive volcanism in central France (Raynal et al., 1982, 1985).

TL MEASUREMENTS

TL measurements are designed to obtain an accurate value for the radiation dose received by the sample since the zeroing event. This dose is usually referred to as the Equivalent Dose (ED) or Palaeodose. The ED is obtained by comparing the natural

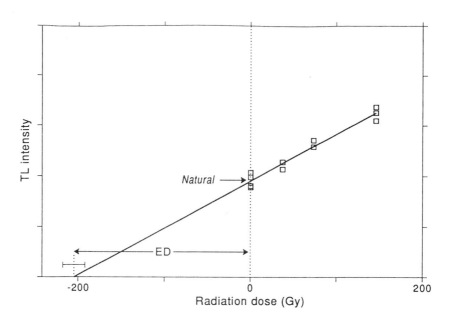

Figure 6.3a *TL response at 300 °C showing apparent linear response for added doses up to 150 Gy for QTL120B. Apparent ED = 204 ± 13 Gy.*

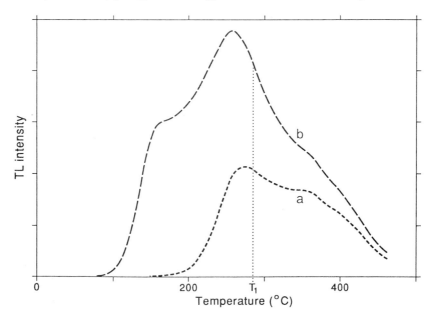

Figure 6.3b *TL glow curves for QTL120B: a) natural TL, b) TL as a result of adding a 150 Gy radiation dose.*

112

TL of the sample with the TL signal induced in it by exposure to a calibrated laboratory radiation source. The response to the laboratory source is a measure of the TL sensitivity. For heated materials (and also for calcite) the additive dose procedure, as illustrated in Figures 6.1 and 6.3a, is used to obtain the ED. This approach can be applied provided that:

1) the sample contained no trapped electrons at the time of the event being dated,

2) the sensitivity to radiation in the laboratory is the same as it was in nature (i.e. it is not affected by the much higher laboratory dose rate),

3) the growth response can be characterised mathematically.

Comparison of Figures 6.1 and 6.3a shows that applying a linear fit to a limited set of TL measurements does not adequately characterise the TL response of this sample and leads to gross overestimation of the ED. The shape of the growth curve as it approaches saturation must be obtained so that the correct extrapolation is made. For loess samples this is required for EDs over 100 Gy.

The intercept on the dose axis is thus the value of the ED to be put in the age equation:

$$\text{Age (years)} = \frac{\text{ED (grays)}}{\text{dose rate (grays/year)}} \qquad (6.1)$$

(Note: The ED is given in grays (abbreviation Gy), the SI unit of absorbed dose. In earlier papers the old unit of dose, the rad, was usually used. 1 rad $= 10^{-2}$ gray, 1 krad $= 10$ gray.)

The data points in Figure 6.3a are obtained from a set of glow curves which look similar to those in Figure 6.3b. These are plots of TL signal as a function of temperature and are obtained as the sample is heated from room temperature (about 20 °C) to 500 °C at a heating rate of 2-10 °C/s. To prevent non-radiation-induced TL signals being produced by surface interaction with oxygen, the measurements are made in an inert atmosphere after the oven volume has been evacuated (Aitken, 1985). The TL signal is detected with a photomultiplier tube, in front of which are placed colour filters which select particular wavelength regions.

Measurements are most commonly made either on fine grains (4-11 μm) containing a mixture of minerals (the TL signal from this grain size is usually dominated by that from the feldspars (Wintle, 1982)), or on coarse grains (typically 100-300 μm) to which mineral separation techniques can be applied. The measurements are then made on either potassium or sodium feldspars, or quartz extracts, which have had their surfaces removed by HF acid etching to remove the effect of natural alpha radiation.

The natural glow curve for any material which is several thousand years old will exhibit no TL signal below 175 °C. This is because the electron traps which would give rise to such a signal are thermally unstable and are kept empty at ambient temperature when exposed to the low natural irradiation rates. When such a sample is irradiated in the laboratory at much higher irradiation rates, the shallower traps are populated and a TL signal is obtained which would subsequently undergo decay with time. This part of the glow curve is thus unsuitable for dating. At higher glow curve temperatures, the electrons remain trapped for a long time and can be used for dating. The stable region of the glow curve can be ascertained by obtaining the ED at 5 °C intervals; above a temperature around 230 °C (shown as T1 in Figure 6.3b) the ED value will be constant. This approach is the basis of the "plateau test" for long term stability of the TL signal (Aitken, 1985).

Feldspars of volcanic origin are affected by a different type of loss of electrons known as anomalous fading (Wintle, 1973). This is the name for the rapid decay of TL which can be observed when some samples are irradiated in the laboratory. It does not obey conventional decay behaviour but shows up in the glow curve between 100 and 400 °C. Anomalous fading has also been reported for sediments from particular geographical areas, for example eastern Canada (Lamothe, 1984). Successful dating of feldspars extracted from lava flows has only been achieved using the TL signal above 500 °C, which does not appear to be prone to this decay (Guerin et al., 1981). Dating of volcanic glass from ash layers is possible, provided that the glass extract contains no feldspars (Berger and Huntley, 1983, Berger, 1985).

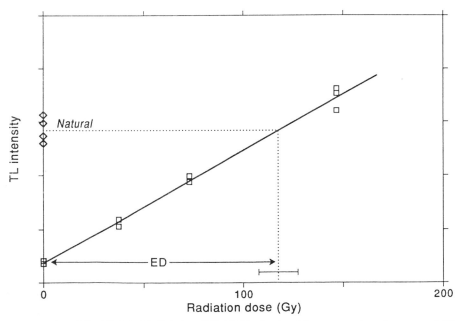

Figure 6.4 *ED (116 ± 10 Gy) for QTL120B obtained by comparing the natural TL with the TL response generated by doses up to 150 Gy after a long light exposure.*

The simple additive method of Figure 6.3a cannot however be applied to sediments because of a residual TL signal in the sample at deposition. Residual TL signals have been reported for modern silts (Berger, 1988) and may result from an equilibrium between trap filling and emptying and/or from minerals whose TL signal is unaffected by light. The residual signal is greater at higher glow curve temperatures and thus would cause a monotonically increasing ED with glow curve temperature when the additive dose procedure is used.

To get around this, several methods of ED determination have been proposed (Wintle and Huntley, 1980). Figure 6.4 illustrates the simplest method, in which the natural TL is compared with the TL induced in similar samples which have been bleached to a residual level in the laboratory and then irradiated. This method makes many assumptions concerning the effects of the light source used for the bleaching experiments. Further discussions of laboratory techniques may be found in reviews by Singhvi and Mejdahl (1985) and Berger (1988).

DOSE RATE DETERMINATION

The denominator of the age equation (6.1) is obtained by measurement of the radioactive content of the pottery, or sediment, combined with knowledge of the water content and radiation environment of the grains used for the TL measurements.

Radioactive Content

The beta and gamma dose due to ^{40}K may be obtained by measuring the total potassium content by an analytical technique, such as atomic absorption spectrometry, and using the known relative abundance of ^{40}K and the dose rate conversion factors obtained from the energy release and lifetime of the decay process (Aitken, 1985).

The alpha, beta and gamma contributions from the uranium and thorium decay chains may be determined by measuring the bulk alpha activity of the sample provided that the sample is uniform and the grain diameter is predominantly less than 40 μm in diameter (the average range of an alpha particle in sedimentary minerals is about 25 μm). The gently crushed sample is placed on a ZnS screen about 4 cm in diameter for at least 24 hours; the scintillations produced by alpha particles from radionuclides in the uranium and thorium decay chains impinging on the screen are observed with a photomultiplier tube and counted (Aitken, 1985). Only alpha particles originating within about 25 μm of the screen are able to reach it and this limits the amount of material being monitored to not much more than 100 mg. This is the best method for determining the alpha dose rate (which is directly proportional to the alpha count rate), which is then combined with a measured TL efficiency factor (obtained by comparing the relative TL response to laboratory alpha and beta radiation) to produce the effective alpha dose rate which is used in the age equation. Because the alpha count is derived from such a small amount of material, beta and gamma dose rates are best obtained by other techniques described later.

Other methods may also be used to measure the uranium and thorium decay chains in the laboratory. These include neutron activation analysis, used to determine the concentration of the parent radioisotopes of each chain, and gamma spectrometry, which enables many of the individual daughter isotopes to be measured and thus permits detection of possible disequilibrium in the decay chains. The individual beta and gamma dose rates can then be calculated using appropriate conversion factors (Aitken, 1985). Neutron activation measurements are also made on small samples and hence are not appropriate for the determination of the beta and gamma dose rates. Laboratory gamma spectrometers are capable of measuring radiation in samples from 7 g to 70 kg, depending upon the type of detector and the feasibility of transporting sufficient sediment to the laboratory.

Instead of measuring the concentrations of radionuclides in the samples, it is also possible to make direct measurements of the beta and gamma dose rates by TL dosimetry. For measurement of the beta dose rate, very sensitive TL phosphors such as natural fluorite (CaF_2) or artificial calcium sulphate ($CaSO_4$:Dy) are placed next to a fixed weight of sample and are stored in a shielded environment for several months (Bailiff and Aitken, 1980). The phosphor will then give a TL signal which is proportional to the beta dose rate.

In situ Gamma Dosimetry

A similar approach may be used for measuring the gamma dose rate from the decay chains and also from potassium. A copper capsule, about 2 cm long, containing grains of CaF_2 or $CaSO_4$:Dy is left in the deposit being dated and retrieved for measurement a year later. The capsule is inserted in the sediment to a depth of 30 cm, allowing the effect of the gamma radiation produced within a sphere of 30 cm radius to be recorded. The volume of this sphere is dictated by the maximum range of gamma rays and corresponds to about 300 kg of sediment. The alpha and beta radiation does not reach the grains because the copper walls are almost 1 mm thick, but the cosmic ray contribution is recorded. The capsules are heated at a temperature of at least 300 °C (e.g. in a gas flame) for a few minutes prior to their insertion in a hole made with an auger. This operation may be carried out by the archaeologist or geologist collecting the samples for dating. When the capsules are collected from the field, they should be returned immediately to the TL laboratory from which they were obtained, along with another capsule which is heated as before, but on the day of collection. This capsule monitors the "travel dose" received by all the capsules as they are brought back in luggage or sent through the post. This is particularly important if they return by air and are exposed to the increased cosmic radiation tens of thousands of feet above the ground, or are X-rayed.

Placing a dosimeter capsule has the advantage that it measures the dose rate experienced by the sample on an annual basis and will include effects due to absorption of the gamma radiation by water in the sediments (as discussed in the next section) and any inhomogeneities in the 30 cm radius sphere of sediment surrounding the sample. This approach is of particular importance for samples from archaeological sites which have a complex stratigraphy.

If a return visit to the site is impossible, a portable gamma spectrometer can be taken to the site and inserted 30 cm into the sediment using a 6.5 cm auger and the instantaneous gamma dose rate can be measured within an hour. The minor disadvantage of this approach is that it does not allow for annual changes in water content. However, there is no guarantee that the average water content in a particular year is representative of the average water content since deposition.

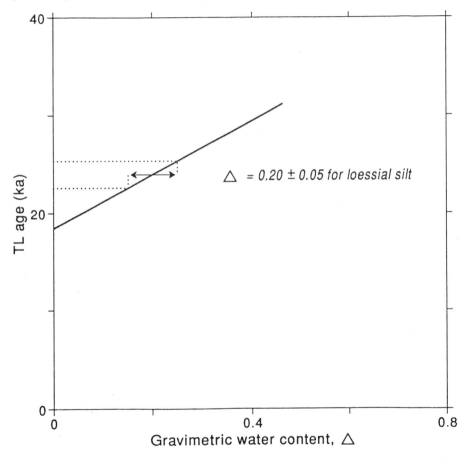

Figure 6.5 *TL age calculated for the same ED and radioactivity content but for different water content. Figure shows error in age resulting from typical uncertainty in past water content for silt.*

Effect of Water Content

The major correction that must be applied to the radiation dose rate is one which allows for the fraction of energy which is dissipated in water present in the sediment rather than in the mineral grains (Aitken, 1985). The presence of water in a sediment will result in a lower ED for a wet sediment than for a dry sample of the same age and with the same concentration of radionuclides. Hence, if no correction is applied to the alpha, beta and gamma dose rates calculated for a dry sample, the age obtained will be too young (Figure 6.5). The effective water content over the time of burial is difficult to estimate for sediments. It is easier for pottery which has a relatively low saturation water content due to its fixed, small pore structure. For aeolian sediments with a narrow grain size distribution and which have not experienced structural collapse, the water content has probably remained fairly constant. For loessic silts a fractional water content of 0.20 ± 0.05 is used. The effect of even this small uncertainty is illustrated in Figure 6.5. For lake sediments, with high initial water content but which have dried out at some unknown time in the past, the uncertainty in the age may be very large.

Radiation Dosimetry and Grain Size

Within a sediment, or a piece of pottery, there are different mineral grains of various sizes and with various radioactive contents. The TL measurements are carried out on narrow grain size fractions so that the appropriate dose rate is applied in the age equation.

One commonly used grain size is between 2 and 11 μm and this is used in the fine grain technique (either 2-8 or 4-11 μm). No mineral separation is performed and, in the case of sediments, the TL signal is usually dominated by that from feldspar grains. Because the maximum grain diameter is smaller than the ranges of all three radiation components, the grains will receive the full dose rate. This is about 4 Gy/ka for many loess deposits.

The quartz inclusion technique was developed for 90-125 μm quartz grains in pottery and takes advantage of the fact that quartz has a very low radioactive content. The outside 10 μm of each grain is removed by etching before TL measurement. This removes the alpha irradiated volume and the ED obtained for such grains can be considered as being due to beta and gamma radiation only. The technique has been applied to late glacial cover sands (Kolstrup et al., 1991) and to dune sands connected with interglacial high sea level stands. The dating of the latter is possible only when the radioactive content of the dune is very low e.g. in Australia (Huntley et al., 1985a). Gardner et al. (1987) used TL dating of quartz grains from dunes in a large dune field to demonstrate the existence of an early dune-building phase around 250 ka.

For more radioactive environments, TL dating of potassium feldspars is more promising. The approach is based on the feldspar inclusion dating method developed for pottery (Mejdahl and Winther-Nielsen, 1982) for which grains up to 500 μm diameter have been used. The advantage of using these grains is that a large fraction of the beta dose comes from the decay of ^{40}K in the crystal lattice. Lundqvist and Mejdahl (1987) recently reported the dating of fossil dune sands in central Sweden using this technique, but the ages were rather young compared with ages based on corrected radiocarbon dates and varve chronology. A systematic 40% underestimation has been reported for interglacial marine sands from north west Europe (Balescu et al., 1991) when the ages are compared with estimates based on their stratigraphic position. Further work on samples of known age has shown that this resulted from the choice of colour filter for the TL measurements (Balescu and Lamothe, 1991).

TIME LIMITS

The lower end of the dating range is set by the TL sensitivity of the sample and by the efficiency of the zeroing mechanism. For pottery or burnt stones, the sample is sufficiently heated for TL dating provided the whole sample has reached at least 450 °C. This is likely for pottery, but is sometimes difficult to assess visually for stones which may have only been in the fire for a short time. For fired materials, the TL sensitivity combined with the dose rate is the important factor; if both are high then pottery as young as 100 years old may be dated. On the other hand, flints tend to have very low sensitivity and also low alpha and beta dose rates because of the low concentration of radioactive nuclides. Hence it has been found difficult to date flints with ages as old as 10 ka (Huxtable and Jacobi, 1982).

Sediments also have variable TL sensitivity and for fine grains this depends upon the amount and type of feldspar present. For most fine grain samples, the increase in TL signal due to a 1 ka radiation exposure can be measured. However, the lower age limit is more realistically set by our ability to assess the residual TL level contained within the natural TL signal. Studies of fine grains from modern aeolian silt (Berger, 1987) and a modern soil developed on loess (Wintle and Catt, 1985), as well as coarse grained quartz from beach and dune sand show that long laboratory light exposures can reduce the signal in modern samples which might otherwise be thought to have been well bleached in their natural environment. If such long bleaching times were used in the ED determination, most aeolian samples would have their TL age overestimated by about 2 ka.

Much greater errors would occur if similar long bleaching times were applied to waterlaid materials. Grains carried by rivers are exposed to a restricted light spectrum (Berger and Luternauer, 1987), particularly as a result of scattering by sediment particles. Such grains are likely to have been exposed to wavelengths greater than 500 nm and hence laboratory light sources containing shorter wavelengths (all sun-lamps or solar simulators) should not be used without appropriate optical filters (Berger, 1984, 1985b).

The upper end of the dating range is controlled by two phenomena; (a) saturation and (b) instability of the TL signal. The TL growth curve is not linear, although for young samples (less than 20 ka) such an approximation may be made (Figure 6.4). At higher doses the response curve flattens (Figure 6.1) and is better expressed by a saturating exponential curve. For the ED to be obtained by the additive dose method, extrapolation of the response curve relies on the use of correct curve fitting. Figure 6.3a shows how an ED of 204 Gy would be obtained if linear growth was assumed using added doses up to 150 Gy, whereas, if doses up to 500 Gy were applied and an exponential fit used, an ED of 138 Gy would be obtained. Extrapolation becomes more difficult as the natural TL approaches the saturation level.

For quartz, the upper age limit is about 70 ka, unless the sample is from a sand dune with very low radioactivity (Huntley et al., 1985a). The saturation level is higher for potassium feldspars, corresponding to about 1 Ma. However, the practical limit of dating is lower because of long term instability of the TL signal. Mejdahl (1988) has suggested that significant correction factors should be applied to samples over 100 ka. As yet there have been insufficient tests on known age samples to determine the range of thermal instability found in potassium feldspars around the world. The behaviour is complicated by the occurrence of anomalous fading in some feldspars, particularly those derived from volcanic eruptions.

Thermal stability is also the limiting factor for the preferred TL peak of stalagmitic calcite; however, comparisons with a more stable peak, which has a non-linear response, indicate that the lower temperature peak can be used for stalagmites up to 100 ka (Debenham, 1983).

SOURCES OF ERROR

Some sources of error have already been discussed in the foregoing sections and will be summarised here. A detailed discussion of the sources of error and the incorporation of both random and systematic error into the age equation has been given by Aitken (1985).

Error in ED Determination

There are systematic errors of about ± 3% associated with the calibration of laboratory radiation sources. Systematic underestimation of the ED will result if the TL peak used is thermally unstable or if the mineral exhibits anomalous fading. Systematic overestimation will result if the additive dose method is used and linear curve fitting applied when the sample has a non-linear response. The measured random error in the quoted ED results from the reproducibility of the TL measurements; multiple measurements have an uncertainty of around ± 5% which will be worse for samples for which the most TL sensitive minerals make up only a small fraction of the bulk of the sample.

Error in Dose Rate Measurement

Provided that the sample is homogeneous, the potassium content is the best known value, with a random error of less than ± 2%. The alpha counting method for alpha dose rate measurement has a random error of $\pm 3\%$ when 1,000 counts are accumulated and a calibration error of about $\pm 2\%$. However, it is only appropriate for homogeneous fine grain sediments or finely-crushed pottery sherds.

However, there are some factors which can cause more significant errors. For example, the uranium and thorium may be concentrated in minerals such as zircon, which is found in the heavy fraction of many sediments. Also, some pottery fabrics are liable to release radon, a short-lived but very mobile gaseous element in the uranium decay chain. Loss of radon would mean the loss of the dose rate from its daughter products. There are also other sources of disequilibrium in the uranium decay chain, the most significant resulting from the difference in solubility of uranium and thorium. The lack of solubility of ^{230}Th results in it not being incorporated into stalagmitic calcite at formation (Wintle, 1978), but results in it being deposited out of deep ocean water to give an excess in ocean floor sediments (Wintle and Huntley, 1980). Both these situations result in time dependent dose rates for the age equation as equilibrium is approached in the radioactive decay chains. Changing dose rates can also be caused by migration of radioelements through a sediment section resulting either in the loss of near-surface atoms by leaching or incorporation of additional radionuclides in an iron-rich coating on the surface of grains. These effects have not been fully assessed.

Specific Problems

The main source of error for stalagmites is the assessment of the environmental dose rate. The calcite has low uranium content in contrast to the sediments washed into the caves which have a much higher activity. A recent comparative study of TL and uranium series dating of stalagmites has shown that it is possible, but very difficult, to obtain TL dates in cave environments (Debenham and Aitken, 1984).

The main source of error for aeolian sediments is the uncertainty in the past water content, as discussed in an earlier section. For waterlaid sediments, the main source of error is connected with the incomplete zeroing at deposition. This can either result from different minerals being bleached by different amounts (as might be expected for quartz and feldspar grains carried in a river with a high sediment load) or from a mixture of bleached and unbleached grains being deposited together (as might be expected for a glacial lake with an aeolian input mixed with a sub-glacial input). There are still many uncertainties relating to the long term stability of the TL signal from sediments.

SAMPLE COLLECTION

Slightly different procedures are required for the different types of sample that may be used for dating. It is preferable that a scientist from the dating laboratory should visit the site, not only to ensure that samples are taken correctly, but also so that either a dosimeter can be placed in the section or *in situ* measurement of the gamma radiation can be made with a gamma spectrometer. In the event that this is not possible, a brief outline of collection procedures for different materials is given below.

Pottery. An information sheet with detailed pottery collection procedures was produced by the Research Laboratory for Archaeology, Oxford, and was reprinted in Aitken's books (Aitken, 1974, 1985). Pottery should be collected as excavated and put immediately into sealed, plastic bags (to allow laboratory measurement of their water content) and then placed in an opaque container, such as a thick, black plastic bag. A bag containing at least 10 g (preferably 500 g to allow laboratory gamma spectrometry measurements) of soil that was immediately surrounding the pot must be collected. It should also be double bagged and sealed to retain the *in situ* water content. This does not need shielding from light.

Burnt flints and stones should be collected as excavated and put straight into a light-tight container or wrapped in aluminium foil. Flints do not absorb significant amounts of water and it is not necessary to double bag them. The pieces of flint should be at least 1 cm thick so that the surface 2 mm can be removed easily in the laboratory. It is most important to collect a large bag of the surrounding soil (about 500 g) since the environmental dose rate often dominates the total dose rate.

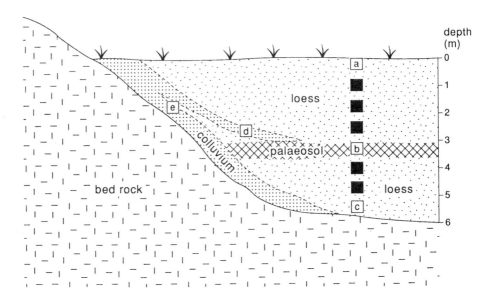

Figure 6.6 *Schematic section showing good sampling strategy,* ■ *, and position of poor samples, a too close to surface, b palaeosol could be affected by leaching or pregenetic signal, c too close to bedrock which may have very different radioactivity, d colluvium containing reworked grains which may not have been exposed to light, e too close to bedrock and colluvium may contain unbleached grains.*

Calcite and volcanic ash dating is so specialised that samples should not be collected without the TL scientist being present.

Compact sediments such as loess, should be collected from freshly cleaned faces by cutting a solid piece with a minimum dimension of 3 cm. It is recommended that the sample is put in a rigid, light-tight container (a beer can would do!). A second sample should be collected in doubled plastic bags so that the *in situ* water content can be measured immediately the sample arrives at the laboratory. A larger sample (10-500 g) should also be collected for laboratory gamma spectrometry measurements if no field measurement is made.

Samples should be taken from the centre of a uniform sediment layer at least 50 cm thick. If this is not possible, additional samples for radioactivity analysis should be collected from 10 cm above and below the sample to be dated; these samples can be collected in transparent plastic bags, but should be sealed to retain their natural water content. Examples of good and poor sampling are shown in Figure 6.6.

The most suitable samples are aeolian, e.g. loess (Wintle, 1987, 1990), because they have had the longest exposure to sunlight, have very uniform radioactivity and are most likely to have had a constant water content in the past. Other sediments which have been dated are silts deposited in braided river channels (Nanson and Young, 1987), slowly deposited lacustrine silts (Berger, 1988), dune sands (Gardner et al., 1987), beach sands (Huntley et al., 1985a) and cover sands (Kolstrup and Mejdahl, 1986). TL dating cannot usually be applied to sediments deposited in ice-marginal areas (Forman, 1989).

CONCLUSIONS

Three decades of research into the principles underlying the TL dating method have enabled it to be used almost routinely for heated materials such as pottery or burnt stone. They have also provided the basis for the development of its application to sediments. The different depositional environments have presented us with mineral grains which have been exposed to light of different wavelengths and intensities. Also, the ten fold increase in the time scale of application from 10 ka to 100 ka has tested different parameters, such as the long term stability of the TL signal or the characterisation of the growth curve shape. In spite of a decade's research on sediments, the variety of responses from minerals from different geographic areas and the greater variety of laboratory procedures to make allowances for the depositional TL level has not yet led to a routine approach. In particular, consensus has not been reached on the approach to be used for samples over 50 ka and results obtained should be judged in the context of the dates produced by individual laboratories for samples which have independently determined ages.

An exciting new development, which is likely to be of particular use for sediments which experienced limited light exposure prior to incorporation in the sediment, involves measuring the optically-stimulated luminescence (OSL) from particular minerals. This was first proposed by Huntley et al. (1985b) for fine grained sediments with stimulation being provided by the green light from a laser. The OSL represents the emptying of electrons from the most light-sensitive traps. This was confirmed by a truly negligible OSL signal being obtained for a recent dune sand.

More recent studies have shown that quartz is particularly sensitive to this stimulation wavelength and promising results have been obtained on sediments with a wide range of ages (Smith et al., 1990). The OSL signal has been linked to a particular quartz TL peak which bleaches very rapidly.

Certain feldspars also exhibit OSL when exposed to infra-red wavelengths (Hutt et al., 1988) and this has allowed the development of a simple stimulation system based on infra-red emitting diodes (Poolton and Bailiff, 1989). These new approaches are likely to be of considerable benefit to the Quaternary community when they have been fully developed.

REFERENCES

Aitken, M.J. 1974. *Physics and Archaeology*, Oxford University Press, Oxford pp. 291.

Aitken, M.J. 1985. *Thermoluminescence Dating*, Academic Press, London pp. 359.

Aitken, M.J. 1990. *Science Based Dating in Archaeology*, Longman, London pp. 274.

Bailiff, I.K. and Aitken, M.J. 1980. Use of thermoluminescence dosimetry for evaluation of internal beta dose-rate in archaeological dating. *Nuclear Instruments and Methods*, **173**, 423-429.

Balescu, S. and Lamothe, M. 1991. The blue emission of K feldspar coarse grains and its potential for overcoming TL age underestimation. *Quaternary Science Reviews*, in press.

Balescu, S., Packman, S.C. and Wintle, A.G. 1991. Chronological separation of interglacial raised beaches from Northwestern Europe using thermoluminescence. *Quaternary Research*, **35**, 91-102.

Berger, G.W. 1984. Thermoluminescence dating studies of glacial silts from Ontario. *Canadian Journal of Earth Sciences*, **21**, 1393-1399.

Berger, G.W. 1985a. Thermoluminescence dating of volcanic ash. *Journal of Volcanology and Geothermal Research*, **25**, 333-347.

Berger, G.W. 1985b. Thermoluminescence dating applied to a thin winter varve of the Late Glacial South Thompson silt, south-central British Columbia. *Canadian Journal of Earth Sciences*, **22**, 1736-1739.

Berger, G.W. 1987. Thermoluminescence dating of the Pleistocene Old Crow tephra and adjacent loess, near Fairbanks, Alaska. *Canadian Journal of Earth Sciences*, **24**, 1975-1984.

Berger, G.W. 1988. Dating Quaternary events by luminescence. *Geological Society of America Special Paper*, **227**, 13-50.

Berger, G.W. and Huntley, D.J. 1983. Dating volcanic ash by thermoluminescence. *PACT*, **9**, 581-592.

Berger, G.W. and Luternauer, J.J. 1987. Preliminary fieldwork for thermoluminescence dating studies at the Fraser River delta, British Columbia. *Geological Survey of Canada Paper*, **87-1A**, 901-904.

Debenham, N.C. 1983. Reliability of thermoluminescence dating of stalagmitic calcite. *Nature*, **304**, 154-156.

Debenham, N.C. and Aitken, M.J. 1984. Thermoluminescence dating of stalagmitic calcite. *Archaeometry*, **26**, 155-170.

Debenham, N.C., Driver, H.S.T. and Walton, A.J. 1982. Anomalies in the TL of young calcites. *PACT*, **6**, 555-562.

Drozdowski, E. and Fedorowicz, S. 1987. Stratigraphy of Vistulian glaciogenic deposits and corresponding thermoluminescence dates. *Boreas*, **16**, 139-153.

Fleming, S.J. 1979. *Thermoluminescence Techniques in Archaeology*, Clarendon Press, Oxford, pp. 233.

Forman, S.L. 1989. Applications and limitations of thermoluminescence to date Quaternary sediments. *Quaternary International*, **1**, 47-59.

Gardner, G.J., Mortlock, A.J., Price, D.M., Readhead, M.L. and Wasson, R.J. 1987. Thermoluminescence and radiocarbon dating of Australian desert dunes. *Australian Journal of Earth Sciences*, **34**, 343-357.

Guerin, G., Gillot, P.Y., Le Garrec, M.J. and Brousse, R. 1981. Age subactuel des dernieres manifestations eruptives du Mont-Dore et du Cezallier. *Comptes Rendus Academie Sciences*, Serie II, **292**, 855-857.

Huntley, D.J., Hutton, J.T. and Prescott, J.R. 1985a. South Australian sand dunes: A TL sediment test sequence. *Nuclear Tracks*, **10**, 757-758.

Huntley, D.J., Godfrey-Smith, D.I. and Thewalt, M.L.W. 1985b. Optical dating of sediments. *Nature*, **313**, 105-107.

Hutt, G., Jaek, I. and Tchonka, J. 1988. Optical dating: K-feldspars optical response stimulation spectra. *Quaternary Science Reviews*, **7**, 381-385.

Huxtable, J. and Jacobi, R.M. 1982. Thermoluminescence dating of burnt flints from a British Mesolithic site: Longmore Inclosure, East Hampshire. *Archaeometry*, **24**, 164-169.

Kolstrup, E. and Mejdahl, V. 1986. Three frost wedge casts from Jutland (Denmark) and TL dating of their infill. *Boreas*, **15**, 187-191.

Kolstrup, E., Grun, R., Mejdahl, V., Packman, S.C. and Wintle, A.G. 1990. Stratigraphy and thermoluminescence dating of Late-Glacial cover sands in Denmark. *Journal of Quaternary Science*, **5**, 207-224.

Lamothe, M. 1984. Apparent thermoluminescence ages of St-Pierre sediments at Pierreville, Quebec, and the problem of anomalous fading. *Canadian Journal of Earth Sciences*, **21**, 1406-1409.

Lamothe, M. 1988. Dating till using thermoluminescence. *Quaternary Science Reviews*, **7**, 273-276.

Lundqvist, J. and Mejdahl, V. 1987. Thermoluminescence dating of aeolian sediments in central Sweden. *Geologiska Foreningens i Stockholm Forhandlingar*, **109**, 147-158.

Mckeever, S.W.S. 1985. *Thermoluminescence Dating of Solids*, Cambridge University Press, Cambridge, pp. 370.

Mejdahl, V. 1988. Long-term stability of the TL signal in alkali feldspars. *Quaternary Science Reviews*, **7**, 357-360.

Mejdahl, V and Winther-Nielson, M. 1982. TL dating based on feldspar inclusions. *PACT*, **6**, 426-437.

Nanson, G.C. and Young, R.W. 1987. Comparison of thermoluminescence and radiocarbon age-determinations from late-Pleistocene alluvial deposits near Sydney, Australia. *Quaternary Research*, **27**, 263-269.

Poolton, N.R.J. and Bailiff, I.K. 1989. The use of LEDs as an excitation source for photoluminescence dating of sediment. *Ancient TL*, **7**, 18-20.

Raynal, J.P., Daugas, J.P., Paquereau, M.M., Miallier, D., Fain, J. and Sanzelle, S. 1982. Premiere datation du maar basaltique de Clermont Ferrand (Puy-de-Dome, France): stratigraphie, palynologie, thermoluminescence. *Comptes Rendus Academie Sciences*, **Series II**, **295**, 1011-1014.

Raynal, J.P., Paquereau, M.M., Daugas, J.P., Miallier, D., Fain, J. and Sanzelle, S. 1985. Contribution a la datation du volcanisme Quaternaire du Massif Central Francais par thermoluminescence des inclusions de quartz et comparaison avec d'autres approches: implications chronostratigraphiques et paleoenvironmentales. *Bulletin de l'Association Francaise pour l'Etude du Quaternaire*, **no 4**, 183-207.

Singhvi, A.K. and Mejdahl, V. 1985. Thermoluminescence dating of sediments. *Nuclear Tracks*, **10**, 137-161.

Smith, B.W., Rhodes, E.J., Stokes, S., Spooner, N.A. and Aitken, M.J. 1990. Optical dating of sediments: initial quartz results from Oxford. *Archaeometry*, **32**, 19-31.

Valladas, H., Geneste, J.M., Joron, J.L. and Chadelle, J.P. 1986. Thermoluminescence dating of Le Moustier (Dordogne, France). *Nature*, **322**, 452-454.

Valladas, H., Joron, J.L., Valladas, G., Arensburg, B., Bar-Yosef, O., Belfer-Cohen, A., Goldberg, P., Laville, H., Meignen, L., Rak, Y., Tchernov, E., Tillier, A.M. and Vandermeersch, B. 1987. Thermoluminescence dates for the Neanderthal burial site at Kebara in Israel. *Nature*, **330**, 159-160.

Valladas, H., Reyss, J.L., Joron, J.L., Vallladas, G., Bar-Yosef, O. and Vandermeersch, B. 1988. Thermoluminescence dating of Mousterian 'Proto-Cro-Magnon' remains from Israel and the origin of modern man. *Nature*, **331**, 614-616.

126

Wintle, A.G. 1973. Anomalous fading of thermoluminescence in mineral samples. *Nature*, **245**, 143-144.

Wintle, A.G. 1978. A thermoluminescence dating study of some Quaternary calcites: potential and problems. *Canadian Journal of Earth Sciences*, **15**, 1977-1986.

Wintle, A.G. 1980. Thermoluminescence dating: a review of recent applications to non-pottery materials. *Archaeometry*, **22**, 113-122.

Wintle, A.G. 1982. Thermoluminescence properties of fine grain minerals in loess. *Soil Science*, **134**, 164-170.

Wintle, A.G. 1987. Thermoluminescence dating of loess. *Catena, Supplement* **9**, 103-115.

Wintle, A.G. 1990. A review of current research on TL dating of loess. *Quaternary Science Reviews*, **9**, 385-387.

Wintle, A.G. and Catt, J.A. 1985. Thermoluminescence dating of soils developed in late Devensian loess at Pegwell Bay, Kent. *Journal of Soil Science*, **36**, 293-298.

Wintle, A.G. and Huntley, D.J. 1980. Thermoluminescence dating of ocean sediments. *Canadian Journal of Earth Sciences*, **17**, 348-360.

Wintle, A.G. and Huntley, D.J. 1982. Thermoluminescence dating of sediments. *Quaternary Science Reviews*, **1**, 31-53.

Chapter 7

ELECTRON SPIN RESONANCE (ESR) DATING

P.L. Smart

The use of Electron spin resonance (ESR) for dating was first considered by Zeller et al. (1967), but it was not until Ikeya (1975), demonstrated its use for the dating of speleothem calcite that it was more widely considered. Although ESR has been used to date a large range of materials in a great variety of environments (see reviews of Hennig and Grün (1983), Ikeya (1985) and Grün (1989), it is still considered by many workers as an experimental rather than routine dating technique. In fact, within the limitations discussed below, ESR can provide a reliable routine technique for the dating of some materials such as speleothem calcite. Indeed, Grün (1989) provides complete protocols for the routine dating of speleothem (see also Smith et al., 1986), molluscs, corals and tooth enamel. These protocols are particularly useful in assessing the reliability of published ESR dates, which in much early work are deficient both with respect to field (dosimetry) and laboratory (Equivalent Dose determination) techniques. ESR has particular utility in being applicable to small samples (<2 g), to materials which cannot be dated using other techniques such as fossil teeth (Grün et al., 1987) or detritally contaminated speleothem (Smith et al., 1985b) and to samples whose age is greater than the applicable range of other methods.

PRINCIPLES OF ESR DATING

ESR dating is essentially identical in principle to TL dating; the sample acts as a natural dosimeter recording the cumulative radiation dose received at the sample site since deposition. ESR simply provides a means of measuring the cumulative effects of this radiation on the sample, and of calibrating the sensitivity of the sample to radiation.

Ionising radiation, X-rays and cosmic rays cause excition of electrons in solids, the majority of which recombine with holes (positive charge sites) relatively rapidly. However, some of the excited electrons become trapped at charge deficit sites associated with defects and impurities in the crystal lattice. For instance in calcite, Y^{3+} sometimes replaces Ca^{2+} and stabilises CO_3^{3-} formed by trapping of an electron on a CO_3^{2-} site. These trapped electrons form paramagnetic centers or radicals whose density may be measured directly and non-destructively by ESR. The intensity of the natural ESR signal in a sample (I_t) is thus dependent on four things, the average radiation flux or dose rate at the sample site (D), the sample age (t) and the sensitivity of the sample in terms of change of ESR signal intensity per unit radiation (S).

$$I_t = t \times D \times S \qquad (7.1)$$

The ESR sensitivity is obtained by application of an additional gamma radiation dose to the sample in the laboratory using the additive dose method (Figure 7.1). In practice the natural intensity and sensitivity are combined to determine the equivalent dose (ED), which is a direct estimate of the cumulative radiation dose to which the sample has been exposed. If the average dose rate for the sample is known, then the age can be calculated directly:

$$t = \frac{ED}{D} \qquad \text{when: } ED = \frac{I_t}{S} \qquad (7.2)$$

Precise and accurate estimates of both the ED and radiation dose are thus needed to obtain reliable ESR ages.

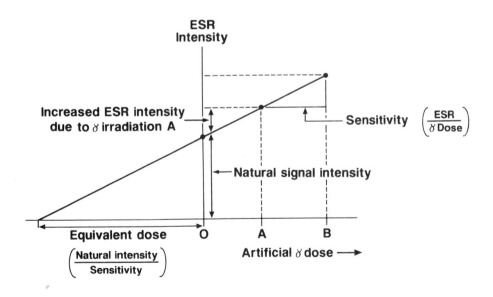

Figure 7.1 *The additive dose method for determination of the sensitivity of a sample to radiation, and estimation of equivalent dose (ED) from the sensitivity and natural ESR signal intensity. In practice a minimum of 6 or 7 gamma irradiations are employed, rather than the two (A and B) illustrated in the Figure, and the ED determined from the best fit regression line.*

There are two potential problems in this simple scheme; firstly the ESR signal must be zeroed on incorporation into the deposit ($I_t = 0$ at $t = 0$), and secondly the radiation flux at the sample site must have remained constant through time (or have varied in a predictable manner, for instance by ingrowth of radioactive daughters in a chain). Newly formed materials such as speleothem calcite or aragonite in mollusc shells contain no trapped electrons, and thus are zeroed on initial deposition. In other cases, the signal may be zeroed by some physical process such as the heating of flints in a fire, which then constitutes the target event to be dated (Griffiths et al., 1983). In some cases resetting of the ESR signal may not be complete, and the estimated age will be too large. For instance where exposure to sunlight does not completely reset all the traps in quartz, only those associated with the Ge center may possibly be used for dating surficial sediments such as loess (Buhay et al., 1988). The adequate demonstration of the zeroing of the ESR signal is thus critical in development of new ESR dating methods.

The radiation dose received by a sample comes primarily from radionuclides in the uranium and thorium decay series, and from ^{40}K, with a contribution from cosmic radiation at near-surface sites. Within the sample alpha and beta radiation which have relatively short ranges (c 20 μm and c 2 mm respectively) are important, but because of the longer range of gamma radiation, unless the sample is greater than 30 cm in size, radiation from the deposits enclosing the sample must also be considered. Ideally both sample and surrounding deposits should form an unchanging and geochemically closed system with respect to the important isotopes. However in some samples, for instance molluscs, and in many sedimentary deposits there may be leaching or accumulation of uranium, and in some cases erosion or further deposition of relatively radioisotope rich sediments surrounding the sample. Such change can have a profound effect on the accuracy of ESR dates where the present radiation flux is assumed to have affected the sample all its life.

ESR DATING METHODS

Selection of ESR Signals for Dating

For any particular material, a variety of electron traps (and associated non-paramagnetic hole centers) may be present. Each paramagnetic center is associated with a specific ESR signal, whose intensity (proportional to the number of trapped electrons or 'spins') may be measured on an ESR spectrometer under characteristic operating conditions (Figure 7.2). A detailed account of the theory of ESR measurement is beyond the scope of this review, and the reader if referred to Symons (1978) and Grün, (1989, appendices B and C). Briefly, an ESR spectrometer can be considered analogous to a visible light spectrophotometer, the adsorption of microwaves being measured as the spectrometer is scanned from a low to high magnetic field intensity. Individual signals are identified with respect to their peak width and g value (technically the spectroscopic splitting factor), the ESR equivalent of wavelength, which for a particular microwave frequency is determined by the magnetic field intensity. Unlike light spectra, ESR spectra are normally recorded as the first differential, enabling simple determination of intensity when there are shifts in the background by direct measurement of peak to peak height. The g-value for ESR signals is generally close to g= 2.000, the value for a free electron.

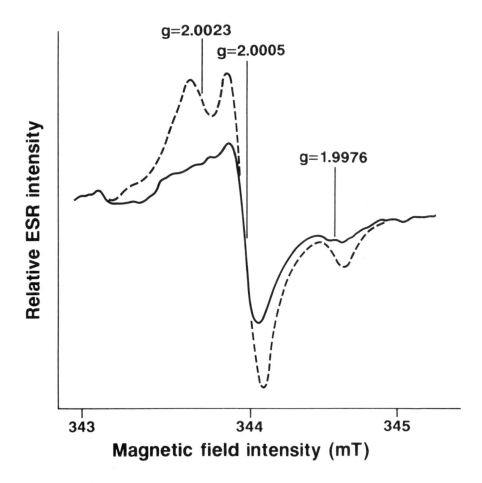

Figure 7.2 *Natural ESR spectrum for speleothem calcite, with spectrum for same sample after 50 Gy gamma irradiation (scan speed 10^{-3} T/min, modulation amplitude 5×10^{-5} T, microwave power 5 mW). The g = 2.0005 signal is used for dating.*

In physics and chemistry, the identification of the paramagnetic center associated with specific signals is often of considerable importance. However, in geochronological applications, emphasis is placed on the characteristics of the signal (see for example Smith et al. (1985a) for an evaluation of the suitability of the ESR signals in speleothem calicite). Specifically:

— is it of zero intensity at the time of the target event?

— does it grow with irradiation?

— is it stable under ambient light and temperature conditions?

Signal stability is particularly important because it is one of two major controls on the applicable range of the dating method, the second being the total number of trap sites available.

Under ideal conditions, the number of potential trap sites is very large compared to the number of energetic electrons produced by irradiation of the solid. The trapping rate is then essentially constant, and there is a simple linear relation between the radiation dose and ESR intensity. However, where this is not the case, the number of available trap sites decreases through time as electrons are trapped, reducing the trapping efficiency (and thus ESR sensitivity per unit irradiation) until all sites are full, and no further increase in ESR signal intensity can occur. This limiting condition is termed saturation, and its onset in indicated by non-linearity in the ESR intensity/radiation dose plot. In some materials such as aragonitic molluscs, the onset of saturation occurs at relatively low ages for typical natural radiation doses (c 100 ka, for the $g = 2.0012$ center used for dating; Molodkov, 1989).

Not all electrons initially held in traps are retained, there is a spontaneous thermally dependent release, the rate of which depends on the depth of the trap. For shallow traps, the rate of release at ambient temperature is high, the mean life-time of electrons in the trap is therefore low, and significant underestimation of ages may occur. The thermal stability of traps associated with particular ESR signals is normally estimated from thermal annealing experiments. The rate of decrease of ESR intensity in a natural sample with time is determined at fixed temperatures, and the results extrapolated to give stability estimates at ambient sample temperature (Figure 7.3). The precision of estimates of mean life at ambient temperature is relatively poor, because considerable extrapolation is required from the relatively elevated annealing temperatures needed to obtain measurable rates of ESR intensity decrease over a reasonable experimental period.

An alternative approach advocated by Grün (1989) is to obtain samples known to be well in excess of the applicable range (>5 mean lives). In such samples, a steady state has been obtained between the rates of trapping and thermal release, and by measurement of the ESR intensity and the natural dose rate, the mean life may be estimated (Deybust et al., 1984). However, this relationship poses a further problem, the steady state is esentially a dynamic equilibrium; irradiation of the sample at a higher rate will cause a further increase in ESR intensity, because vacant trap sites still remain. This is of course precisely the procedure used in the additive dose technique, laboratory irradiation rates (typically Grays per minute) being many orders of magnitude greater than that received naturally by the sample (typically milliGrays per year). Thus significant underestimation of the equivalent dose can be obtained for samples which show no evidence of saturation in the laboratory, but which have

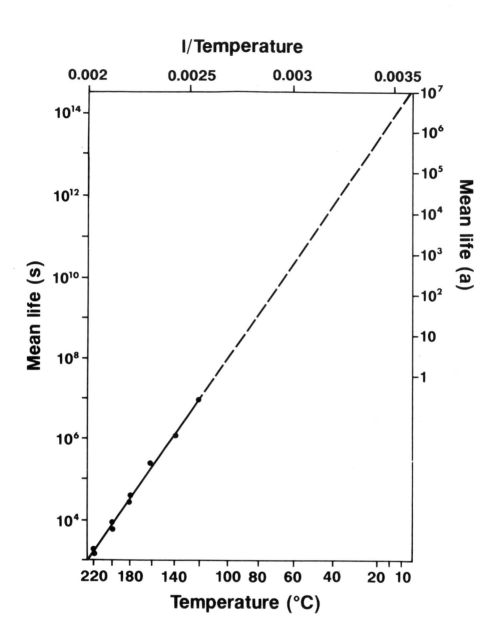

Figure 7.3 *Results of isothermal annealing experiments for speleothem calcite; note the large extrapolation from experimental to field temperatures, and that the mean life at 30°C is less than 10⁵ years compared to 7.3 × 10⁶ years at 10°C (after Henning and Grün, 1983).*

a trap life comparable to the sample age (Figure 7.4). Procedures to identify and correct for this problem theoretically have been presented by Molodkov (1989) and Hutt and Jaek (1989), but have not yet been routinely applied. Thus in general, the practicable limit of ESR dating is defined as 0.2 times the mean life, beyond which thermal detrapping leads to systematic underestimation of the age by greater than 10%. Table 7.1 presents estimated applicable ranges for ESR dating of various materials at 10°C; values will be less in warmer climates.

Table 7.1 *Potential applicable ranges for ESR dating of various materials at 10°C based on published estimates of mean life.*

Material	Applicable Range (ka)
Calcite — Speleothems	0 — 800
Aragonite — Molluscs	0 — 100
Aragonite — Corals	0 — 250
Quartz — Faults and sediments	0 > 2000 ?
Hydroxyapatite — tooth enamel	0 — 2000
Gypsum	0 — 1000

Determination of the Equivalent Dose

The total cumulative radiation dose received by an ESR sample is known as the equivalent dose (ED). Other terms used in the literature include accumulated dose (AD) and total dose (TD). The ED is determined in the laboratory by the additive dose method, a minimum of seven aliquots of the sample are irradiated with increasing gamma radiation doses from a calibrated laboratory source, and the relation between ESR intensity and dose determined. The ED is obtained by linear extrapolation of a best fit straight line through the data, the uncertainty being estimated from the variance of experimental points about the error-weighted regression line. As discussed previously some samples may show a pronouced non-linearity, the ESR intensity exponentially approaching the saturation value (Figure 7.4). This is indicative that the trapping process follows first order kinetics. The relationship may be linearised by plotting: $\ln(1-(I/I_{max})$ against the gamma dose but I_{max} (the ESR intensity at saturation) must be determined iteratively and the logarithmic transformation introduces bias into the estimates of the standard errors.

An alternative approach has been suggested by Grün and MacDonald (1989). The relation between ESR intensity and ED is expressed as:

$$I = (1 - \exp(-a(D-ED)))I_{max} \qquad (7.3)$$

where:
I = ESR intensity,
a = a constant,
D = radiation dose,
I_{max} = ESR intensity at saturation.

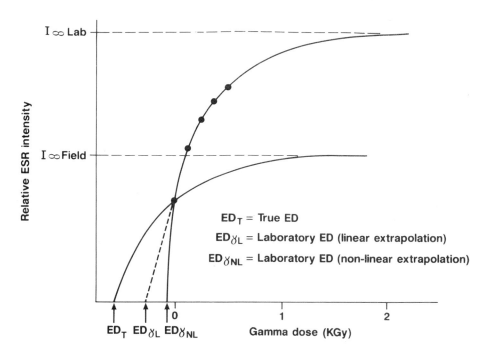

Figure 7.4 *Effect of non-linear and linear extrapolation on estimation of ED, and of potentially erroneous ED estimates if trap has a relatively low thermal stability.*

The three unknowns are determined simultaneously using a sum of squared deviations minimisation model, the standard errors being determined by jackknifing (a FORTRAN program FITT is available from the authors). Grün and MacDonald (1989) also demonstrate that although the linear fit generally used to determine ED may give a high correlation coefficient and an apparently good fit to the data, this is significantly improved by use of this exponential function, which also yields a systematically lower value for the ED (Figure 7.4). Careful consideration should therefore be given to the distribution of residuals around linear regression lines fitted to intensity/dose plots, and the exponential model adoped if there is any evidence of systematic underestimation at intermediate radiation doses.

The uncertainty of individual ESR measurements is typically better than ± 3%, but depends on signal strength (Figure 7.5). For young or insensitive samples, or those which have interfering ESR signals, the large uncertainities associated with determination of very weak signals effectively define the lower applicable limit of the dating method. Optimisation of spectrometer sensitivity is thus critical. The resolution of individual ESR signals is controlled by the modulation amplitude and scan speed, slow scan speeds (less than 10^{-3} T/min) are universally employed, but there is less agreement on the optimum protocol with respect to modulation

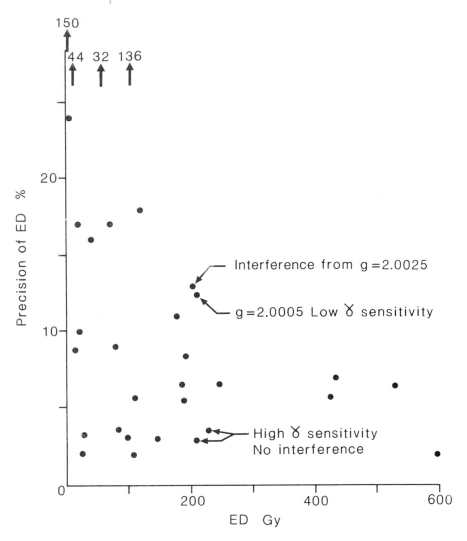

Figure 7.5 *The precision of ED determinations for the g = 2.0005 signal in speleothem calcite in relation to magnitude of ED showing effect of interfering signals and low gamma radiation sensitivity (Smart et al., 1988). Arrows indicate four samples with very large uncertainties.*

amplitude. For some applications, it is important to resolve individual sharp signals, such as the g = 2.0005 signal in calcite, from other potentially interfering signals. Thus Smith et al (1986) recommend a low modulation amplitude (less than 10^{-4} T). In other applications use of a high modulation amplitude (10^{-3} T) to saturate intense, superimposed signals is recommended, for instance in molluscan aragonite (Molodkov, 1988; Figure 7.6). Modulation amplitude also controls signal intensity, larger signals being obtained with high modulation amplitude and high microwave power, giving improved signal to noise ratio and thus precision. Lyons et al (1988) have demonstrated that interference may be reduced for some signals by use of high microwave power (50 mW, a factor of 10 higher than normal) and provide a procedure to test if this is the case. It is thus important to provide not only details of both the g value and peak width of the signal used for dating, but also the spectrometer operating conditions (scan speed, modulation amplitude, microwave power) when documenting ESR spectra. Sensitivity is also controlled by optimal tuning of the spectrometer for each individual sub-sample, and by sample size and placement in cavity. Grün (1989) advocates the use of small samples placed centrally in the spectrometer cavity, while Smith et al. (1986) suggest that the gain in sensitivity is offset by a reduction in reproductibility because of minor differences in sample height and orientation. They therefore recommend use of larger samples which pass right through the cavity.

Normally in ESR dating, uncertainty in the determined ED is controlled by the variance of the best-fit line to the ESR growth curve obtained from the additive dose technique. To some extent this is dependent on the range and number of irradiations employed and their spacing (Grün and McDonald 1989), but it is also dependent on the standardisation of operating conditions between individual sub-samples. Normally sub-samples are all determined during a single spectrometer run after spectrometer sensitivity has stablised following an initial warm-up period (1 to 2 hours). Reproductibility is checked by redetermination of the first sub-sample (often the unirradiated natural sample) during the course of or at the end of the run. All sub-samples should be determined in a matched set of 2 mm diameter quartz sample tubes selected to ensure no signal blank, and marked to ensure equal packing. Each sub-sample should be of equal weight (normally 100 or 150 ± 0.1 mg), and all should be given identical simultaneous pre-treatment (such as low-temperature annealing — see below). Reproducibility is also enhanced by use of multiple scans (>10), or computer signal averaging, the former being preferred as blurring of the signal due to minor shifts of the signal base are more readily recognised and corrected. For the best samples uncertainties in estimation of ED may be as low as ± 2 %, with ± 10% being acheivable for the majority of samples.

In most cases, sample preparation for ESR dating is relatively simple, most samples are run in powdered form (typically of 125 — 250 µm grain size) thus the ESR signals represent averages of the separate signals observed in oriented whole crystals. Because of the thermal dependence of the mean life, it is important that excessive heating is avoided during sample preparation. Samples should be cut using water-cooled saws, and excessive grinding avoided. Similarly samples which have been directly exposed to solar-heating in the field should be treated with caution. In some materials grinding may induce radiation sensitive paramagnetic centers on grain surfaces. Interferences from these may be overcome by etching in a suitable acid, for instance 2 minutes in 10% acaetic acid elimates the strong grinding signal in calcite (Smith et al., 1986). Etching also elimates the contribution from external alpha and

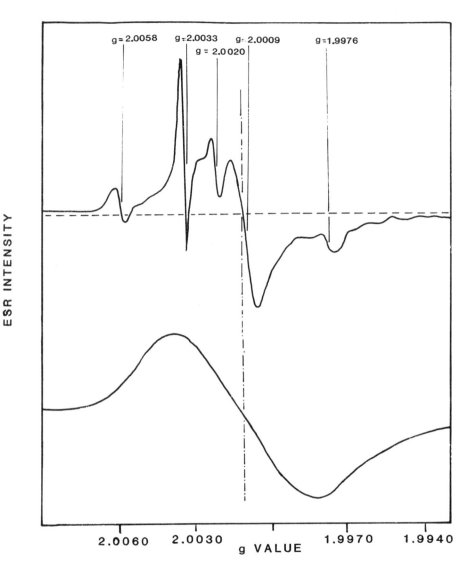

Figure 7.6 *ESR signal for molluscan aragonite. Solid line, complex signal recorded using low modulation (2 × 10⁻⁴ T) and low microwave power (2 mW). Dotted line: same spectrum recorded using strong overmodulation (1 × 10⁻³ T) and high microwave power (50 mW) to reduce signal inteference on the g = 2.0012 signal (after Molodkov, 1988).*

(potentially) beta radiation. Laboratory gamma irradiation may also induce short-lived but intense interfering signals which are absent from natural samples. As shown by Smith et al. (1986) these may have a significant systematic effect (c 20%) on determined ED values. A brief low temperature annealing (120°C for four hours for calcite (Figure 7.7) can often remove or reduce these interferences without adversely affecting the intensity of the more stable signal employed for dating. A simple test of the stability of the dating signal in calcite may also be employed by heating an unirradiated sub-samples to 200°C.

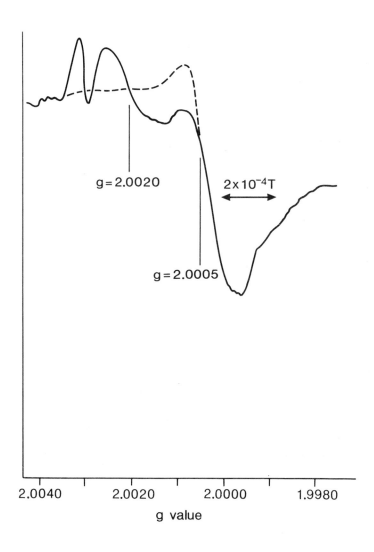

Figure 7.7 *ESR spectrum of calcite flowstone showing interference between the g = 2.0020 and g = 2.0005 signals, resulting in supression of the g = 2.0005 signal upswing and a systematic over estimation of ED. The g = 2.0020 signal can be eliminated by annealing for several hours at 120°C (dashed line).*

Estimation of Dose Rate

The second major element required to determine an ESR age is an estimation of the dose rate received by the sample. The SI unit of radiation dose is the Gray (Gy), but in older references the rad may be used (100 rad = 1 Gy). Dose rates are normally averaged over one year for dating purposes, and are often quoted in mGy/a. The dose rate comprises three components, that from cosmic radiation, that derived from radionuclides within the sample (Internal Dose), and that derived from radionuclides in the environment surrounding the sample (External Dose). The cosmic dose rate is dependent on altitude, latitude and attenution by rocks and sediments overlying the sample. At the surface it is equal to about 280 mGy/a at sea-level, but below a depth of c 25 m it is negligible. It may be estimated from the equation given by Prescott and Hutton (1988).

The relative importance of the internal and external dose depends on the size of the sample in relation to the average ranges of alpha (c 20 μm), beta (c 2 mm) and gamma (c 30 cm) radiation in geological materials (Figure 7.8). Where possible the outer 2 mm of the sample are removed to eliminate the effects of external alpha and beta radiation, then only external gamma radiation must be considered. For large samples such as speleothems, this radiation is progressively attenuated as it penetrates the sample, and for diameters in excess of 30 cm, can be completely ignored (see Debenham and Aitken, 1984 for details of gamma attenuation factors in calcite, and Grün, 1989 for other materials). For smaller samples such as quartz grains, etching may need to be more limited, and may only remove the region affected by external alpha radiation; external beta radiation must then be considered. Finally, for very small samples such as foraminifera which have a wall thickness of only slightly greater than the alpha particle range, all sources of external radiation much be included. A potential source of uncertainty in estimating external radiation dose from sediments is the water content, which may vary seasonally, or have changed significantly during the course of time. High water contents reduce external dose by enhanced adsorption of radiation (Aitken, 1985). External dose rates may be determined from the uranium, thorium and potassium concentrations in sediments (Bell, 1979, Nambi and Aitken, 1986) or be measured *in situ* by encapsulated themoluminescent dosimeters or portable gamma spectrometers (Fain et al., 1985, Murray et al., 1979). Dosimeters have the advantage of integrating seasonal variations as they are normally left in place for at least 1 year.

The internal dose is derived largely from the uranium decay chain, and is dominated in small samples by the alpha and beta contributions. It may be determined from tables or by calculation from measurements of the uranium concentration (Nambi and Aitken, 1986, Grün, 1989). However there are three problems which must be considered. In many samples, the decay chain is not at equilibrium at the time of deposition, and ingrowth of the daughter isotopes occurs with time. In speleothem calcite for instance only uranium is present initially, and ingrowth of ^{230}Th (and its shorter lived daughters) occurs over some 400 ka. This increases the dose by

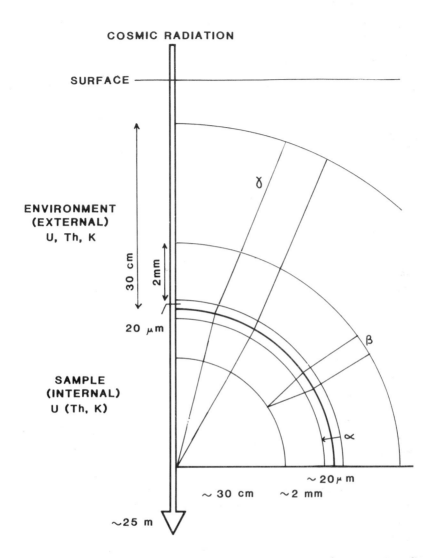

Figure 7.8 *Schematic illustration of source volumes and penetration distances (horizontal axis) for external alpha, beta and gamma radiation and cosmic radiation in one quadrant of a spherical sample.*

a factor of 3. Normally an iterative procedure must therefore be used, an initial estimate of the age is used to derive the dose, then this is recalculated using the determined ESR age until convergence occurs. The second problem involves changes in the isotopic composition of the sample due to uptake of uranium. Uranium concentrations three to four orders of magnitude greater than in living specimens are commonly reported for many fossils, particularly molluscs, bones and teeth. Correction for uptake of uranium is problematic because it is generally not known whether this has occurred very rapidly *post-morten* or progressively through time (the case for many molluscs, Kaufman et al., 1971). A pragmatic solution is to determine age estimates based on both models which may bracket the true sample age, although this is of limited utility in many geochronological investigations because of the large age range which may result. For instance in the case of ESR dates for tooth enamel from the Bilzingsleben archaeological site, the range is in excess of 100 ka, and the site cannot be unambiguously attributed to either oxygen isotope stage 9 or 11 (Schwarcz et al., 1988). A final problem in estimating internal dose rates is that breaks in the decay chain may occur if loss of radon gas (or other isotopes) occur. Selection of "tight" samples may eliminate this problem.

The term 'equivalent' dose is used to describe the total cumulative radiation dose received by the sample because it is the gamma irradiation equivalent of the field dose, which includes both an alpha and beta component. While the density of excited electrons generated in solids by beta and gamma radiation is essentially identical and relatively low, that for the much more massive alpha particle (a helium nucleus) is very much higher. The trapping efficiency of the electrons produced by the ionising radiation is thus much lower for alpha than beta and gamma irradiation because local saturation of all ESR traps occurs in the vicinity of the alpha-particle tracks. The relative efficiencies of alpha, compared to beta and gamma radiation in inducing changes in the intensity of ESR signals are indicated by the a value (Aitken and Bowman, 1975, Lyons and Brennan, 1989). For calcite this value is typically 0.3, and a correction must be included in field dose rate determinations. In fact routine measurements of values for materials used in ESR dating are extremely difficult because of the limited range of alpha penetration and the need for a minimum of 100 mg of sample for ESR measurement. To overcome these problems, Lyons (1988) has used a particle accelerator. An alternative strategy is to select samples for which uncertainty in the a value has a limited effect on the precision of the calculated age because the alpha component of the total radiation received is minor. This would for instance be the case for a speleothem with low uranium concentration which was buried in a sediment containing much higher uranium, potassium and thorium concentrations.

Precision and Accuracy

The precision of ESR age estimates is generally rather low because of the considerable number of measurements required in determination of both ED and radiation dose (Table 7.2). It also varies significantly between individual samples (thus, as discussed above, the precision of ED determination may vary from ± 2% to in excess of ± 100% in samples with a weak ESR signal), and between types of sample (tooth enamel requires estimation of many more parameters than speleothem calcite because of the complexity of dose estimation). It is however important that realistic precisions are quoted which contain all sources of uncertainty (see recommended protocol for TL dating (Aitken, 1976). As an alternative Grün (1989) recommends estimation of precision from multiple analyses of different samples from the same unit, which will also permit inclusion of uncertainty due to diagenetic and other field effects such as inhomogeneities in the host sediments.

Table 7.2 *Factors which may determine radiation dose rate in ESR dating.*

Cosmic Radiation Dose
Latitude and altitude of sample location.
Thickness and density of overlying sediments or rock.

External and Internal Radiation Dose
Uranium, thorium and potassium concentrations.
Extent of radioactive disequilibrium in decay chains.
Occurrence of breaks in decay chains due to loss of mobile radioisotopes.
Rate, timing and extent of post-depositional radionuclide uptake/loss.
Water content.
Sample thickness and extent of surface etching.
Attenuation of alpha, beta and gamma radiation in sample.
'a' value for sample.

Systematic errors may also be important, resulting from the methods employed and the calibration of the laboratory gamma radiation source (typically $\pm 6\%$ based on intercalibration of beta sources for TL dating (Haskell, 1983). Note that the gamma source calibration should also account for attenuation in the sample container which is neccessary to obtain secondary electron equilibrium in the sample. In the case of speleothems, differences in sample treatment, such as failure to remove interfering signals by etching and annealing, can lead to systematic errors of 20%, and erroneous trap transfer procedures (Yokoyama et al., 1983) may produce even larger effects on accuracy. Such differences in procedure may explain the poor results obtained from the first ESR Interlaboratory Comparison Project (Hennig et al., 1988), although with the wider dissemination of information on problems and techniques, much better results would now be anticipated. In fact comparative studies using ESR and the ^{230}Th/^{234}U uranium series dating techniques show a satisfactory concordance for speleothem calcite and aragonitic corals (Smart et al., 1988, Grün 1985a, Radtke and Grün 1988a). The agreement for travertine calcite and mollusc shells is not as good (Radtke et al., 1985, Grün et al., 1988b) but it must be remembered that this may result from the open system nature of these materials which affects both methods. Adequate comparative studies from other materials are not available, and the dating of foraminifera, teeth, bone, burnt flint, volanic rocks and fault movements must be considered to be still at the experimental stage.

APPLICATIONS OF ESR DATING

Calcite — Speleothems, Calichés and Travertines

Numerous studies have been made of the ESR spectra of calcite (Grün and DeCanniere 1984, Smith et al., 1985a, Wieser et al., 1985). Seven natural ESR

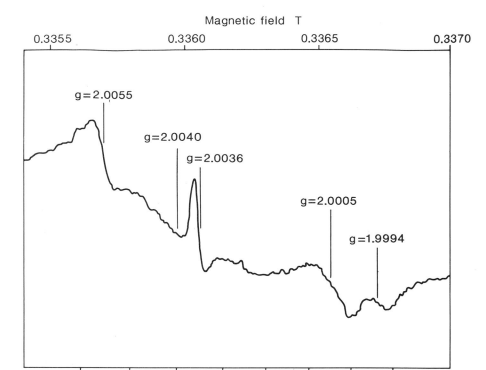

Figure 7.9 *Natural ESR spectrum for a calcite flowstone showing most of the signals commonly observed in speleothem calcite. There is a broad organic signal centered at g = 2.0040 upon which the other marked signals are superimposed. Some calcites also show a signal at g = 2.0025 and g = 1.9970. Modulation amplitude 4 × 10^{-5} T, scan speed 10^{-3} T/min, microwave power 5 mW.*

signals have been observed in calcite, five of which are shown in Figure 7.9, but only that at g = 2.0005 ± 0.0003 (sometimes quoted by other workers as g = 2.0007) with a peak to peak width of 2 × 10^{-4} is useful for dating (Figure 7.2). It is found widely in speleothems, being absent from only 9% of the 70 samples studied by Smart et al. (1988), and weak or insensitive to radiation in a further 23%. In other deposits, this preferred signal is very much less common; it was found to occur in only 15% of the travertines examined by Grün et al. (1988b), and 4% of the caliche crusts and nodules sampled by Radtke et al. (1988b). In both these materials the main ESR signal is centered at g = 2.0045 ± 0.0005 and is relatively broad (peak width 6 × 10^{-4}). This signal, which is also widely reported in speleothems (c 50%) is attributed to the presence of humic acids by Grün and

DeCanniere (1984), and is frequently not zero in modern calcites. Its use for dating may thus lead to an over estimation of the true sample age. In Spanish calcretes this over estimation was as large as 200 ka, but became less important for older samples (Radtke et al. 1988b). Relatively porous calcretes may also act as open systems, accumulating uranium, and showing multiple phases of carbonate deposition. Dating of calcretes by ESR is thus difficult. Similar problems are also encountered in travertine samples, although Grün et al. (1988b) demonstrate that careful selection of dense stalactitic and stalagmitic samples formed in cavities underlying the barriers both increased the probability of the presence of the preferred g = 2.0005 signal (46%), and eliminated problems related to the presence of acid insoluble residues.

The stability of the g = 2.0005 signal in speleothem calcite determined by isothermal annealing (Figure 7.3) is relatively high, published values of the mean life at 10°C being in the range 3×10^6 to 7×10^7 years (Hennig and Grün 1983, Wieser et al., 1985, Smith et al., 1985a). In some samples an unstable component does however appear to be present, which should be checked by annealing a sub-sample at 200°C for 15 minutes (Smith et al., 1986). The applicable range for ESR dating of calcite using the g = 2.0005 signal is thus 800 ka, but in many samples two other effects become more significant in limiting the method. Saturation of the signal becomes evident at total doses from as low as 200 Gy (but in other samples not until doses as high as 600 Gy), and at sample sites associated with sediments this may become a limiting problem in old speleothems (Smith et al., 1985a). Recrystalisation of old speleothem is also a problem, especially in warmer climates (Grün, 1985a, Smart et al., 1988; Figure 7.10). Recrystalisation is indicated by a low or negligible sensitivity of the g = 2.0005 signal to gamma irradiation, a considerable scatter in values of ED for adjacent samples, similar estimates of ED thorough a stratigraphic sequence and, in some samples, the presence of a non-radiation sensitive signal at g = 1.9994 (± 0.0003).

There are no simple criteria to aid selection of speleothem samples, but several different samples associated with the deposits of interest should be collected. Because the external gamma dose from sediments will generally be much higher than the internal dose from the speleothem calcite, in situ dosimetry is recommended. Samples should be selected from sites where the geometric relations to the sediment body are clear and relatively simple. Sites where changes since sample deposition are at a minimum are preferred, dewatering, erosion or sedimentation causing considerable uncertainties in estimation of palaeodose from present day conditions. A particular problem in this respect is that of radon accumulation within the cave void, which varies with changes in ventilation. The beta dose derived from radon, together with plate-out of randon daughters on exposed surfaces of inactive speleothems can significantly affect the ED (Hennig and Grün, 1983). Samples from within 2 mm of growth hiatuses should therefore be avoided. Radon loss from dense speleothem calcite does not appear to be significant (Lyons et al., 1989). Routine preparation and instrumental techniques for determination of speleothem calcite EDs are now well known (for instance Smith et al., 1986). Care is particularly required to avoid

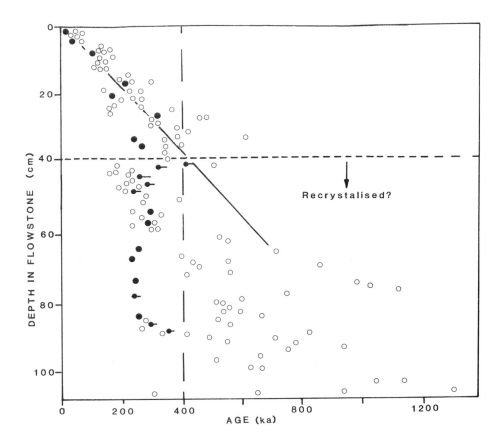

Figure 7.10 *Relation between uranium series (solid circles) and ESR ages (open circles) with increasing depth in a flowstone from Wilhelmshohle, Germany. Below 40 cm the larger scatter in ESR ages suggests that partial recrystalisation has occurred, as is also indicated by the disequilibrium in the uranium decay chain (after Grün, 1985b).*

the effects of interfering signals, particularly those from sample crushing (acid etch before analysis) and the g = 2.0023 signal (low temperature pre-annealing 2 hrs at 120°C (Figure 7.7) and/or use of high microwave power). The technique of Yokoyama et al (1983) which transfers charge from the g = 2.0005 signal to that at g = 2.0058 is not recommended. The typical precision for ED determination is about ± 7% but this depends strongly on signal sensitivity and the extent of interference (Figure 7.5). When combined with the uncertainties in dosimetry the achievable precision is typically ± 15%, but rarely better than ± 10%. A particular source of uncertainty is the a-value for conversion of alpha to gamma equivalent dose. This is rather difficult to determine routinely (Lyons and Brennan 1989), an average value of 0.34 ± 0.08 being recommended (Grün 1985b). However, the effect of this uncertainty is minor, providing the external radiation dose is dominant, as is generally the case.

ESR dating of speleothem calcite, despite its relatively large uncertainty, offers some advantages compared with the $^{230}Th/^{234}U$ method. It utilises very small samples, provides reliable results even for detritally contaminated speleothem, and yields useful results in the interval 250 to 1000 ka. Encouraging results have been obtained from foraminifera in deep sea cores (Siegele and Mangini, 1985) but dating of calcitic molluscs is not possible due to signal interference.

Example: Speleothems — Smart et al. (1988)
              Travertines — Grün et al. (1988b)

Aragonite — Corals and Molluscs

Both molluscs, which are frequently found in Quaternary deposits, and corals which can be used to date raised marine terraces, comprise aragonite and development of reliable dating methods for these using ESR has received significant attention. The ESR spectrum of molluscan aragonite is relatively complex with 5 signals distinguishable in the powder spectrum, two of which are not radiation sensitive (Figure 7.6). Overlap of these signals can cause difficulty in obtaining reliable ED estimates (Molodkov, 1988, Kai and Ikeya, 1989, Katzenberger et al., 1989). The most satisfactory solution is to employ the signal at g = 2.0012 recorded using moderate microwave power (50 mW) and strong over-modulation (1 mT). The aragonite spectrum of corals is rather simpler, showing two non-radiation sensitive signals at g = 2.0058 and 2.0032, and a gamma sensitive signal at g = 2.0007 which can be used for dating (Figure 7.11). The mean life determined for the dating signal in molluscs is relatively low (approximately 3×10^5 years at 10°C, Molodkov 1988), thus serious underestimation of the age will occur for Quaternary samples unless they are derived from circumarctic areas (the mean life at 0°C being 3×10^6 years). Molodkov (1989) has suggested a correction procedure, but while elegant this requires detailed annealing experiments which could not be undertaken routinely. Although stability estimates for coraline aragonite are somewhat higher (the experimentally determined mean life at 26°C is of the order 5×10^5 years; Hennig and Grün, 1983), fossil samples are also preserved at a much higher ambient temperature. In practice Radtke and Grün (1988) obtained good agreement between ESR and uranium series ages up to 300 ka for corals on Barbados, and were able to determine maximum ages of 800 to 900 ka, well in excess of the theoretical mean life (Figure 7.12).

Aragonite is metastable under ambient conditions, and recrystalises to calcite with time, the rate depending primarily on the effective rainfall in the area. The resulting resetting of the ESR dating signal will produce an underestimate of the ED. All samples should therefore be screened by X-ray diffraction, and those showing the presence of calcite (effectively less than 1 — 2%) should be discarded. While corals

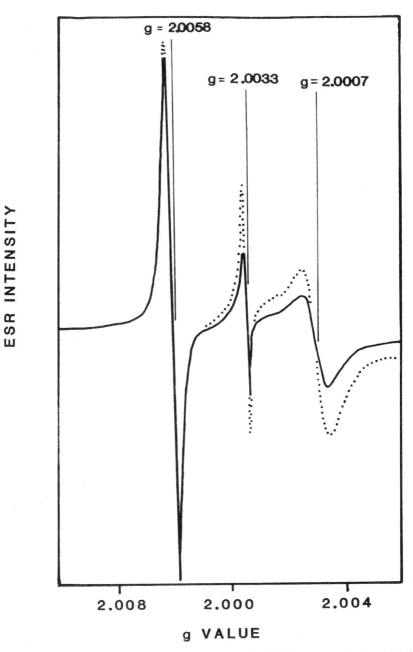

Figure 7.11 *ESR signal for coraline aragonite (solid line natural signal, dashed line gamma irradiated); modulation amplitude 1 × 10⁻⁴ T, scan speed 10⁻³ T/min, microwave power 4 mW (after Radtke and Grün, 1988).*

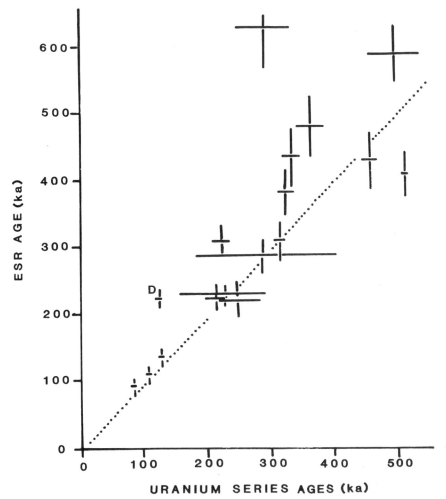

Figure 7.12 *Comparison of average ESR ages for raised coral reefs on Barbados with [230]Th/[234]U uranium series age (less than 300 ka) and He-U age (after Radtke and Grün, 1988). For clarity He-U ages for terraces younger than 300 ka are not included but are comparable to [230]Th/[234]U estimates with the exception of point D. Bars indicate ± 1 standard deviation uncertainty derived from multiple samples. The systematic underestimation for He-U ages may indicate that coraline aragonite is not closed with respect to helium. The thermal stability of the ESR signal appears to be much higher than estimated from thermal annealing experiments.*

show relatively little uptake of uranium with time, most fossil molluscs accumulate uranium post-morten. This is not, however, too serious a problem as the internal radiation dose is generally only about 10% of the total (Ikeya and Ohmura, 1984). A uranium uptake model may be used for high uranium specimens as discussed below for tooth enamel. Information on the uranium isotope ratios is useful for terrestrial deposits, but in marine samples determination of the uranium concentration alone is sufficient. Corals appear to be closed to radon loss. External dose should preferably be measured *in situ*, especially in heterogeneous sediments, but the external beta and gamma components may be eliminated for corals and thick-walled molluscs by removing the outer 2 mm of the sample. For this reason, and because they are more prone to diagenetic change, thin-walled molluscs (eg. *Glycimeris*) are less useful than thick-walled species (eg. *Mercenaria*).

The achievable precision for ESR dating of molluscs appears to be good, the estimated error for individual dates ($\pm$ 10%) being comparable to that derived from multiple samples at one site. However, for older dates and for samples with considerable uranium uptake, the accuracy may be poor unless the ambient temperature is low or a correction for thermal detrapping is applied. For corals the precision for multiple determinations is somewhat lower ($\pm$ 15%), but accuracy appears to be surprisingly good even for samples in excess of 200 ka.

Example: Corals — Radtke et al. (1988a)
          Molluscs — Molodkov (1988)

Hydroxyapatite — Bones and Tooth Enamel

Bones and teeth comprise hydroxyapatite which has a well known and highly sensitive ESR signal at g = 2.0018 (Figure 7.13). The stability of this signal is high (10^7 years, Ikeya and Miki 1980, Grün et al., 1987), and thus it offers considerable potential for the dating of archaeological sites where other dateable material is absent. Unfortunately in bone the proportion of hydroxyapatite is relatively low (c 50%), the remainder comprising collagen (a protein), fat and water. Organic radicals developed on irradiation interfere with the hydroxyapatite signal and cause considerable uncertainties in the determination of the ED. Furthermore, approximately 40% of the mineral phase in bone comprises spherical aggregates of amorphous calucium phosphate ($Ca(PO_4)_6$). Recrystalisation of this material to hydroxyapapite occurs through time *post morten*, generating vacant traps and resulting in an underestimation of the ED determined by the additive dose method (Grün and Schwarcz, 1987). Conversion of hydroxyapatite ($Ca_{10}(PO_4)_6(OH)_2$) to fluorapatite ($Ca_{10}(PO_4)_6F_2$) may also occur, reducing the ESR sensitivity (Ikeya, 1985, Grün and Schwarcz, 1987). Finally, bones form geochemically open systems, uranium derived from percolating water is imobilised under the reducing conditions which occur during *post-morten* organic decomposition. Uranium concentrations in fossil bones are thus often several orders of magnitude higher than in recent samples, and it is necessary to make unproveable assumptions regarding the dynamics of this uptake in order to determine the radiation dose. For these reasons, bone represents a difficult system to date, and no reliable methods are yet available.

Similar problems are also observed for cement and dentine in teeth. However tooth enamel is 96-97% mineral, with only about 1% organic material and is well

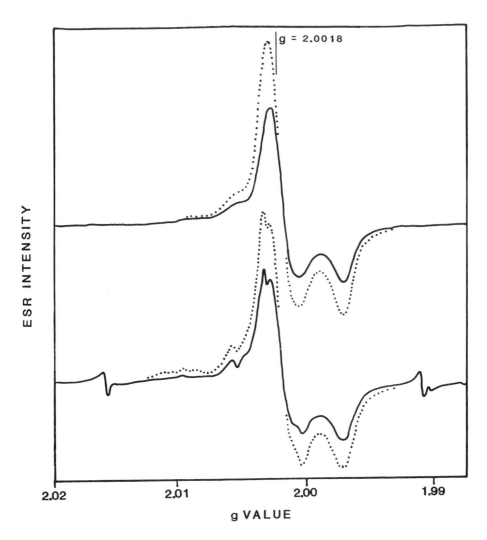

Figure 7.13 *ESR spectra for tooth enamel. Solid line natural sample; dotted line irradiated sample. The lower spectra show interference by organic signals as is commonly seen in dentine and bone (Grün, 1989).*

crystalised. Methods have therefore been developed to date tooth enamel (Grün et al., 1987). There are two major problems, firstly the difficulty of dose rate estimation in the complex layering of dentine, cement and enamel which constitutes the tooth, and secondly the need to model uranium uptake. Two models are normally applied, early uptake, in which most uranium is accumulated immediately after burial, and the continuous linear uptake model, where there is a constant rate of uranium accumulation with time (Ikeya 1985, Grün et al., 1987). The age difference between the two models for a given ED increases with the extent of uranium uptake, the

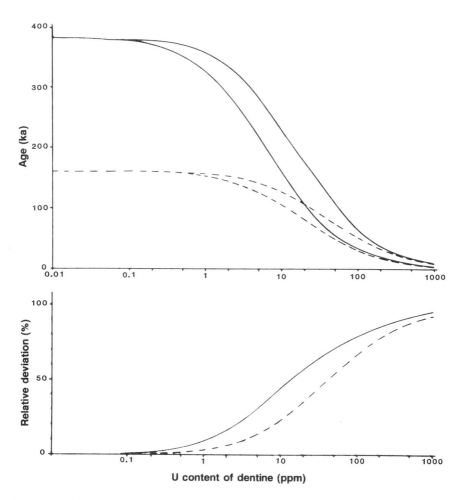

Figure 7.14 *Top: Dependence of calculated age on uranium content of dentine (assuming U enamel = 0.1 U dentine) for sand (solid line) and clay (dotted line). The clay gives a higher external dose and thus younger age for a particular ED. The upper curve is for the continuous linear uptake model (LU), and lower for early uptake (EU). Bottom: Relative percentage deviation of the linear uptake and early uptake model ages expressed as a function of the early uptake age ($100(t_{LU}-t_{EU})/t_{EU}$), from Grün et al. (1987).*

linear uptake model giving an age twice as high as the early uptake model for uranium concentrations in excess of 500 µg/g (Figure 7.14). One approach to this problem is to attempt to model the uptake iteratively using a combined uranium series/ESR age model (Grün et al., 1988a). While offering promise, this method has not yet been adequately tested. The second technique is to select samples where uranium uptake is at a minimum, and the external dose is of greater importance in estimating the age. Because enamel is less porous than cement and dentine, it accumulates uranium more slowly and has lower uranium concentrations (often by a factor of 10). This effect can be extended if relatively large dense teeth, such as those from a mammoth are selected for dating (Grün and Invernati, 1985), uranium accumulating in the outer layers (and cement and dentine) in preference to the interior enamel. A second possibility is to sample small chips of enamel which are separated from the high uranium concentration dentine and cement. Although uranium uptake remains a problem, the geometry required for dosimetry is simplified, and external gamma dose may be predominant. In either case, careful removal of the surface 20 μm layer of enamel is necessary to eliminate external alpha radiation contributions. External beta radiation dose must however be included, together with an estimate of its attenuation within the sample. A typical precision of $\pm$ 20% can be achieved from multiple samples in the dating of tooth enamel. Accuracy is dependent on the extent of uranium uptake and the validity of the model applied, but for younger samples (<300 ka) it seems possible to assign material to a particular interglacial period or oxygen isotope stage.

Example: Tooth enamel — Grün et al. (1987)

Quartz — Volcanic Rocks, Sediments and Fault Movement

There is considerable potential for the ESR dating of quartz as it is a ubiquitous geologic material. The ESR centers in quartz are relatively well known, and include three centers associated with germanium (Ge), titanium (Ti) and aluminium (Al) impurities together with the E' (SiO_3^{3-}) and OHC (OH^-) centers. The ESR signals associated with these centers are much more complex than those observed in calcites, and in the case of the Al and Ti centers have to be recorded at low temperatures (Figure 7.15). High modulation amplitude (5×10^{-4} T) has been used to simplify the complex signals for routine dating studies (Imai and Shimokawa, 1988). The E' center also saturates if high microwave powers are employed (>0.5 mW). The OHC and E' centers appear to be the most stable with mean lives at 20°C of 3.4 $\times$ 10^9 and 6.7×10^8 years, while the Ge and Al centers yield estimates of 3.1×10^7 and 2.4×10^6 years respectively (Shimokawa and Imai, 1987, Huang et al., 1988).

The ESR signals in quartz are zeroed on initial crystalisation, but more importantly in dating applications may be reset by exposure to sunlight or heating. Only the Ge center is totally bleached by 7 to 8 hours sunlight exposure (Buhay et al., 1988), and has been used for dating sediments by Tanaka et al. (1985). Preliminary results have also been reported for a magnetically reversed loess from China (Huang et al., 1988), suggesting that ESR dating of sediments may not be age-limited, as is the case for TL dating using feldspars.

The Al and Ti centers in quartz (and Al center in feldspars) have been used to date volcanic ash, volcanic glass and rhyolite (Imai and Shimokawa, 1988, Imai et al.,

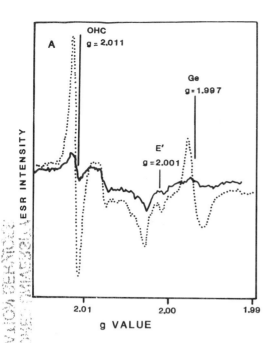 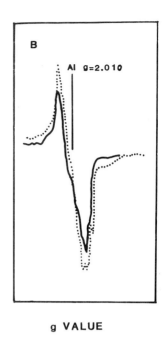

Figure 7.15 A) *ESR signals from granite (solid line), and mylonite (dotted line) showing the OHC, E' and Ge signals typically found in quartz at room temperature. Modulation amplitude 8 × 10⁻⁵ T, scan speed 2 × 10⁻⁵ T/s, microwave power 1mW.*

B) *ESR spectra for same samples recorded at low temperature (77°K) showing Al signal. Modulation amplitude 5 × 10⁻⁴ T, scan speed 1 × 10⁻⁴ T/s, microwave power 1mW (after Fukuchi, 1988). A more complex spectrum due to hyperfine splitting is displayed by the signal if lower modulation amplitudes are used (see Buhay et al., 1988 for example).*

1985, Imai and Shimokawa, 1989). Above 400°C both centers are completely annealed, but regrow on cooling and irradiation (Imai and Shimokaw, 1989), although the sensitivity of the Ti center is much reduced. Results show good stratigraphic accord in the range 0 to 0.8 Ma and satisfactory agreement with independent dating methods up to 1.2 Ma (Imai et al., 1985). Rigorous estimation of the uncertainties has not been undertaken, however they are probably large (± 20%) due to the weakness of the ESR signal, and uncertainties in dose rate estimation due to inhomogeneities in the isotopic composition of both individual grains, and the rock matrix. ESR dating of burnt flint from archaeological sites has potential, but a routine methods has not yet been developed.

A novel and unique application of ESR, which has been developed mainly in Japan, is the dating of movement on fault planes from quartz grains in the fault gouge.

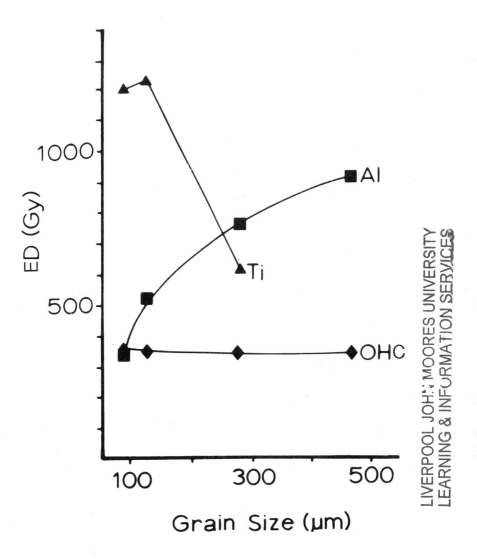

Figure 7.16 *ED determined from the OHC, Ti and Al centers in quartz grains of different grain size from the San Jacinto Fault. The OHC signal displays a plateau indicating all grain sizes were reset during the last significant movement event, while the Al center (which is more stable) was reset only for the finest grain size. There is no systematic pattern for the Ti center (after Buhay et al., 1988).*

Resetting of the signal appears to be due to frictional heating as laboratory experiments demonstrate that static pressure alone gives only partial zeroing (Sato et al., 1985). Thus the extent of the movement, depth of burial and type of movement control the resetting process (Fukuchi, 1989, Ito and Sawada, 1985). Reverse faults involving compressive stress give a high reliability for samples greater than 20 m deep at the time of movement, but for strike slip the depth should be in excess of 70 m and for normal faults in excess of 100 m. Buhay et al. (1988) suggest a practical test for complete resetting. For sub samples of different grain sizes, there should be agreement of ED estimates between at least two signals for the finest grain size, and ED estimates for the most unstable signal (OHC) should not vary with grain size (Figure 7.16). Results to date show promise, age estimates agreeing with the observed order of multiple movements in a single fault zone, although comparison with independent dating techniques is difficult. However, careful sampling is critical to obtain samples from within the zone of displacement, *in situ* estimates of external dose at the exact sample site are essential due to the variable nature of fault zones, although surface etching of sample quartz grains is normal to eliminate the contribution of external beta and gamma dose. Changes in the water saturation state of the fault gouge may also have occurred as surface exposure of the initially buried fault has occurred. These will be less significant in crystaline rocks, and in clayey gouge.

Example: Fault movement — Kosaka and Sawada (1985).
         Volcanic rocks — Imai and Shimokawa (1988).

Other Materials

A number of other materials have been examined to determine their potential for use in ESR dating. The radiation-sensitive ESR signal in zircons is too weak to utilise for dating (Taguchi et al., 1985), results from nacholite and halite appear to underestimate actual ages (Ikeya and Kai, 1988), while studies with gypsum suggest some potential (Chen et al., 1988). Nambi and Sankaran (1985) have reported the dating of laterite, but further work is needed.

REFERENCES

Aitken, M.J. 1976. Thermoluminescent age evaluation and assessment of error limits: revised system. *Archaeometry*, **18**, 233-238.

Aitken, M.J. 1985. *Thermoluminescence Dating*, Academic Press, London, pp. 359.

Aitken, M.J. and Bowman, S.G.E. 1975. Thermoluminescence dating: assessment of alpha particle contribution. *Archaeometry*, **17**, 132-138.

Bell, W.T. 1979. Thermoluminescence dating: radiation dose-rate data. *Archaeometry*, **21**, 243-245.

Buhay, W.M., Schwarcz, H.P. and Grün, R. 1988. ESR dating of fault gouge: the effect of grain size. *Quaternary Science Reviews*, **7**, 515-522.

Chen, Y., Lu, J., Head, J., Arakel, A.V. and Jacobson, G. 1988. ^{14}C and ESR dating of calcrete and gypcrete cores from the Amadeus Basin, Northern Territory, Australia. *Quaternary Science Reviews*, **7**, 447-453.

Debenham, N.C. and Aitken, M.J. 1984. Thermoluminescence dating of stalagmitic calcite. *Archaeometry*, **26**, 155-170.

Debuyst, R., Dejehet, F., Grün, R., Apers, D. and DeCanniere, P. 1984. Possibility of ESR dating without determination of annual dose. *Journal of Radioanalytical Nuclear Chemistry Letters*, **86**, 399-410.

Fain, J., Enramli, H., Miallier, D., Montret, D. and Sazelle, S. 1985. Environmental gamma dosimetry using TL dosimeters: efficiency and absorption calculations. *Nuclear Tracks*, **10**, 639-646.

Fukuchi, T. 1989. Theoretical study on frictional heat by faulting using ESR. *Applied Radiation and Isotopes*, **40**, 1181-1193.

Griffiths, D.R., Seeley, N.J., Chandra, H. and Symons, M.C.R. 1983. ESR dating of heated chert. *PACT*, **9**, 399-409.

Grün, R. 1985a. ESR dating of speleothems: limits of the method. In *ESR Dating and Dosimetry* (eds Ikeya M. and Miki, T.), Ionics, Tokyo, 61-69.

Grün, R. 1985b. Beitrage zur ESR-Datierung. *Sonderveroffentlichungen des Geologischen Institut der Universitat zu Koln*, **59**, 1-157.

Grün, R. 1990. Electron spin resonance (ESR) dating. *Quaternary International*, **1**, 65-109.

Grün, R. and DeCanniere, P. 1984. ESR dating: problems encountered in the evaluation of the naturally accumulated dose (AD) of secondary carbonates. *Journal of Radioanalytical Nuclear Chemistry Letters*, **85**, 213-226.

Grün, R. and Invernati, C. 1985. Uranium accumulation in teeth and its effect on ESR dating — a detailed study of a mamoth tooth. *Nuclear Tracks*, **10**, 869-878.

Grün, R. and MacDonald, P.D.M. 1989. Non-linear fitting of TL/ESR dose-response curves. *Applied Radiation and Isotopes*, **40**, 1077-1080.

Grün, R. and Schwarcz, H.P. 1987. Some remarks on ESR dating of bones. *Ancient TL*, **5**, 10-19.

Grün, R., Schwarcz, H.P. and Chadam, J.M. 1988a. ESR dating of tooth enamel: coupled correction for U uptake and U series disequilibrium. *Nuclear Tracks*, **14**, 237-241.

Grün, R., Schwarcz, H.P. and Zymela, S. 1987. ESR dating of tooth enamel. *Canadian Journal of Earth Sciences*, **24**, 1022-1037.

Grün, R., Schwarcz, H.P., Ford, D.C. and Hentzsch, B. 1988. ESR dating of spring deposited travertines. *Quaternary Science Reviews*, **7**, 429-432.

Haskell, E.H. 1983. Beta dose-rate determination: preliminary results from an interlaboratory comparison of techniques. *PACT*, **9**, 77-85.

Hennig, G.J. and Grün, R. 1983. ESR dating in Quaternary geology. *Quaternary Science Reviews*, **2**, 157-238.

Hennig, G.J., Grün, R. and Brunnacker, K. 1983. Interlaboratory comparison project of ESR dating, phase 1. *PACT*, **9**, 447-452.

Huang, P.H., Jin, S-Z., Peng, Z-C, Liang, R-Y., Quan, Y. and Wang, Z-R. 1988. ESR dating and trapped electron lifetime of quartz grains in loess of China. *Quaternary Science Reviews*, **7**, 533-536.

Hutt, G. and Jaek, J. 1989. Dating accuracy from laboratory reconstruction of palaeodose. *Applied Radiation and Isotopes*, **40**, 1057-1061.

Ikeya, M. 1975. Dating a stalactite by electron paramagnetic resonance. *Nature*, **255**, 48-50.

Ikeya, M. 1985. Dating methods of Pleistocene deposits and their problems, electron spin resonance. *Geoscience Canada Reprint Series*, **2**, 73-87.

Ikeya, M. and Kai, A. 1988. ESR dating of saline sediments using $NaHCO_3$ and NaCl. *Quaternary Science Reviews*, **7**, 471-475.

Ikeya, M. and Miki, T. 1980. Electron spin resonance dating of animal and human bones. *Science*, **207**, 977-979.

Ikeya, M. and Ohmura, K. 1983. Comparison of ESR ages of corals from marine terraces with ^{14}C and $^{230}Th/^{234}U$ ages. *Earth and Planetary Science Letters*, **65**, 34-38.

Imai, N. and Shimokawa, K. 1988. ESR dating of Quaternary tephra from Mt. Osore-Zan using Al and Ti centers in quartz. *Quaternary Science Reviews*, **7**, 523-527.

Imai, N. and Shimokawa, K. 1989. ESR dating of the tephra 'Crystal Ash' distributed in Shinshu, Central Japan. *Applied Radiation and Isotopes*, **40**, 1177-1180.

Imai, N., Shimokawa, K. and Hirota, M. 1985. ESR dating of volcanic ash. *Nature*, **314**, 81-83.

Ito, T. and Sawada, S. 1985. Reliable criteria for selection of sampling points for ESR fault dating. In *ESR Dating and Dosimetry* (eds Ikeya, M. and Miki, T.), Ionics, Tokyo, 229-237.

Kai, A. and Ikeya, M. 1989. ESR study of fossil shell in sediments of Hamana Lake. *Applied Radiation and Isotopes*, **40**, 1139-1142.

Katzenberger, O., Debuyst, R., DeCanniere, P., Dejehet, F., Apers, D. and Barabas, M. 1989. Temperature experiments on mollusc samples: on approach to ESR signal identification. *Applied Radiation and Isotopes*, **40**, 1113-1118.

Kaufman, A., Broecker, W.S., Ku, T.L. and Thurber, D.L. 1971. The status of U-series methods of mollusc dating. *Geochimica Cosmochimica Acta*, **35**, 1155-1189.

Kosaka, K. and Sawada, S. 1985. Fault gouge analysis and ESR dating of the Tsurukawa Fault, West of Tokyo. In *ESR Dating and Dosimetry* (eds Ikeya, M. and Miki, T.), Ionics, Tokyo, 257-266.

Lyons, R.G. 1988. Determination of alpha effectiveness in ESR dating using linear accelerator techniques: methods and energy dependence. *Nuclear Tracks*, **14**, 275-288.

Lyons, R.G. and Brennan, B.J. 1989. Alpha particle effectiveness in ESR dating: energy dependence and implications for dose rate calculations. *Applied Radiation and Isotopes*, **40**, 1063-1070.

Lyons, R.G., Bowmaker, G.A. and O'Connor, C.J. 1988. Dependence of accumulated dose in ESR dating on microwave power: a contra-indication to the routine use of low power levels. *Nuclear Tracks and Radiation Measurements*, **14**, 243-251.

Lyons, R.G., Crossley, P.C., Ditchburn, R.G., McCabe, W.J. and Whitehead, N. 1989. Radon escape from New Zealand speleothems. *Applied Radiation and Isotopes*, **40**, 1153-1158.

Molodkov, A. 1988. ESR dating of Quaternary shells: recent advances. *Quaternary Science Reviews*, **7**, 477-484.

Molodkov, A. 1989. The problem of long-term fading of absorbed palaeodose on ESR-dating of Quaternary mollusc shells. *Applied Radiation and Isotopes*, **40**, 1087-1093.

Murray, A.S., Bowman, S.G.E. and Aitken, M.J. 1979. Evaluation of the gamma dose rate contribution. *PACT*, **2**, 84-96.

Nambi, K.S.V. and Aitken, M.J. 1986. Annual dose conversion factors for TL and ESR dating. *Archaeometry*, **28**, 202-205.

Nambi, K.S.V. and Sankaram, A.V. 1985. ESR dating of laterite of basaltic origin. In *ESR Dating and Dosimetry* (eds Ikeya, M. and Miki, T.), Ionics, Tokyo, 54-59.

Prescott, J.R. and Hutton, J.T. 1988. Cosmic ray and gamma dosimetry for TL and ESR. *Nuclear Tracks and Radiation Measurements*, **14**, 223-227.

Radtke, U., Bruckner, H., Mangini, A. and Hausmann, R. 1988b. Problems encountered with absolute dating (U. Series, ESR) of Spanish calcretes. *Quaternary Science Reviews*, **7**, 439-445.

Radtke, U. and Grün, R. 1988. ESR dating of corals. *Quaternary Science Reviews*, **7**, 465-470.

Radtke, U., Grün, R. and Schwarcz, H.P. 1988a. New results from ESR dating of Pleistocene coral reef tracts of Barbados (W.I.). *Quaternary Research*, **29**, 197-215.

Sato, T., Suito, K. and Ichikawa, K. 1985. Characterisitics of ESR and TL signals on quartz from fault regions. In *ESR Dating and Dosimetry* (eds Ikeya, M. and Miki, T.), Ionics, Tokyo, 54-59.

Schwarcz, H.P., Grün, R., Latham, A.G., Mania, D. and Brunacker, K. 1988. New evidence for the age of the Bilzingsleben archaeological site. *Archaeometry*, **30**, 5-17.

Shimokawa, K. and Imai, N. 1987. Simultaneous determination of alteration and eruption ages of volcanic rocks by electron spin resonance. *Geochimica et Cosmochimica Acta*, **51**, 115-119.

Siegele, R. and Mangini, A. 1985. Progress of ESR studies on $CaCO_3$ of deep sea sediments. *Nuclear Tracks*, **10**, 937-943.

Smart, P.L., Smith, B.W., Chandra, H., Andrews, J.N. and Symons, M.C.R. 1988. An intercomparison of ESR and uranium series ages for Quaternary speleothem calcites. *Quaternary Science Reviews*, **7**, 411-416.

Smith, B.W., Smart, P.L. and Symons, M.C.R. 1985a. ESR signals in a variety of speleothem calcites and their suitability for dating. *Nuclear Tracks*, **10**, 837-844.

Smith, B.W., Smart, P.L., Symons, M.C.R. and Andrews, J.N. 1985b. ESR dating of detritally contaminated calcites. In *ESR Dating and Dosimetry* (eds Ikeya, M. and Miki, T.), Ionics, Tokyo, 49-59.

Smith, B.W., Smart, P.L. and Symons, M.C.R. 1986. A routine ESR technique for dating calcite speleothems. *Radiation Protection Dosimetry*, **17**, 241-245.

Symons, M.C.R. 1978. *Chemical and Biochemical Aspects of Electron Spin Resonance Spectrocopy*, Van Nostrand Reinhold, London, pp. 190.

Taguchi, S., Harayama, M. and Hayashi, M. 1985. ESR signal of zircon and geologic age. In *ESR Dating and Dosimetry* (eds Ikeya and Miki, T.) Ionics, Tokyo, 191-196.

Tanaka, T., Sawada, S. and Ito, T. 1985. ESR dating of late Pleistocene near shore and terrace sands in southern Kanto, Japan. In *ESR Dating and Dosimetry* (eds Ikeya, M. and Miki, T.) Ionics, Tokyo, 54-59.

Wieser, A., Goksu, H.Y. and Regulla, D.F. 1985. Characteristics of gamma-induced ESR spectra in various calcites. *Nuclear Tracks*, **10**, 831-836.

Yokoyama, Y., Quaegebeur, J.P., Bibron, R. and Leger, C. 1983b. ESR dating of Palaeolithic calcite: thermal annealing experiment and trapped electron lifetime. *PACT*, **9**, 371-379.

Zeller, E.J., Levy, P.W. and Mattern, P.L. 1967. Geologic dating by electron spin resonance. *Proceedings of the Symposium on Radioactive Dating and Low-Level Counting*, IAEA, Vienna, 531-540.

Chapter 8

AMINO ACID DATING

G. Sykes

HISTORICAL BACKGROUND

In 1954, Abelson demonstrated the presence of amino acids in fossils, the oldest being Devonian fish bone from the Ohio Black Shale (Abelson, 1954). It was soon realised that the systematic changes undergone by amino acids following the death of an organism could be used to provide an index of the age of a fossil (Abelson, 1956). This was further studied by Vallentyne (1964, 1969) who heated modern materials to determine the order of stability of amino acids and the temperature dependence of their decay. A major advance was made by Hare and Mitterrer (1967) who discovered an increase in non-protein D-amino acids in fossils of increasing age. Improvements in techniques and instrumentation (Benson and Hare, 1975) have increased the sensitivity and speed of amino acid analysis, enabling measurements of the D/L ratio to be used for dating fossils.

CHEMICAL BACKGROUND

Proteins are built from a strings of amino acids which are joined together by peptide bonds. Sometimes several amino acid chains are joined by disulphide (-S-S-) bridges (Stryer, 1988, Metzler, 1977 (Figure 8.1)). The sequence of amino acids is unique to a given protein and determines its biological function. Proteins are generally composed of 20 α-amino acids along with the imino acids, proline and hydroxyproline, the latter being very abundant in bone collagen. Amino acids (with the exception of glycine) can all exist as two non-superimposable mirror images, rather like right and left hands. These non-superimposable mirror images are called optical isomers and are designated L-amino acids and D-amino acids (Figure 8.2). The asterisked carbon atom in Figure 8.2 is known as a chiral carbon atom, and it is this carbon atom which is the centre of asymmetry that allows the formation of two optical isomers. The amino acids threonine and isoleucine have two chiral carbon atoms, giving a set of four diastereoisomers (Figure 8.3).

161

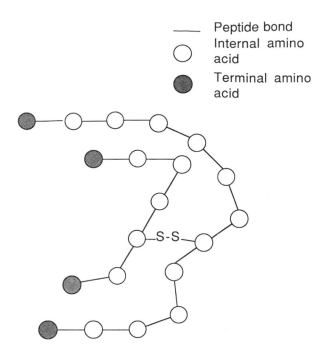

Figure 8.1 *Proteins consist of a "chain" of amino acids joined together by peptide bonds. Several of these "chains" may be joined together by -S-S— bridges.*

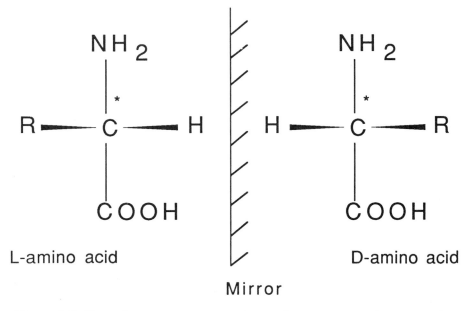

Figure 8.2 *Generalized representation of D- and L- amino acids. The side chain (R) is different for each amino acid. * = chiral carbon atom.*

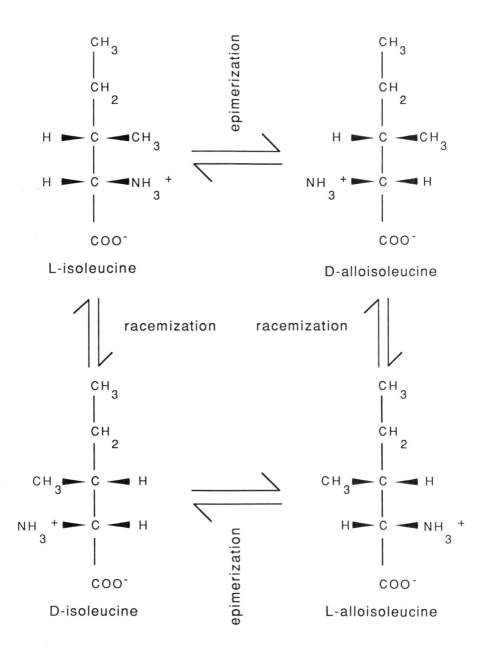

Figure 8.3 *Diastereoisomers of isoleucine.*

PRINCIPLES OF AMINO ACID DATING

Only the L-isomers of amino acids occur in the proteins of living organisms. After death, however, amino acids are no longer maintained in the L-configuration, but interconvert (racemize) with the D-configuration until equilibrium is reached. If the rate of this interconversion can be calculated, the time elapsed since the death of an organism can be determined from the ratio of D/L amino acids. In most geochronology applications, the amino acid L-isoleucine (L-Ile), which interconverts (epimerizes) with its diastereoisomer, D-alloisoleucine (D-aIle), is used. This process is known as epimerization, ie. the inversion of the chiral α-carbon atom, as opposed to racemization which is the inversion of all chiral carbon atoms (see Figure 8.3). L-Ile and D-Ile are relatively easy to separate by ion exchange chromatography. Mixtures of D/L amino acids can also be separated by gas liquid chromatography. Determining the rate of epimerization of L-Ile to D-aIle is not a straightforward task because the chemistry of the process is complex. However, studies at elevated temperatures have produced a model of protein diagenesis; amino acids at the terminal position of proteins (see Figure 8.1) epimerize much faster than internally bound or free amino acids (free amino acids are those released by hydrolysis of the protein) (Kriauskul and Mitterer, 1980). In addition, terminal amino acids can be released as dipeptides by internal aminolysis and form diketopiperazines which epimerize rapidly (Steinberg and Bada, 1983, Mitterer and Kriauskul, 1984). Protein diagenesis is therefore a complex process involving the interaction of protein hydrolysis and the relative rates of amino acid epimerization at different positions in a protein chain. The sequence of events is summarized in Figure 8.4. This reaction sequence gives rise to a kinetic model that has an initial component where the reaction follows first order reversible kinetics, followed by a slowing down phase, ending in a second, but slower reversible first order reaction. For the initial reversible first order portions of the reaction sequence (0 to 20 hours in Figure 8.4), it is easy to relate the D/L ratio to time:

$$\ln \left[\frac{1 + \frac{(D)}{(L)}}{1 - K' \frac{(D)}{(L)}} \right] = k_1 \left(1 + K' \right) t + c' \tag{8.1}$$

where,
(D) = concentration of D amino acid,
(L) = concentration of L amino acid,
K' = 1/equilibrium constant,
k_1 = rate constant for L to D interconversion,
t = time,
c' = constant of integration.

Several factors affect the relationship between D/L ratio and time and these are considered below.

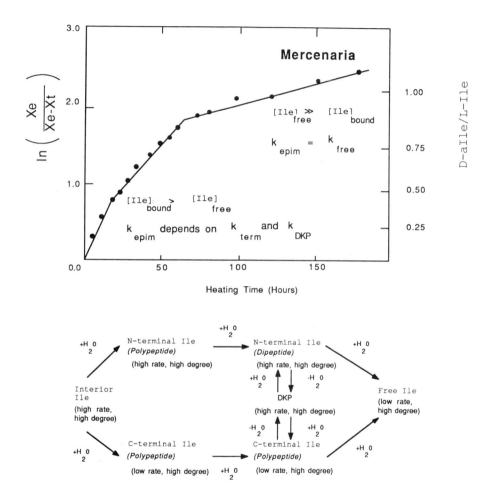

Figure 8.4 *Kinetics of epimerized* Mercenaria *at 150°C (top) and schematic representation of a possible reaction sequence for isoleucine epimerization in a carbonate matrix based on studies with di and tri peptides (bottom). DKP = diketopiperazine. (Kriauskul and Mitterer, 1980, Mitterer and Kriauskul, 1984).*

165

Temperature

Of all environmental factors, temperature has the largest effect on the D/L ratio. From studies that measure the rate of epimerization in various molluscs, it has been shown that a temperature rise of 4°C doubles the rate of epimerization (Mitterer, 1975, McCoy, 1987a). The equation that relates the increase in reaction rate to temperature is:

$$k = A.e^{\frac{E_a}{RT}}$$
(8.2)

where,
k = rate constant,
A = pre-exponential factor,
E_a = activation energy,
R = universal gas constant,
T = temperature.

While it is potentially possible to use this equation to correct for paleotemperature and calculate ages from the D/L ratio, uncertainties in measurements of paleotemperature and the values in equation (8.2) can lead to errors of up to ±50%. However, for samples of known age, it is possible to calculate average paleotemperatures since the death of an organism with a high degree of accuracy (McCoy, 1987a).

Two strategies have been developed to overcome the problems associated with temperature effects. The first, the aminostratigraphic approach of Miller and Hare (1980), considers D/L ratios from a limited geographical area. A similar climatic history is thus assumed for the area and this is often confirmed by independent evidence such as pollen data. The D/L ratios are arranged into groups which are constrained by lithostratigraphy, biostratigraphy, statistical analysis and geomorphology. These groups were named aminozones by Nelson (1978). More recently, Bowen et al. (1985) have introduced the term D/L stage, where stratigraphically the designation stage is more appropriate than zone. The fossiliferous beaches of South West Britain have been divided into three D/L stages. Of these, the Pennard (youngest) and Minchin Hole (oldest) are lithostratigraphically separated at Minchin Hole, Gower. The status of the middle, unnamed D/L stage was uncertain, but it may now be more appropriately regarded as a substage of the Minchin Hole stage (Bowen, 1989a,b). If independently determined ages are available, aminozones or D/L stages can be tied to a geochronology. In the case of south west Britain, calibration with the available radiometric dates gives an age of 122 ka for the Pennard D/L stage (0.105 ± 0.003, n=196). It is therefore likely that the Minchin Hole stage is the same age as oxygen isotope stage 7.

The second strategy was pioneered by Kennedy et al. (1982), who used a limited number of radiometric ages to calibrate D/L ratios over a wide range of mean annual temperatures and to produce isochrons relating D/L ratio to age along the west coast of North America. Hearty et al. (1986) have produced similar isochrons for the Mediterranean (Figure 8.5).

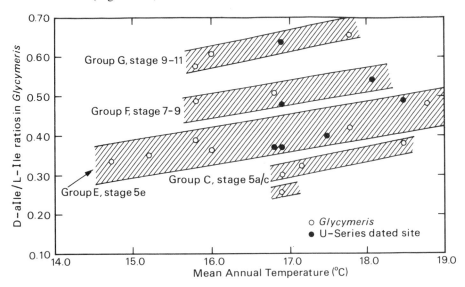

Figure 8.5 *Plot of mean D-alLe/L-Ile ratios in* Glycimeris *by group against present day mean annual temperatures. The trend of increasing D-alLe/L-Ile ratios with increasing temperature reflects the control of the temperature on the epimerization rate. (Hearty et al., 1986).*

Species Effect

Different taxa have been shown to epimerize at different rates. It is therefore important to analyse monospecific samples, identifying individuals to at least genus level (King and Hare, 1972, King and Neville, 1977). Ideally, several samples each of different species should be analysed from the same stratigraphic unit. Species can be divided into 3 broad categories, based on rate of epimerization. These categories are fast *(Divaricella divaricata, Lucinoma borealis)*, moderate *(Arctica, Macoma)*, and slow *(Patella, Littorina)* (Miller and Mangeraud, 1985). Within a given category, it is possible to make adjustments to correct for the slight differences between species (Bowen et al., 1985).

In some depositional environments, shelly material is very fragmented and may be difficult to identify unambiguously. Fortunately, the amino acid composition of such shells can be used to assist in species identification (Andrews et al., 1985).

Essentially, the taxonomic effect on the rate of epimerization does not represent a serious constraint on the method, provided that a site contains identifiable species, and that D/L ratios have been measured for these species at other sites.

Intra-shell Variation

Some taxa have been found to show differences in D-alle/L-Ile proteins from different parts of the same shell (Brigham, 1983, cf. also Miller and Hare, 1980). Ideally the same portion of a shell should be used for analyses. Where this is not possible, it is important to record which part of a shell was used. In the future, it should be possible to correct for intra-shell variation in the same way that it is presently possible to compensate for inter-species differences.

Contamination and Exchange of Amino Acids with the Environment

Although contamination is potentially a source of very large errors in amino acid geochronology, it does not seem to present a problem for molluscs. Miller and Hopkins (1980) found that shells from last interglacial sites on St. Pauls Island, Alaska, which had their amino acids either destroyed (Upper Marine Beds), or taken to equilibrium by the transient heat of a lava flow (Lower and Basal Marine Beds), had not exchanged amino acids with the environment (Table 8.1). Armstrong et al. (1983) have shown that in pre-Quaternary fossil bone there is considerable contamination of bone protein. Bone, however, appears to be unreliable, even for dating relatively recent material (Blackwell and Rutter, 1987a). Contamination by groundwater and leaching are also potential sources of error. In either case, the amino acid fingerprint and the free (naturally hydrolysed) amino acid component of the fossil material would be altered (Schroeder, 1975). To minimize the effects of environmental contamination, the samples should be cleaned, first mechanically and then by dissolution of the outside third of the shell with 2M HCl. Contamination in the laboratory by handling after cleaning can be detected by anomalously high serine levels.

Table 8.1 *D/L ratios from molluscs affected by lava flows on St Paul, Alaska (Miller and Hopkins, 1980).*

Location	Age (ka)	Relation to lava flow	D-alle/L-Ile
Tolstoi Point Einahunto Bluffs	125	4.3 - 5 m below subaerial lava	0.18
Upper Marine Bed	125	1.0 - 2.5 m below subaerial lava	amino acids destroyed levels <1%
Lower marine Beds	125	<1.2 m below pillow lava	1.26
Basal Marine Beds	>125	0.3 - 1.5 m below pillow lava	1.22

Any process which produces an open system allowing exchange of amino acids with the environment could invalidate the method. Therefore results from worn and abraded shells should be treated with caution and chromatograms examined for signs of contamination or leaching. Criteria for examining chromatograms have been suggested by Sykes and Bowen (1991).

pH and Trace Elements

pH has a major effect on the epimerization rate of fossil protein in aqueous solution (Blackwell and Rutter, 1987a). However, in practice this is less of a problem because calcareous material or hydroxyapatite should act as buffers against changes in environmental pH. Catalysis by metal ions, particularly Cu^{2+} and Mg^{2+}, increases the epimerization rate of free amino acids (Bada and Schroeder, 1975), although the effect of metal ions on protein-bound amino acids should be negligible (Williams and Smith, 1977). Ionic strength can also affect epimerization rate but this would present less of a problem for proteins in a carbonate or hydroxyapatite matrix (Williams and Smith, 1977).

Table 8.2 *Preparation techniques, sample prefix and code numbers and reference sources for published amino acid data for British Pleistocene molluscs. Preparation A is the currently used standard technique. Samples analysed using Preparation B do not give statistically reproducible results.*

Preparation technique	Sample prefix and code number	Reference source
A	> AAL-2790 > ABER-300 ABER (all non-marine mollusc data) LOND (all data)	Andrews et al. (1984) Bowen et al. (1985) Miller et al. (1987b) Bowen et al. (1989) Bowen and Sykes (1988)
B	AAL-1300 to AAL-1550 < ABER 300 (marine mollusc data)	Miller et al. (1979) Andrews et al. (1979) Davies (1983) Davies and Keen (1985)
C	AAL-1330 to AAL-1550	Miller (1984)

Sample Preparation

It has been shown that different methods of sample preparation introduce differences into the measured D/L ratio. Methods that involve dissolution of a sample in a glass vessel, followed by transfer to a glass vial, lead to fractionation of the high molecular weight component of the sample which is preferentially adsorbed on to the glass wall (Miller et al., 1987). Amino acid laboratories have now standardized on a sample preparation technique in which dissolution and hydrolysis of the sample all take place in the same glass vessel. A summary of the procedures is given in Figure 8.6. Miller

169

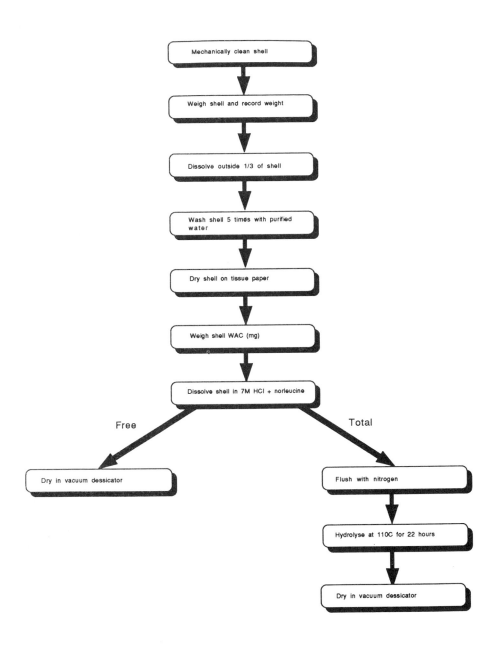

Figure 8.6 *Flow diagram of the preparation procedure for amino acid geochronology.*

(1984) has calculated correction factors for some species to compensate for differences between three sample preparation techniques, but samples analysed under the old preparation method do not give statistically reproducible results (Miller, 1984). The differences between techniques for total D-alle/L-Ile are summarised below (Miller, 1984) and details of results relating to the British Pleistocene are tabulated by preparation method in Table 8.2.

The total amino acid fraction measures both the free and bound amino acids. Samples can also be prepared to measure the free amino acid fraction; that is, those amino acids which are hydrolysed during diagenesis. The free amino acid fraction gives higher D/L ratios than the total fraction and is therefore useful for dating younger material. (Note that the free amino acid D-alle/L-Ile ratios are the same for preparation methods A, B and C which eliminates instrumental variability as a cause of the measured differences (Miller, 1984)). In addition, comparison of the absolute concentrations of free and total amino acids may help identify samples that have been leached as the low molecular weight, free amino acids should be leached faster than higher molecular weight, bound amino acids.

Consistent differences between D/L ratios measured by different laboratories have been shown to exist (Wehmiller, 1984). Note, however, that the differences between the amino acid laboratories at the University of London (Royal Holloway and Bedford New College) and the University of Colorado (at Boulder) are not significant (Bowen et al., 1985).

Datable Materials

Shell. The most widely dated material has been molluscan shell, which seems to form a tightly closed system that is affected by a minimum of external factors. Several studies show a consistent increase in D/L ratio from deposits known to increase in age. These studies have been mainly on marine mollusca (Wehmiller, 1982, Hearty et al., 1986, Miller and Mangerud, 1985, Bowen et al., 1985), although the method has recently been successfully applied to the continental record (Miller et al., 1987b, McCoy, 1987, Hughes, 1987). Foraminifera have also been used to date sediments. Here an increase in D/L ratio in a down core direction from deep ocean sediments has been demonstrated (King, 1980).

Bone, antler and dental tissue. Several studies using bone have produced contentious results (see for example Bischoff and Rosenbauer, 1981). Recently it has been shown that the D/L ratios in bone, antler and dental tissues do not increase consistently with age over a period of 200 ka (Blackwell and Rutter, 1987a). Furthermore, the extrapolation of linear kinetics in experiments on bones and teeth at elevated temperatures has been called into question, as the reaction kinetics have been shown to be complex (Blackwell and Rutter, 1987c).

Wood. Amino acid dating of wood has produced reliable results in some

171

environments, but it should be remembered that proteins in wood are not buffered against changes in environmental pH (as they are in non-carbonate systems) and great care must be taken in evaluating results (Pillans, 1983).

Sample Collection

It is important that the position of samples within a stratigraphic unit is known as accurately as possible. Accordingly, samples should always be accompanied by at least the following information; collector, collection date, country of origin, region, site, unit, position within unit, grid reference, age of sample if known and dating method, any biostratigraphic data and a stratigraphic diagram. Other information such as depth of burial, depositional environment and lithology of units may also prove useful when evaluating results.

Several factors which could affect the D/L ratios can be eliminated by appropriate sampling strategies and subsequent sample preparation procedures. Some of these strategies are obvious but are outlined here. Samples should be well embedded in the stratigraphic unit to eliminate the possibility of contamination by modern material. Miller et al. (personal communication) have shown that shells from the Arctic that lie close to the surface of a unit may also be affected by diurnal and annual temperature fluctuations although a burial depth of more than 2 m for most of the history of the site eliminates this source of uncertainty. Samples from near the surface of recently exposed units should not be affected (this could apply to durations of exposure of several hundred years).

Ideally the samples should be collections of *in situ* deposits as the D/L ratios are then characteristic of the time of deposition. It is possible to identify mixed populations of shells, for example from glacial deposits, and, in these cases, the youngest faunal element gives the maximum age of a stratigraphic unit. One additional use of amino acid geochronology is to screen populations and select the youngest faunal element for other dating techniques, such as ^{14}C dating (Miller and Hare, 1980).

Contamination by handling is generally not a problem because the samples are rigourously cleaned during preparation for amino acid analysis. Chemical reagents should be avoided during sample preparation, as strong acids will dissolve shelly material and strong alkalis may catalyse the epimerization of L-isoleucine. Oxidizing agents such as hydrogen peroxide could oxidize amino acids and should be avoided. Sediments being sampled for amino acid analysis are best disaggregated in water alone, although this may be time consuming. Heat should also be avoided during sample preparation. Samples for amino acid analysis should therefore be air and not oven dried.

CONCLUSION

In conclusion, amino acid geochronology has already contributed to our understanding of the Quaternary and, as more absolute dates become available for use in calibration, the potential of the method will become even greater. With the accuracy currently achievable, the relative speed and low cost of the amino acid technique permit correlative dating of large numbers of sites, particularly given the ubiquitous distribution of molluscs in both marine and terrestrial Quaternary deposits. Large scale correlation of Quaternary events over the last 2.4 Ma of earth history is therefore potentially possible.

REFERENCES

Abelson, P.H. 1954. Paleobiochemistry. *Carnegie Institute Washington Yearbook*, **53**, 97-101.

Abelson, P.H. 1956. Paleobiochemistry. *Scientific American*, **195**, 85-92.

Andrews, J.T., Bowen, D.Q. and Kidson, C. 1979. Amino acid ratios and the correlation of beaches in southwest England and Wales. *Nature*, **281**, 556-568.

Andrews, J.T., Gilbertson, D.D. and Hawkins, A.B. 1984. The Pleistocene succession of the Severn Estuary: a revised model based on amino acid racemization studies. *Journal of the Geological Society of London*, **141**, 967-974.

Andrews, J.T., Miller, G.H., Davies, D.C. and Davies, K.H. 1985. Generic identification of fragmentary Quaternary molluscs by amino acid chromatography: a tool of Palaeontological research. *Geological Journal*, **20**, 1-20.

Armstrong, W.G., Halstead, L.B., Reed, F.B. and Wood, L. 1983. Fossil proteins in vertebrate calcified tissues. *Philosophical Transactions of the Royal Society of London Series B*, **301**, 301-343.

Bada, J.L. and Schoeder, 1975. Amino acid racemization reactions and their geochemical implications. *Naturwissenschaften*, **62**, 71-79.

Benson, J.R. and Hare, P.E. 1975. o-Phthaldehyde: fluorogenic detection of primary amines in the picomole range. Comparison of fluorescamine and ninhydrin. *Proceedings of the National Academy of Sciences of the USA*, **72**, 619-622.

Bischoff, J.L. and Rosebauer, R.L. 1981. Uranium series dating of human skeletal remains from the Telar and Sunnyvale sites, California. *Science*, **213**, 1003-1005.

Blackwell, B. and Rutter, N. 1987a. Problems in amino acid racemization dating from Lachaise and Montgaudier (Charente, France). *Proceedings of the 12th INQUA Congress*, 130.

Blackwell, B. and Rutter, N. 1987b. pH variations in amino acids racemization and interacid ratios in mammalian dentine. *Proceedings of the 12th INQUA Congress*, 130.

Blackwell, B. and Rutter, N. 1987c. Amino acid racemization kinetics in mammalian bone and teeth. *Proceedings of the 12th INQUA Congress*, 130.

Bowen, D.Q. 1989a. An introduction to the Quaternary. In *Quaternary of Wales* (eds. Campbell, S. and Bowen, D.Q.), Nature Conservancy Council, Peterborough, 7-14.

Bowen, D.Q. 1989b. The Quaternary rocks and Landforms of Wales. In *Quaternary of Wales* (eds. Campbell, S. and Bowen, D.Q.), Nature Conservancy Council, Peterborough, 15-20.

Bowen, D.Q. and Sykes, G.A. 1988. Correlation of marine events and glaciations on the Northeast Atlantic margin. *Proceedings of the Royal Society of London B*, **318**, 619-635.

Bowen, D.Q., Sykes, G.A., Reeves, A.R., Miller, G.H., Andrews, J.T., Brew, J.S. and Hare, P.E. 1985. Amino acid geochronology of raised beaches in South West Britain. *Quaternary Science Reviews*, **4**, 279-318.

Bowen, D.Q., Hughes, S., Sykes, G.H. and Miller, G.H. 1989. Land sea correlations in the Pleistocene based on isoleucine epimeisation in non marine mollusus. *Nature*, **350**, 49-51.

Brigham, J.K. 1983. Intrashell variations in amino acid concentration and isoleucine epimerization ratio in fossil *Hiatella arctica*. *Geology*, **11**, 509-513.

Davies, K.H. 1983. Amino acid analysis of Pleistocene marine molluscs from the Gower Peninsula. *Nature*, **302**, 137-139.

Davis, K.H. and Keen, D.H. 1985. The age of PLeistocene marine deposits at Portland, Dorset. *Proceedings of the Geological Association*, **96**, 217-225.

Hare, P.E. and Mitterer, R.M. 1967. Nonprotein amino acids in fossil shells. *Carnegie Institute of Washington Yearbook*, **65**, 362-364.

Hearty, P.J., Miller, G.H., Stearnes, C.E. and Szabo, B.S. 1986. Amino-stratigraphy and Quaternary shorelines in the Mediterranean basin. *Geological Society Bulletin*, **97**, 850-858.

Hughes, S. 1987. *The Aminostratigraphy of British Quaternary non-marine deposits*. Ph.D. thesis, University of Wales.

Kennedy, G.L., Lajoie, K.R. and Wehmiller, J. 1982. Aminostratigraphy and faunal correlations of the later Quaternary marine terraces, Pacific coast, USA. *Nature*, **299**, 545-547.

King, K. Jr. 1980. Application of amino acid biogeochemistry for marine sediments. In *The Biogeochemistry of Amino Acids*, (eds P.E. Hare, T.C. Hoering and K. King Jr.), Wiley, New York, 377-389.

King, K. and Hare, P.E. 1972. Species effects in the epimerization of L-isoleucine in fossil planktonic Foraminifera. *Carnegie Institute of Washington Yearbook*, **71**, 599-608.

King, K. and Neville, C. 1977. Isoleucine epimerization for dating marine sediments, the importance of analysing monospecific samples. *Science*, **195**, 1333-1335.

Kriauskul, N. and Mitterer, R.M. 1978. Isoleucine epimerization in peptides and proteins: kinetic factors and application to fossil proteins. *Science*, **201**, 1011-14.

Kriauskul, N. and Mitterer, R.M. 1980. Some factors affecting the epimerization of isoleucine in peptides and proteins. In *The Biogeochemistry of Amino Acids*, (eds P.E. Hare, T.C. Hoering and K. King Jr.), Wiley, New York, 283-296.

Kriauskul, N. and Mitterer, R.M. 1984. Comparison of rates and degrees of isoleucine epimerization in dipeptides and tripeptides. *Organic Geochemistry*, **7**, 91-8.

McCoy, W.P. 1987a. The precision of amino acid Geochronology and Palaeothermometry. *Quaternary Science Reviews*, **6**, 43-48.

McCoy, W.P. 1987b. Quaternary Aminostratigraphy of the Bonneville basin, Western United States. *Geological Society of American Bulletin*, **98**, 99-112.

Metzler, D.E. 1977. The molecules of which we are made. In *Biochemistry: The Chemical Reactions of Living Cells*, Academic Press, New York, 47-150.

Miller, G.H. 1984. Aminostratigraphy of Baffin Island shell bearing deposits. In *Quaternary Environments*, (ed J.T. Andrews), Allen and Unwin, Boston, 395-427.

Miller, G.H. and Hare, P.E. 1980. Amino acid geochronology: integrity of the carbonate matrix and potential of molluscan fossils. In *The Biogeochemistry of Amino Acids*, (eds P.E. Hare, T.C. Hoering and K. King Jr.), Wiley, New York, 415-443.

Miller, G.H., Brigham, K.J. and Andrews, J.T. 1979. Aminostratigraphy of the U.K. Pleistocene deposits. *Nature*, **281**, 539-543.

Miller, G.H. and Hopkins, D.M. 1980. Degradation of molluscan shell protein by lava-induced transient heat flow, Pribilof Islands, Alaska: implications for amino acid geochronology and radiocarbon dating. In *The Biogeochemistry of Amino Acids*, (eds P.E. Hare, T.C. Hoering and K. King Jr.), Wiley, New York.

Miller, G.H. and Mangerud, J. 1985. Aminostratigraphy of European marine interglacial deposits. *Quaternary Science Reviews*, **4**, 215-278.

Miller, G.H., Brigham, K.J. and Clark, P. 1987a. Alteration of total aIle/Ile ratio of different methods of sample preparation. *Amino Acid Geochronology Laboratory Report of Current Activities*, Institute of Arctic and Alpine Research, University of Colorado, 9-20.

Miller, B.B., McCoy, W.D. and Bleur, N.K. 1987b. Stratigraphic potential of amino acid ratios in Pleistocene terrestrial gastropods: an example from West-central Indiana, USA. *Boreas*, **16**, 133-138.

Mitterer, R.M. 1975. Ages and diagenetic temperatures of pleistocene deposits of Florida based on isoleucine epimerization in Mercenaria. *Earth and Planetary Science Letters*, **28**, 275-282.

Nelson, A.R. 1978. *Quaternary Glacial and marine stratigraphy of Qivitu Peninsula, Northern Cumberland Peninsula, Baffin Island, Canada*, Ph.D. thesis, University of Colorado, Boulder, Colorado.

Pillans, B. 1983. Upper Quaternary marine terrace chronology and deformation, South Taranki, New Zealand. *Geology*, **11**, 292-297.

Schroeder, R.A. 1975. Absence of beta-alanine and gamma-aminobutyric acid in cleaned foraminiferal shells: implications for use as a chemical critierion to indicate removal of non-indigenous amino acid contaminants. *Earth and Planetary Science Letters*, **25**, 274-278.

Steinberg, S.M. and Bada, J.L. 1983. Peptide decomposition in the neutral pH region via the formation of diketopiperazines. *Journal of Organic Chemistry*, **48**, 2295-2298.

Stryer, L. 1988. Protein structure and function. In *Biochemistry*, Freeman, W.H. and Company, New York, 15-42.

175

Sykes, G.A and Bowen, D.Q. 1991. Screening chromatograms for amino acid dating. *Proceedings of the American Geological Society, Denver meeting (in press).*

Vallentyne, J.R. 1964. Thermal reaction kinetics and transformation products of amino compounds. *Geochimica et Cosmochimica Acta*, **28**, 157-188.

Vallentyne, J.R. 1969. Pyrolysis of amino acids in *Mercenaria* shells. *Geochimica et Cosmochimica Acta*, **33**, 1453-1458.

Wehmiller, J.F. 1982. A review of amino acid racemization studies in Quaternary molluscs. *Quaternary Science Reviews*, **1**, 83-120.

Wehmiller, J.F. 1984. Interlaboratory comparisons of amino acid enantiomeric ratios in Pleistocene mollusks. *Quaternary Research*, **22**, 109-120.

Williams, K.M. and Smith, G.G. 1977. A critical evaluation of the application of amino acid racemization in geochronology and geothermometry. *Origins of Life*, **8**, 91-144.

Chapter 9

PALAEOMAGNETIC DATING

R. Thompson

The key that would eventually unlock the chronology
of the Pleistocene (was) found in 1906 in a French
Brickyard by Bernard Brunhes, a geophysicist
investigating the earth's magnetic field.

Imbrie and Imbrie (1979).

INTRODUCTION

Palaeomagnetic stratigraphy involves the measurement of the natural remanent
magnetism of sediments or rocks and then the matching or correlating of the measured
remanences with other previously dated palaeomagnetic records or geomagnetic field
behaviour. The most important remanence changes for Quaternary studies are those
associated with polarity reversals of the geomagnetic field.

The Earth's magnetic field is presently of normal polarity while Jupiter's and Saturn's
fields are of reversed polarity. The north seeking end of a compass needle on Jupiter
and on Saturn would point south rather than to the north as here on Earth. Around
730 ka, the Earth's magnetic field switched from also pointing South, from a state
of reversed polarity, to its present state of normal polarity. Seven such polarity
switches occurred on Earth during the Pleistocene.

Figure 9.1 illustrates the Pleistocene polarity time scale with its four normal polarity
subchrons, four reversed polarity subchrons and seven polarity transitions. The most
recent of the polarity switches is referred to as the Matuyama-Brunhes boundary,
having been named in honour of two pioneering workers in the study of polarity
reversals. The Olduvai, Jaramillo, Matuyama-Brunhes boundary sequence of
Pleistocene geomagnetic polarity markers has been recognised in a range of
remarkably diverse geological situations including continental lava flows, deep sea
sediment sequences, lake sediments, European and Asian loess deposits and sea floor
magnetic anomalies from all of the world's oceans. The Cobb Mountain polarity
event which took place 1.10 Ma ago is a recently established geomagnetic feature
(Mankinen et al., 1978) that only lasted for about 10 ka. The Pleistocene polarity

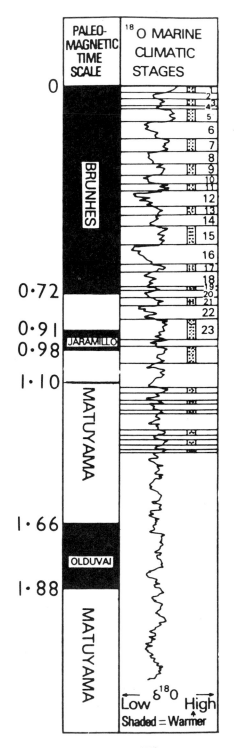

Figure 9.1 *Pleistocene time scales. The polarity time scale after Mankinen and Dalrymple (1979) and Mankinen and Grommé (1982). The* [18]*O record after Shackleton and Opdyke (1976). (Modified from Harland et al., 1982.)*

timescale has been dated through potassium-argon age determinations on some 170 lavas (Mankinen and Dalrymple, 1979, McDougall, 1979). It is unlikely that any further long lasting (more than 20 ka) Pleistocene polarity changes remain to be discovered.

The geomagnetic field varies on all time scales from short pulsations lasting a fraction of a second, through secular changes varying in length from months to hundreds of years, on through large secular changes and aborted polarity reversals taking thousands of years, through full polarity reversals to changes in the average frequency and polarity bias of reversals which take place over periods of hundreds of millions of years. While Pleistocene geomagnetic fluctuations of shorter duration than 10 ka have certainly taken place and while they are of undoubted geomagnetic interest and of potential chronological value, they have proved to be extremely difficult to document unequivocally. Consequently the value of short duration geomagnetic changes for dating purposes is extremely doubtful.

One type of temporary field change falling into this category is commonly referred to as an excursion. Although scores of excursions have been inferred from palaeomagnetic data, duplication between neighbouring sites or real synchronicity have rarely been demonstrated. Perhaps two examples of the likely recognition of Brunhes age excursions, or extremely short reversals, in igneous rocks are the Emperor and Laschamp/Maelifell palaeomagnetic features with ages of around 490 ka and 47 ka respectively (Champion et al., 1981, Bonhommet and Babkine, 1967, Levi et al., 1990).

Secular magnetic direction changes with amplitudes of a few tens of degrees and lifetimes of a few hundred years have been recorded by direct observation from 1500 AD onwards (e.g. Bauer, 1896, Thompson, 1983). They have also been documented in certain regions through archaeomagnetic studies (e.g. Aitken, 1974, Hirooka, 1971). Secular magnetic variations may have some correlation or dating significance at these shorter time scales.

Palaeomagnetic remanence intensities do not directly reflect ancient geomagnetic field intensities, but are predominantly related to magnetic mineralogy, grain size and iron oxide concentration. Nevertheless by using careful, controlled laboratory magnetization techniques, to correct for mineral variations, reliable palaeointensity determinations have been obtained from thermoremanences (e.g. Aitken, 1974). However, attempts to use the depositional remanence of sediments have failed to produce clearly repeatable palaeointensity results. This is because little progress in developing laboratory methods for correcting sedimentological modulations of palaeomagnetic remanence intensity has been made since the pioneering sediment magnetism studies of Johnson et al. (1948) and Ising (1942) half a century ago. In practice, palaeointensity studies have yet to be shown to form the basis of a viable dating method.

The main value of palaeomagnetic studies in Pleistocene dating undoubtedly lies with the polarity reversal time scale of Figure 9.1. The Quaternary reversal time scale has been gainfully employed in many varied and important branches of the Earth sciences. These include the dating of deep sea and lacustrine cores for sedimentological and climatic studies (Opdyke, 1972, Singh et al, 1981), the determination of rates and directions of sea floor spreading, Vine (1966), providing age information about volcanic rock sequences (Einarsson, 1957) and linking the terrestrial and marine climatic records (Kukla, 1970).

THE PALAEOMAGNETIC METHOD

The palaeomagnetic method involves:- (1) collecting orientated samples, (2) determining the direction of any remanent magnetization held by the samples, (3) confirming the stability of the remanence, (4) checking that the measured remanences relate to the geomagnetic field direction at sample formation time and (5) matching the measured remanences with a previously-dated pattern of geomagnetic behaviour. The first three steps of collection, measurement and partial demagnetization are relatively straightforward. The fourth step, in particular, is a vital part of the palaeomagnetic method and is to be ignored only at peril.

Collection

The more sample orientation data obtainable, the safer the palaeomagnetic method will be. Complete orientation information of way-up and azimuth is best, although often with core materials way-up alone or just relative azimuth have to suffice. Way-up allows magnetic inclination to be measured while azimuth allows declination to be measured. Sediment cores can either be sub-sampled while fresh using small (approximately 10 ml volume), thin-walled plastic boxes or sawn into suitably sized samples if dry. Sediment sections can also be sub-sampled with plastic boxes, using a clean vertical face. Igneous rocks can be sampled either by collecting blocks some 10 to 20 cm across, or else by drilling cores, some 25 mm in diameter and several centimetres in length, using a portable rock drill with a diamond impregnated bit. Full orientation information can be obtained for a block by noting the strike and dip of a convenient flat face and for a core by noting the direction and dip of its long axis and its way-up.

There are no fixed rules about which sediment and igneous rock types yield useful palaeomagnetic information. Most lavas carry a usable remanence whereas most sediments do not. Less than one sediment sequence in five turns out to be amenable to palaeomagnetic dating (Stupavsky and Gravenor, 1984, Thompson and Oldfield, 1986). In general, any sediments that were deposited in high energy environments, have been distorted since deposition, are entirely minerogenic, are almost completely organic or contain an appreciable coarse silt or sand fraction are very unlikely to yield dependable palaeomagnetic results. Eminently usable palaeomagnetic data have been obtained, however, from a whole range of materials including deep sea clays, loess deposits, moderately organic lake sediments, red siltstones and sandstones, basalts and andesites. The most persistently troublesome materials have been minerogenic varves and shallow marine deposits.

Measurement

Easy to use, robust, portable, sensitive, fluxgate magnetometers are to be found in dozens of laboratories around the world. These instruments are ideal for Pleistocene palaeomagnetic work. Their operation can be mastered in seconds and samples measured at rates of around twenty to sixty per hour. The more specialised superconducting magnetometers can also be employed. They have recently become very reliable and easy to use, and can be extremely valuable for specialised studies of small or very weakly magnetized samples. Remanence directions can be measured to within a couple of degrees with most types of magnetometer, so that instrumental errors are rarely of concern in palaeomagnetic studies.

Cleaning

The natural remanence (NRM) of rocks and sediments may be made up of several magnetic components lying in different directions. These components can be any combination of primary remanence plus secondary chemical (CRM), viscous (VRM), partial thermal (PTRM) or isothermal (IRM) remanences. Alternating field and thermal partial demagnetization or "magnetic cleaning" techniques have been developed in order to separate out the more stable magnetizations in multicomponent remanences. In many cases these laboratory based treatments have been found to work extremely well and allow stable, characteristic remanences (ChRM) to be isolated. Usually, the most stable component distinguished is taken to be the primary remanence direction, reflecting the geomagnetic field direction at the time of origin of the material under investigation. With Brunhes age sediments, storage in zero field for a few days often provides an effective cleaning method, but for Matuyama or older materials, active demagnetization methods are most desirable. Demagnetization studies should form an integral part of any palaeomagnetic study.

Checking

Although there is no single, simple, definitive method of proving that a palaeomagnetic remanence is a true record of the ancient field, there are a variety of tests and criteria that can demonstrate the converse — ie. that palaeomagnetic data are unreliable. Irving (1964) succinctly summarizes the use of minimum criteria of reliability in palaeomagnetic studies. Thompson (1984) lists ten reliability criteria for magnetostratigraphic, secular variation studies of sediments.

Igneous Rocks The main problem with igneous samples concerns the effect of self reversal, in which the thermoremanence acquired by a rock on cooling grows in the opposite direction to that of the ambient field. Graham (1949) originally suggested the need for a self reversal mechanism to explain combinations of normal and reverse directions in rocks. Neel (1955) described seven theoretical self reversal mechanisms and Nagata et al. (1951) discovered the first natural example of self reversal in a dacitic pumice. Natural self-reversal now appears to be a comparatively rare phenomenon, occurring in less than 1% of all igneous rocks. The best check that self reversal has not taken place in a sample is to monitor remanence changes at elevated temperatures during both demagnetization and remagnetization in a laboratory field. Heller (1980), using this elevated temperature method, has demonstrated self-reversal processes in Olby-Laschamp lavas.

Igneous rocks may be bodily moved following their magnetization, for example through the rolling of blocks at the leading edge of an advancing lava flow. Such transposed remanences are best avoided at the collection stage by sampling the interior of massive lavas, but can also be recognised after collection, through lack of consistency of palaeomagnetic directions. Secondary magnetization may originate in igneous rocks in several ways, for example through the chemical growth of new iron oxide minerals or through viscous effects. The complications of secondary magnetizations are much less in Pleistocene rocks than in older materials. Their effects can generally be satisfactorily removed by thermal or alternating field demagnetization techniques.

Sediments As the majority of sediments do not carry a true record of the ancient field, many checks and reliability criteria need to be employed in palaeomagnetic investigations of sediments. The most diagnostic and most straightforward check is the demonstration of a repeatable signal in duplicate sediment sequences or cores. The further apart the repeatable sequences, while still lithologically or biologically firmly correlatable, the better. Another useful check is to see whether unusual palaeomagnetic directions occur at, or close to, lithological boundaries or close to the ends of core sections. Such features are almost always connected with sedimentological or coring disturbance effects and not with ancient field variations.

Bioturbation can cause remanence acquisition to be delayed until sediments are buried beneath a surface bioturbation zone. Bioturbation depth can be estimated from sediment mixing studies (e.g. Ruddiman and Glover, 1972, Guinasso and Schink, 1975) and from remanence intensity variations through polarity transition records (e.g. Denham and Chave, 1982, Hyodo, 1984) and may amount to tens of centimetres.

Other difficulties associated with sediments are bedding and current effects, compaction, recent weathering, and distortion during subsampling and coring. Bedding errors arise from deposition on sloping surfaces, while current errors are caused by grain rotations connected with water flow-induced shear stresses. Both of the latter effects lead to systematically low inclinations and can lead to errors in declination. Sediment compaction after remanence acquisition can also lead to mechanical flattening of the magnetic inclination.

One of the most difficult problems in palaeomagnetic studies of Pleistocene sediments is recognition of the inclination error of depositional remanence. The effect of inclinational error, caused by particles tending to come to rest with their long axes parallel to the bedding plane, was clearly recognised in one of the first studies of the magnetic remanence of sediments (Ising, 1942) and has since been well documented in laboratory deposition studies (King, 1955). The widespread nature of the effect is illustrated by the low inclinations to be found in many Pleistocene sediments. In comparison, the inclinations found in Pleistocene igneous rocks much more closely resemble those of the present day field. Indeed so many instances of incorrect attribution of low inclinations in sediments to ancient field behaviour (particularly excursions) can now be demonstrated (e.g. Opdyke, 1976, Verosub and Banerjee, 1977 and Banerjee et al. 1979) that serious stratigraphers are strongly advised to disregard low magnetic inclination results in sediments for dating and correlation purposes.

Lovlie (1989), despite all the above difficulties, remains optimistic that additional laboratory based techniques, e.g. magnetic fabric analyses, will one day be sufficiently developed to allow discrimination between sediment records distorted by the various biasing effects, described above, and genuine ancient field signals. He suggests that more extensive determinations of anisotropies of magnetic susceptibility and remanence should allow the establishment of credible excursion and secular variation time scales based on sediment data.

Matching

Johnson and McGee (1983) have discussed limitations of the reversal magnetostratigraphic method when unconformities or hiatuses are present. They have shown a uniform sample spacing through time to be the most effective strategy for promoting good matching of magnetic records. Errors in palaeomagnetic data and gaps in rock or sediment successions can at times obscure correlations to such a degree as to make matching untenable. Seven examples of matching Pleistocene magnetic records with previously dated geomagnetic behaviour patterns are discussed in the following sections.

MAGNETOSTRATIGRAPHIC APPLICATION OF THE PLEISTOCENE POLARITY TIME SCALE

Figure 9.2 illustrates the use of the Olduvai, Jaramillo and Matuyama-Brunhes boundary sequence of geomagnetic markers in dating a sequence of loesses and soils at Lochuan in China. The Lochuan inclination data are of high quality and can be matched with the polarity sequence of Figure 9.1 without difficulty, to yield the five ages listed in Figure 9.2. By contrast the inclination data of the North Sea sediments of Figure 9.3, although spanning a broadly similar time span to the Lochuan sediments and although containing both normal and reverse inclinations, are too

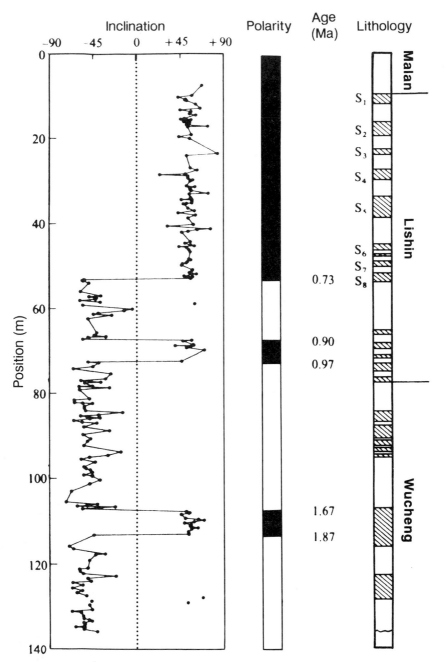

Figure 9.2 *Variation of magnetic inclination with depth in a sequence of loess (white) and soil layers (hatched) in the Lochuan borehole. Ages of the polarity chron boundaries after Mankinen and Dalrymple (1979). (Modified from Heller and Liu 1982.)*

scattered to be matched with any certainty with the polarity sequence of Figure 9.1. The most that can reasonably be gleaned from such poor quality data is that the older sediments with negative, reverse inclinations are likely to be at least 700 ka in age.

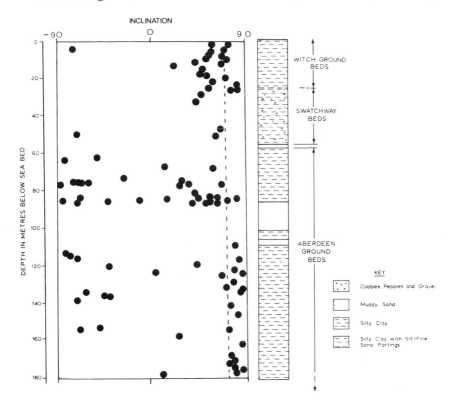

Figure 9.3 *Variation of lithology and magnetic inclination with depth in the North Sea borehole SRN33. No clear sequence of polarity reversals can be distinguished. The negative inclinations in the Aberdeen Ground beds are taken to indicate that the sediments are of Matuyama age or older. The boundary between the normally magnetized Swatchway beds and mixed polarity of the Aberdeen Ground beds is probably a hiatus. The occasional reversed inclination to be found in the Witch Ground beds is interpreted to have been caused either by inadvertent overturning of core segments, by sedimentological effects or by mechanical disturbance. (Modified from Begg 1979.)*

Another example of good quality palaeomagnetic data is provided by the declination logs of two deep sea cores used in oxygen isotope studies, as shown in Figure 9.4. In core Vema 28-239 the Olduvai, Jaramillo and Matuyama-Brunhes boundary sequence can be recognised in the declination changes. The scattered declinations at the top of the core are most probably to be interpreted as deriving from coring disturbances. In core Vema 28-238, the Matuyama-Brunhes boundary is found at

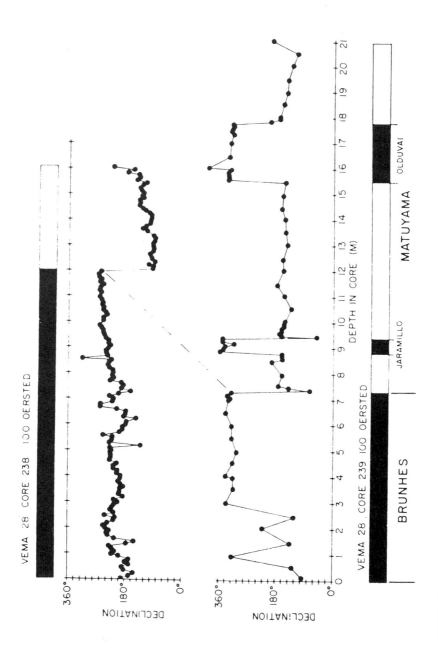

Figure 9.4 *Variation of magnetic declination with depth in cores V28-238 and V28-239. The cores are not orientated with respect to true north. (From Shackleton and Opdyke, 1973.)*

a greater depth than in core 28-239 implying a higher deposition rate for these sediments.

The age of Pleistocene materials may also be determined through use of the polarity time scale when remanence directions have been determined *in situ*. Such *in situ* studies which avoid the need for sample collection are sometimes possible when dealing with the relatively strong magnetization of basalts. *In situ* normally magnetized materials tend to increase the strength of the geomagnetic field while reversely magnetized materials tend to reduce the geomagnetic field strength. The precise effect depends on the shape and orientation of the magnetized material and on the latitude of the site under investigation. Einarsson (1957) demonstrated that the remanence polarity of many Icelandic lavas can be detected *in situ* with the use of an ordinary compass. As an example of this approach, Piper (1971) has produced a palaeomagnetic map of the polarity chrons of the basalts of south-west Iceland by measuring the magnetic anomalies associated with the lavas.

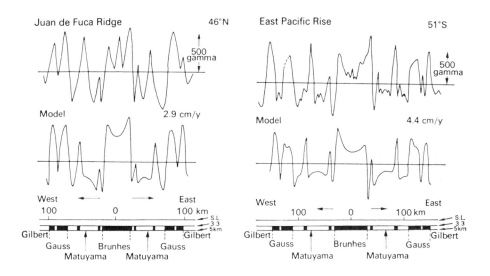

Figure 9.5 *Observed magnetic anomaly profiles across the Juan de Fuca ridge and the East Pacific rise compared with the theoretical magnetic anomaly according to the Vine-Matthews hypothesis assuming the palaeomagnetic polarity time-scale of Figure 9.1. It is assumed that the magnetic blocks are confined to oceanic layer 2. Black denotes normal magnetization, unshaded denotes reverse. (After Bott, 1971 redrawn from Vine, 1966.)*

The greatest use of palaeomagnetic dating of magnetic anomalies has been in marine surveys, through the application of the Vine-Matthews hypothesis of sea-floor spreading. Figure 9.5 plots magnetic anomaly profiles, measured by towing a proton precession magnetometer at the sea surface, across the Juan de Fuca and East Pacific ridges. High field intensities are to be interpreted as being caused by the remanence of normally magnetized ocean floor beneath the magnetometer. The central positive anomalies thus overlie Brunhes age sea floor. The sequences of anomalies can be neatly accounted for by symmetrical blocks of normally and reversely magnetized oceanic crust as illustrated at the bottom of Figure 9.5. The observed and modelled anomaly profiles can be seen to correlate well. Matching of marine anomaly profiles with the palaeomagnetic polarity time scale allows oceanic crust to be dated all around the world in this most elegant manner.

OTHER MAGNETIC CORRELATION METHODS

Secular Variation

Some sediment sequences hold records of palaeomagnetic direction fluctuations which resemble secular geomagnetic changes which have taken place over a time scale of centuries. A potential magnetostratigraphic method is to match these fluctuations with a previously dated, secular variation record (Mackereth, 1971, Thompson 1973). This secular variation approach to magnetostratigraphy is much more difficult to apply than that of polarity reversals because:- (1) secular geomagnetic changes are not global features, (2) type secular variation records are generally based on lake sediments which have proved to be exceedingly difficult to date with better than 10% accuracy, whereas the polarity time scale is based on results from basalts which have proved to be ideal rocks for potassium-argon dating, and (3) secular variation patterns with amplitudes of only some 20° are more susceptible to noise than polarity changes of 180°.

Figure 9.6 plots Holocene palaeomagnetic direction fluctuations from three lakes in Iceland as an illustration of the variation in quality of palaeomagnetic secular variation data. The pre 1500 BP Vatnsdalsvatn record of Figure 9.6a from Thompson and Turner (1985) has been found in four other cores from lake Vatnsdalsvatn and is interpreted as a useful palaeomagnetic signal, largely reflecting direction changes of the ancient geomagnetic field. The Draghalsvatn record of Figure 9.6b is an example of a disappointing site for palaeomagnetic studies at which the noise, particularly in inclination, totally overwhelms any geomagnetic secular variation signal. The Svinavatn records of Figure 9.6c and d are further examples of unusable palaeomagnetic records. Although the Svinavatn sediments have good magnetic stability, strong intensity, reasonable within-core consistency, sensible mean directions and typical amplitudes of variation, they do not repeat between cores and consequently cannot be interpreted as having correctly recorded the ancient geomagnetic field. Coring disturbance, core orientation difficulties, compaction, bioturbation, remagnetization, micro-slumping, grain reorientation, sampling errors, instrumental effects and, in particular, the inclination error of depositional remanence (Ising, 1942) all serve to degrade and distort the palaeomagnetic signal of sediments.

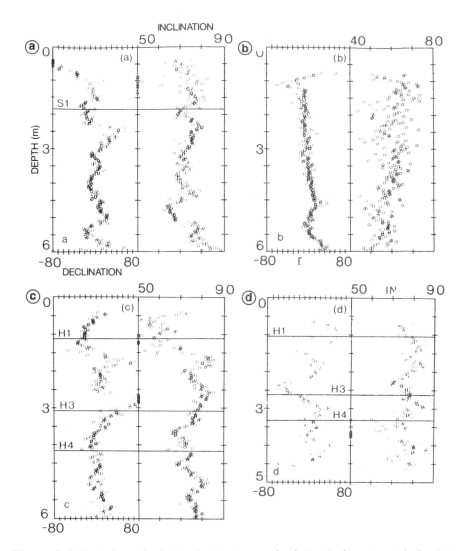

Figure 9.6 *Variation of relative declination and relative inclination with depth in sediment cores from three lakes in Iceland. Tephra horizons, marked as horizontal lines: H-1 Hekla 846 years BP, H-3 Hekla 2980 years BP, H-4 Hekla 4545 years BP, S1 Snaefells 1705 years BP. (a) Vatnsdalsvatn. The palaeomagnetic records are scattered at the top but may reflect the ancient field in the sediments below 1.5 m depth. (b) Draghalsvatn. The inclination record is too scattered for magnetostratigraphic work. (c) and (d) Two Svinavatn cores. The Svinavatn palaeomagnetic directions show some internal coherence, but are not repeatable between cores (compare the records between tephras H-4 and H-3 and between H-3 and H-2). The Svinavatn sediments are also of no magnetostratigraphic value, despite their internal consistency, stability under alternating field demagnetization and mean inclination being close to that of the axial dipole field.*

Not surprisingly, for the great majority of sediments a usable palaeomagnetic record of secular variation is not recoverable with present sampling and measuring techniques.

Mineral Magnetism

Magnetic investigations can provide lithostratigraphies in addition to chronostratigraphies when mineral magnetic as well as palaeomagnetic parameters are measured. As mineral magnetic investigations involve laboratory-induced artificial magnetizations and remanences, they are quite distinct from palaeomagnetic studies of the ancient geomagnetic field. Mineral magnetic stratigraphy is largely related to variations in the concentrations, compositions and grain sizes of the constituent iron oxide minerals (Thompson and Oldfield, 1986). An example of the use of mineral magnetic lithostratigraphy in Pleistocene studies (Oldfield and Robinson, 1985) is shown in Figure 9.7, where the mineral magnetic parameter 'S' is plotted against depth for a sediment core from the North Atlantic. The 'S' parameter of Stober and Thompson (1979) is chosen to emphasise variation in iron oxide composition and grain size. The 'S' ratio is defined as the ratio of the laboratory induced isothermal remanences in fields of 100 mT and 1 T. The mineral magnetic fluctuations in 'S' ratio in the North Atlantic can be correlated with the oxygen isotope variations of the last 20 ka (Imbrie et al., 1984). High 'S' ratios occur in the interglacial deposits. These high ratio values indicate that higher proportions of 'haematite' as opposed to 'magnetite' minerals occur in the interglacials. Oldfield and Robinson (1985) interpret the variations in magnetic ratio as being related to changing atmospheric circulation patterns between glacial and interglacial periods with proportionally more haematite-rich Saharan dust contributing to the sediments at the coring site during interglacials. Another good example of mineral magnetic stratigraphy in ocean sediments is the work of Bloemendal and deMenocal (1989) in the Arabian Sea and the eastern tropical Atlantic. Magnetic susceptibility measurements also offer considerable potential for correlation between marine and terrestrial sequences, as for instance in Kukla et al. (1988) for the Chinese loess.

BRITISH PLEISTOCENE MAGNETOSTRATIGRAPHY

The full complement of Pleistocene polarity changes of the Olduvai, Cobb Mountain, Jaramillo, Matuyama-Brunhes boundary sequence are to be found in the sediments on the west flank of the Rockall bank (Shackleton et al., 1984).

On land, in Britain, reversely magnetized Pleistocene sediments are rare (van Montfrans, 1971 and Table 9.1). In North Sea sediments, reverse magnetizations, presumably of Matuyama age (Begg, 1979, Stoker et al. 1983), are to be found, although as described above the quality of much of the North Sea palaeomagnetic data has been very poor.

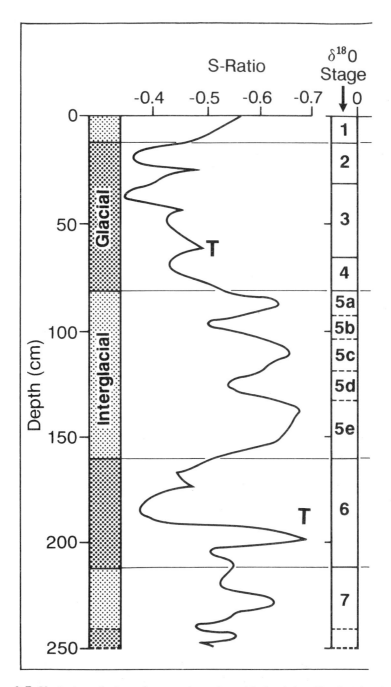

Figure 9.7 *Variation of mineral magnetic ratios with depth in a North Atlantic core. High magnetic ratios corresponding to high 'haematite to magnetite' ratios are found in the interglacial sediments. Tephra layers indicated by the letter T. (After Oldfield and Robinson, 1985.)*

Table 9.1 *Intensity, stability and polarity of some Pleistocene sediments from*

Locality	Lithology or zone	Stage
Gallowflat	clay	Devensian
Maidenhall	silts and clays	Ipswichian
Burtle beds	Underlying silts and clays	Ipswichian
Hoxne	Gipping silts	Early Wolstonian
Marks Tey	Lacustrine laminated clay	Hoxnian
Hitchin	lacustrine zone I	Hoxnian
Gort	lacustrine	Hoxnian
Happisburgh	clay	Anglian
	lower till	Anglian
Sugworth	clay	Cromerian
	sands and silts	Cromerian
Westbury-sub-Mendip	silty clays	Middle Pleistocene
Nettlebed	lacustrine	Pre-Cromerian
Chillesford	blue clay	Pastonian
	fine-grained band in Crag	Waltonian
Aldeburgh	blue clay	Pastonian
Eastern Bavents	brown clay	Baventian
	dark grey clay	Baventian
Cove Bottom	grey clay	Baventian
	dark grey clay	Baventian
Ludham	L4	Baventian
	L2	Thurnian
	L1	Ludhamian
Tattingstone Hall	silt layers in Crag	Ludhamian
Bawdsey	silt band in Crag	Waltonian
North Sea (Fladen) SLN33	(0-20 m)	Witchground beds
	(20-58 m)	Swatchway beds
	(58-182 m)	Aberdeen ground beds
77/2	(0-22 m)	Witch Ground Beds
	(22-35 m)	Swatchway beds
	(35-124 m)	Lower Channel deposits
	(124-200 m)	Aberdeen Ground Beds
North Sea (Forties) 77/3	(0-140 m)	Channel deposits

the British Isles. Polarity N = normal, R = reversed, ? = indeterminate.

Collector	Number of Samples	Intensity of NRM mA/m	Median Destructive Field mT	Polarity
Thompson	15	33	—	N
Wymer	4	2	15	N?
Heyworth	14	0.5	15	N
Gibbard	4	1	—	N
Turner/Thompson	12	16	—	N
	14	10	—	N
Gibbard	15	0.7	—	N
Turner	4	0.2	20	N
Thompson	2	—	—	?
	21	—	—	?
Osmaston	27	470	—	N
	15	6	—	N
Stringer	5	<1	—	N?
Turner	4	0.4	15	N?
Thompson	13	1.8	—	N
	2	2	—	?
Thompson	15	1.5	—	N
Collins/Thompson	28	0.8	5	N
	25	18	10	N
Thompson	10	0.5	6	N
	20	47	10	N
Roy. Soc. Borehole	10	1	10	?
	20	2	<10	N?
	6	1	20	N
Thompson	7	0.8	—	?
Thompson	7	0.7	—	N
BGS Borehole	16	20	35	N
	10	8	30	N
	70	10	50	R+N
BGS Borehole	21	6	—	N
	19	4	—	N
	19	10	—	N
	216	10	>20	R+N
BGS Borehole	51	8	—	N

The lack of reversals in the Pleistocene sediments of East Anglia compared with those of the Netherlands was one of the main reasons that led Zagwijn (1975) to propose that there were long stratigraphic gaps covering the upper part of the Lower Pleistocene and the lower part of the Middle Pleistocene in the known East Anglian successions.

SUMMARY

The state-of-the-art of the five magnetic dating and correlation techniques of Pleistocene materials discussed above is well summarized by the following comments from recent review articles:-

1) Reversal magnetostratigraphy

> Palaeomagnetic stratigraphy offers one of the most promising methods for establishing world-wide correlations of (terrestrial) Quaternary events ... (and) ... of correlating the marine and terrestrial records.
>
> *Lowe and Walker (1984).*

2) Excursions

> Although it seems clear that excursions exist ... it seems premature to use these changes as a dating method.
>
> *Tarling (1983).*

3) Secular variation

> Master curves of palaeomagnetic (secular variations) may provide a rapid means of dating sediment sequences in   lakes ... the precision which may be achieved by palaeomagnetically based (secular variation) dating cannot be estimated accurately from results obtained so far ... it will inevitably vary from lake to lake.
>
> *Oldfield (1977).*

4) Mineral magnetism

> This method would appear to offer considerable potential as a means of correlation in a range of sediments and ... time scales where variations in mineral magnetic properties reflect synchronous environmental properties.
>
> *Lowe and Walker (1984).*

REFERENCES

Aitken, M.J. 1974. *Physics and Archaeology*,Clarendon Press, Oxford, pp. 291.

Banerjee, S.K., Lund, S.P. and Levi, S. 1979. Geomagnetic record in Minnesota sediments — Absence of the Gothenburg and Erieau excursions. *Geology*, **7**, 588-591.

Bauer, L.A. 1896. On the secular motion of a free magnetic needle. II. *Physics Review*, **3**, 34-48.

Begg, P. 1979. Magneto-stratigraphy. Unpublished B.Sc. dissertation, University of Edinburgh.

Bloemendal, J. and DeMenocal, P. 1989. Evidence for a change in the periodicity of tropical climate cycles at 2.4 Myr from whole-core magnetic susceptibility measurements. *Nature*, **342**, 897-900.

Bonhommet, N. and Babkine, J. 1967. Sur la presence d'aimantations oversees dans la Chaine des Puys. *Comes Rendus des Academie des Sciences Paris*, **264**, 92-94.

Bott, M.H.P. 1971. *The Interior of the Earth*,Edward Arnold, London, pp. 316.

Champion, D.E., Dalrymple, G.B. and Kuntz, M.A. 1981. Radiometric and palaeomagnetic evidence for the Emperor reversed polarity event at 0.46 ± 0.05 M.y. in basalt lava flows from the Eastern Snake River Piain, Idaho. *Geophysical Research Letters*, **8**, 1055-1058.

Denham, C.R. and Chave, A. 1982. Detrital remanent magnetization: viscosity theory of the lock-in zone. *Journal of Geophysical Research*, **87**, 7126-7130.

Einarsson, T. 1957. Magneto-geological mapping in Iceland with the use of a compass. *Philiosphical Magazine Supplement Advances in Physics*, **6**, 232-239.

Graham, J.W. 1949. The stability and significance of magnetism in sedimentary rocks. *Journal of Geophysical Research*, **54**, 131-167.

Guinasso, N.L. and Schink, D.R. 1975. Quantitative estimates of biological mixing rates in abyssal sediments. *Journal of Geophysical Research*, **80**, 3032-3043.

Harland, W.B., Cox, A.V., Llewellyn, P.G., Picton, C.A.G., Smith, A.G. and Walters, R. 1982. *A Geologic Time Scale*, Cambridge University Press, New York, pp. 128.

Heller, F. 1980. Self-reversal of natural remanent magnetisation in the Olby-Laschamp lavas. *Nature*, **284**, 334-335.

Heller, F. and Liu, T. 1982. Magnetostratigraphical dating of loess deposits in China. *Nature*, **300**, 431-433.

Hirooka, K. 1971. Archaeomagnetic study for the past 2000 years in Southwest Japan. *Memoirs of the Faculty of Science Kyoto University. Geology and Minerology Series*, **XXXVIII**, 167-207.

Hyodo, M. 1984. Possibility of reconstruction of the past geomagnetic field from homogeneous sediments. *Journal of Geomagnetism and Geoelectricity*, **36**, 45-62.

Imbrie, J., Hays, J.D., Martinson, D.G., McIntyre, A., Mix, A.C., Morley, J.J., Pisias,

N.G., Prell, W.L. and Shackleton, N.J. 1984. The orbital theory of Pleistocene climate: support from a revised chronology of the marine and ^{18}O record. In *Milankovitch and Climate* (ed Berger, A.L.), Part I, Reidel, Boston, 269-305.

Imbrie, J.I. and Imbrie, K.P. 1979. *Ice Ages*, Macmillan, London, pp. 224.

Irving, E. 1964. *Paleomagnetism and its Application to Geological Problems*, Wiley, New York, pp. 399.

Ising, G. 1942. On the magnetic properties of varved clay. *Arkiv for Matematik, Astronomi och Fysik*, **29**, 1-37.

Johnson, E.A., Murphy, T. and Torrenson, O.W. 1948. Prehistory of the Earth's magnetic field. **53**, 349-372.

Johnson, N.M. and McGee, V.E. 1983. Magnetic polarity stratigraphy: stochastic properties of data, sampling problems and the evolution of interpretations. *Journal of Geophysical Research*, **88**, 1213-1221.

King, R.F. 1955. The remanent magnetisation in artificially deposited sediments. *Monthly Notes of the Royal Astronomical Society*, **7**, 115-134.

Kukla, G., Heller, F., Liu, X.M., X.U., T.C., Liu, T.S. and An, Z.S. 1988. Pleistocene climates in China dated by magnetic susceptibility. *Geology*, **16**, 811-814.

Kukla, G.J. 1970. Correlations between loesses and deep-sea sediments. *Geologiska Foreningens i Stockholm Forhandlinghar*, **92**, 148-180.

Levi, S., Audunsson, H., Duncan, R.A., Kristjansson, L., Gillot, P-Y. and Jakobsson, S.P. 1990. Late Pleistocene geomagnetic excursion in Icelandic lavas: confirmation of the Laschamp excursion. *Earth and Planetary Science Letters*, **96**, 443-457.

Lovlie, R. 1989. Palaeomagnetic stratigraphy: a correlation method. *Quaternary International*, **1**, 129-149.

Lowe, J.J. and Walker, M.J. 1984. *Reconstructing Quaternary Environments*, Longman, London, pp. 389.

Mackereth, F.J. 1971. On the variation in direction of the horizontal component of remanent magnetisation in lake sediments. *Earth and Planetary Science Letters*, **12**, 332-338.

Mankinen, E.A. and Dairymple, G.B. 1979. Revised geomagnetic polarity time scale for the interval 0-5 M.y. B.P. Journal of *Geophysical Research*, **84**, 615-626.

Mankinen, E.A. and Gromme, C.S. 1982. Paleomagnetic data from the Coso range, California and current status of the Cobb Mountain normal geomagnetic polarity event. *Geophysics Research Letters*, **9**, 1279-1282.

Mankinen, E.A., Donnelyy, J.M. and Gromme, C.S. 1978. Geomagnetic polarity event recorded at 1.1 M.y. B.P. on Cobb Mountain, Clear Lake volcanic field, California. *Geology*, **6**, 653-656.

McDougall, I. 1979. The present status of the geomagnetic polarity timescale. In *The Earth: Its Origin, Structure and Evolution*, (ed. McElhinny, M.W.), Academic Press, New York.

Montfrans, H.M. Van. 1971. Palaeomagnetic dating in the North Sea Basin, unpublished Ph.D. Thesis, Amsterdam University.

Nagata, T., Atkimoto, S. and Uyeda, S. 1951. Reverse thermoremanent magnetism. *Proceedings of the Japan Academy*, **27**, 643-645.

Neel, L. 1955. Some theoretical aspects of rock magnetism. *Advances in Physics*, **4**, 191-242.

Oldfield, F. 1977. Lakes and their drainage basins as units of sediment-based ecological study. *Progress in Physical Geography*, **1**, 460-504.

Oldfield, F. and Robinson, S.G. 1985. Geomagnetism and palaeoclimate. In *The Climatic Scene*, (eds. Tuley, M.J. and Sheail, G.M.), Allen Unwin: London, 186-205.

Opdyke, N.D. 1972. Palaeomagnetism of Deep-Sea cores. *Reviews in Geophysics and Space Physics*, **10**, 213-249.

Opdyke, N.D. 1976. Discussion of paper by Morner and Lanser concerning the palaeomagnetism of Deep-Sea core A179-15. *Earth and Planetary Science Letters* **29**, 238-239.

Piper, J.D. 1971. Ground magnetic studies of crustal growth in Iceland. *Earth and Planetary Science Letters* **12**, 199-207.

Ruddiman, W.F. and Glover, L.K. 1972. Vertical mixing of ice-rafted volcanic ash in North Atlantic sediments. *Geological Society of America Bulletin*, **83**, 2817-2836.

Shackelton, N.J. and Opdyke, N.D. 1973. Oxygen isotope and palaeomagnetic stratigraphy of equatorial Pacific core V28-238. *Quaternary Research*, **1**, 39-55.

Shacketon, N.J. and Opdyke, N.D. 1976. Oxygen isotope and palaeomagnetic stratigraphy of Equatorial Pacific core V28-239. *Geological Society of American Memoir*, **145**, 449-464.

Shackleton, N.J., Backman, J., Zimmerman, H., Kent, D.V., Hall, M.A., Roberts, D.G., Schitker, D., Baldauf, J.G., Desprairies, A., Homrighausen, R., Huddlestun, P., Keene, J.B., Kaltenback, A.J., Krumsiek, K.A.O., Morton, A.C., Murray, J.W. and Westberg-Smith, J. 1984. Oxygen-isotope calibration of the onset of ice-rafting and history of glaciation in the North Atlantic region. *Nature*, **307**, 620-623.

Singh, G., Opdyke, N.D. and Bowler, J.M. 1981. Late Cainozoic stratigraphy, palaeomagnetic chronology and vegetational history from Lake George, N.S.W. *Journal of the Geological Society of Australia*, **28**, 435-452.

Stober, J.C. and Thompson, R. 1979. An investigation into the source of magnetic minerals in some Finnish lake sediments. *Earth and Planetary Science Letters*, **45**, 464-474.

Stoker, M.S., Skinner, A.C., Fyfe, J.A. and Long, D. 1983. Palaeomagnetic evidence for early Pleistocene in the central and northern North Sea. *Nature*, **304**, 332-334.

Stupavsky, M. and Gravenor, C.P. 1984. Paleomagnetic dating of Quaternary sediments: a review. In *Quaternary Dating Methods*, (ed. Mahaney, W.C.), Elsevier, Amsterdam, 123-140.

Tarling, D.H. 1983. *Palaeomagnetism*, Chapman and Hall, London, pp. 379.

Thompson, R. 1973. Palaeolimnology and palaeomagnetism. *Nature*, **242**, 182-184.

Thompson, R. 1983. ^{14}C dating and magnetostratigraphy. *Radiocarbon*, **25**, 229-238.

Thompson, R. 1984. A global review of palaeomagnetic results from wet lakes sediments. In *Lake Sediments and Environmental History*, (eds. Haworth, E.Y. and Lund, J.W.G.), Leicester University Press, Leicester, 145-164.

Thompson, R. 1984. Geomagnetic evolution: 400 years of change on planet Earth. *Physics of the Earth and Planetary Interiors*, **36**, 61-77.

Thompson, R. and Oldfield, F. 1986. *Environmental Magnetism*, Allen and Unwin, London, pp. 227.

Thompson, R. and Turner, G.M. 1985. Icelandic Holocene palaeomagnetism. *Physics of the Earth and Planetary Interiors*, **38**, 250-261.

Verosub, K.L. and Banerjee, S.K., 1977. Geomagnetic excursions and their palaeomagnetic record. *Reviews of Geophysics and Space Physics*, **15**, 145-155.

Vine, F.J. 1966. Spreading of the Ocean Floor: New evidence. *Science*, **154**, 1405-1415.

Zagwijn, W.H. 1975. Variations in climate as shown by pollen analysis, especially in the Lower Pleistocene of Europe. In *Ice Ages, Ancient and Modern*. (eds. Wright, A.E. and Moseley, F.), *Geophysical Journal Special Issue*, **6**, 137-152.

Chapter 10

OXYGEN ISOTOPE CHRONOSTRATIGRAPHY

A.J Patience and D. Kroon

INTRODUCTION

As a result of a dramatic increase in late Cenozoic palaeoclimatic research, a standard method is required to allow global correlation of ocean sediments. Such a standard correlation technique must use variations in a parameter which can be easily recognised and can be applied globally. In 1955 Emiliani suggested that changes in ocean temperature related to the glacial/interglacial cycles caused a change in the stable isotopic composition of the oceans. This would be directly reflected in the oxygen isotopic composition of foraminifera which are preserved in carbonate bearing ocean sediments retrieved by coring. Subsequently Shackleton (1967) suggested that these variations in the isotopic composition of the oceans were due to changes in the volume of global ice-sheets. The synchroneity of these changes throughout the world provides the potential for a high resolution correlative chronology. Only later was a direct link forged between the climatic effects on isotopic variations and the orbital changes central to the Milankovitch theory (Hays et al., 1976).

There has long been an interest in the effects of orbital variations on the Earth's climate (Croll, 1864, Milankovitch, 1941, Veeh and Chappell, 1970, Berger, 1976, 1988, Imbrie and Imbrie, 1980). The variations in the eccentricity of the Earth's orbit around the sun, the obliquity of the ecliptic and the axial precession of the equinoxes (Figure 10.1) cause changes in the solar insolation specific to each latitude of the globe (Berger, 1988, Broecker and Van Donk, 1970), and form the core of the Milankovitch theory of climate change. The main periodicities (Figure 10.2) of 400 ka and 100 ka (eccentricity), 41 ka (obliquity) and 23 ka and 19 ka (precession) have been calculated from astronomical theory (Berger, 1984). These variations in solar radiation at the Earth's surface have the potential to force changes in global and regional climate, which may, in turn, imprint on the geological record. Thus cyclical changes in the factors directly reflecting climate, such as global ice volume, oceanic water mass chemistry and distribution, marine biogenic diversity, and in the distribution of vegetation and production of sediments on the continents will lead to rhythms in marine sediments. These rhythms can be examined using time series techniques, such as spectral analysis, which have demonstrated there is a close relationship between the predicted Milankovitch frequencies and the periodicities

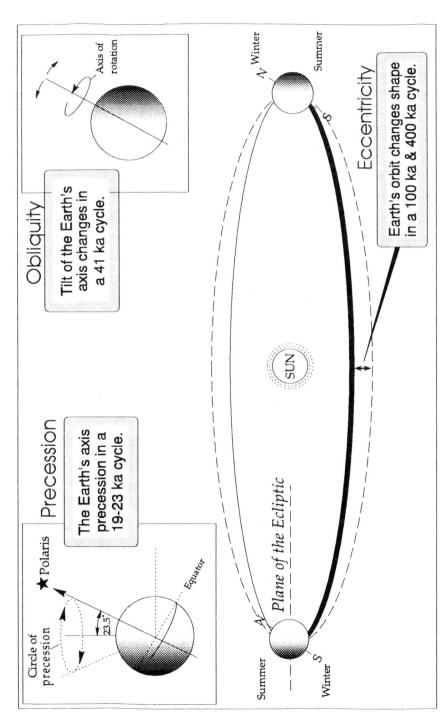

Figure 10.1 *Orbital Eccentricity, Obliquity and Precession; the three astronomical cycles involved in solar input and climate variation.*

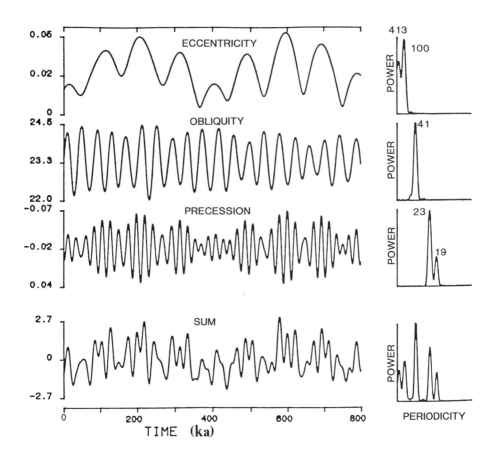

Figure 10.2 *Graphical illustration of the calculated variation in eccentricity, obliquity and precession (0-800 ka). The upper three plots on the left are the result of calculations on solar insolation through the last 800 ka (Berger, 1977). The lower plot is a composite curve called SUM, by Imbrie et al. (1984). Scale for individual cycles in degrees; for SUM, in standard deviation units. Right: variance spectra calculated from these time series, with dominant periods (ka) of conspicuous peaks indicated. (Adapted from Imbrie et al., 1984.)*

dominating the power spectra in ocean sediment cores (Pisias et al., 1973, Pisias, 1976, Hays et al., 1976). The existence of these Milankovitch-driven cycles in sediment cores provides the potential for conversion of cycles of a particular parameter with depth in the sediment to time.

Oxygen isotope curves today form the basis of most detailed correlation in the Pleistocene and late Pliocene marine sedimentary records, because the mixing time of the oceans is relatively short and the palaeoclimate signal is essentially synchronous across the globe. The recognition of the potential of these methods has resulted in the development of the SPECMAP age models (Imbrie et al. 1984), which stack several oxygen isotope curves then smooth, filter and tune the composite curve to the Milankovitch cyclicities. This reference stack can then be used to correlate global isotopic, geochemical and magnetic susceptibility records (Imbrie et al., 1984). Overviews of the development of oxygen isotope dating techniques and their application to chronostratigraphy are presented by Prell et al. (1986), Williams et al. (1988b) and Jansen (1989).

The aim of this review is to critically discuss the problems in the use of oxygen isotopic ratio curves in the development of age models for correlation of late Cenozoic ocean sediments and for mapping climatic variation in space and time. Particular attention will be paid to the difficulties resulting from tuning, stacking, filtering and stretching of profiles, and the problems associated with sampling density and positioning of isotopic stage boundaries.

FACTORS INFLUENCING THE OXYGEN ISOTOPE COMPOSITION OF FORAMINIFERA

There are many factors which contribute to the overall oxygen isotopic signal in the carbonate tests of foraminifera, the most important of which are discussed below.

Ice Volume Effect

The oxygen isotopic composition of the world's oceans is mainly dependent on the balance between low latitude evaporation and high latitude precipitation. This is because the isotopically lighter ^{16}O is preferentially evaporated, while ^{18}O is preferentially condensed. Thus high latitude precipitation is isotopically light ($-30‰$ to $-40‰$; Figure 10.3), and the polar ice sheets are enriched in ^{16}O compared to mean ocean water. If the ice sheets grow as a result of some climatic change, sufficient ^{16}O is removed from the oceans to change the mean oceanic composition (Duplessy, et al., 1970). Conversely, melting of ice sheets will release ^{16}O, decreasing the $^{18}O/^{16}O$ ratio in the oceans. The difference in oceanic oxygen isotopic composition between a full glacial and a full interglacial cycle is estimated to be approximately $1.0‰$ (Berger, 1979). These changes are reflected in the isotopic composition of the tests of foraminifera, which on death fall to the ocean floor, and accumulate to form a sedimentary record (Shackleton 1967, 1977). Comparable records may also be preserved in other marine organisms, such as corals (Shackleton and Matthews, 1977, Fairbanks and Matthews, 1978), which may be preserved in raised reef terraces, the dating of which has also been of considerable significance in establishing the chronology of deep sea cores (Broecker et al., 1968, Bloom et al., 1974).

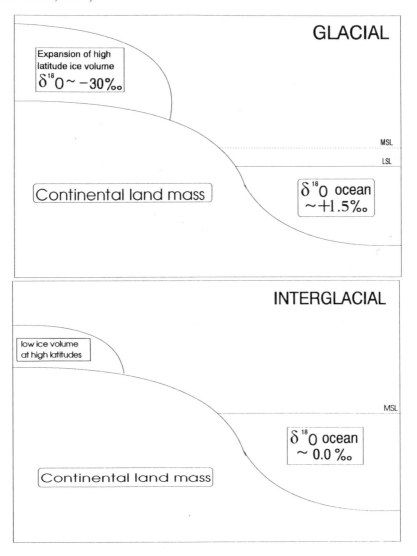

Figure 10.3 *Diagram illustrating the variation in sea level, isotope composition and ice volume between glacial (upper) and interglacial (lower) periods. MSL-Mean Sea Level, LSL-Low Sea Level. During the glacials seawater is depleted in ^{16}O because the lighter isotope has been removed through the meteorological cycle and locked in ice. (After Williams et al., 1988.)*

Temperature Effect

The oxygen isotopic composition of the tests of foraminifera is dependant upon both the isotopic composition of the water from which precipitation occurs, and the temperature. At low temperature there is greater fractionation of ^{18}O relative to ^{16}O, and the tests contain a greater proportion of the heavier istotope than would be the case at higher temperatures (Urey 1948, Shackleton and Opdyke, 1973, Williams et al., 1981). The temperature dependence is about $0.23‰/1°C$ (Epstein et al., 1953).

The world's oceans are essentially divided into three stratified water regimes which have distinctive temperatures and densities (Figure 10.4):-

1) The upper surface mixed layer varies between 10 m (sheltered coasts in summer) to 200-300 m deep (mid latitudes open oceans) and has a wide seasonal variation in temperature.

2) The permanent thermocline zone usually lies between 70-1000 m and shows limited seasonal variation in temperature.

3) The deep water below 1000 m has a fairly constant temperature which often approaches freezing.

Different foraminiferal species inhabit different parts of the water column: planktonic foraminifera in the surface layers and benthic at the bottom of the oceans. Planktonic species living in the top 50 m of the water column are dominantly *spinose* whereas *non-spinose* forms dominate below this level. However, a single foraminifera species may also migrate in the water column during development. Figure 10.4 illustrates the water mass and temperature regimes inhabited by foraminiferal species that are commonly used in oxygen isotope studies.

Clearly, planktonic foraminifera are subject to much greater temperature and salinity variations (especially near continents where fresh water runoff and upwelling occurs) than are benthic species. For instance, Steens et al. (1990) have measured the isotopic composition of two different planktonic foraminifera through time in a core from the western Arabian sea. The surface dweller *Globigerina bulloides* (d'Orbigny) is on average lighter, and shows both different trends and a greater amplitude of oxygen isotope variation from glacial to interglacial conditions than the deeper dwelling *Neogloboquadrina dutertrei* (Figure 10.5). The latter lives between 50-300 m (Hemleben and Spindler, 1983), and is thus subject to less isotopic variation than the near surface dweller *G. bulloides*. Therefore, *N. dutertrei* should more accurately reflect the global isotopic signal of ice volume. Benthic foraminifera however, receive their isotopic signal from the bottom waters which have a more constant temperature, salinity and chemistry and are often directly derived from the polar regions. They thus more directly reflect ice volume, which may be blurred by local isotopic

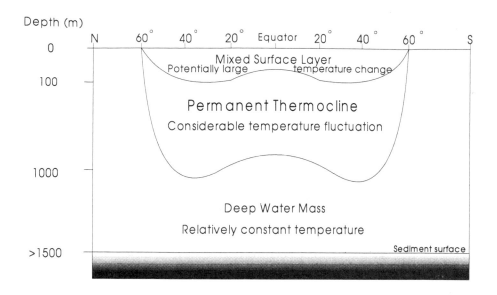

Foraminiferal Species	Approximate Depth Range (m)	Temperature regime/range (°C)
Globigerinoides ruber	0-50	Sub-tropical (20-29)
Globigerinoides sacculifer	0-100	Tropical (15-30)
Globigerina bulloides	0-100	Sub-Arctic/sub-antarctic (0-25)
Globoquadrina pachyderma	50-300	Arctic/Antarctic (2-7)
Neogloboquadrina dutertrei	50-300	Temperate/subtropical (14-25)
Globorotalia crassiformis (LC)	100-300	Sub-tropical (0-25)
Uvigerina spp.	100-2000	(0-20)
Cibicoides spp.	>30	(0-20)

Figure 10.4 *Generalised diagram showing the thermal structure of the oceans, the foraminiferal species most commonly used in oxygen isotope dating and their approximate position in the water column and temperature regimes. LC — left coiling foraminifera. Foraminiferal depth ranges are from Hemleben and Spindler (1983). In general the oxygen isotope profiles generated from benthic foraminifera give the best age models because surface waters experience much greater fluctuation in oxygen isotope ratios.*

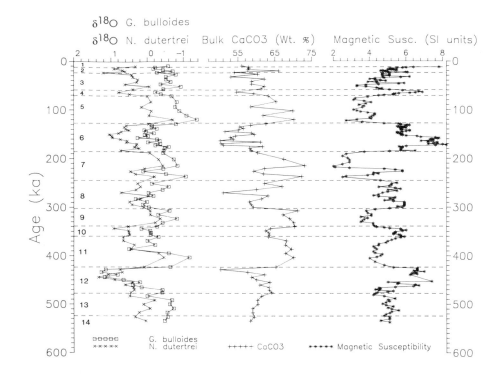

Figure 10.5 *Depth profiles of δ¹⁸O oxygen isotope records from* Globigerina bulloides *(surface dweller) and* Neogloboquadrina dutertrei *(deep dweller), bulk CaCO₃ (%) and magnetic susceptibility over the last 600 ka from ODP core 728A (western Arabian Sea). The oxygen isotope record of* N. dutertrei *has been correlated with the SPECMAP curve to produce this age model. The oxygen isotope record of* N. dutertrei *appeared to be more suitable for dating than that of* G. bulloides, *which is expressed in the power spectra of the two species (see Figure 10.10 e-f). The concentration of variance (power) is more sharply focused in the Milankovitch rhythms in* N. dutertrei *than in the* G. bulloides *record. Figure 10.10 also shows that the magnetic susceptibility and CaCO₃ records are consistent with the stable oxygen isotope curve, which illustrates the potential for use of these records for dating. However such a strategy has many drawbacks and is completely unreliable unless a global oxygen isotope curve is available since local differences may have influenced the signal. Figure generated from data in Steens et al. (1990).*

fractionation effects in planktonic records. The benthic signal should therefore always produce a more globally reliable curve for age model development. Indeed, Shackleton and Berger (in press) show by cross spectral analysis of planktonic and benthic $\delta^{18}O$ curves from the same core, that the benthic signal displays greater coherency with the orbital parameters than does the planktonic (Figure 10.6). This diagram also shows the greater amplitude of the $\delta^{18}O$ excursions in the planktonic compared to the benthic record, because the former includes the combined effect of ice volume and temperature fluctuations, whereas the latter predominantly reflects ice volume variations. However, despite this advantage, benthic foraminifera are often scarce in deep sea sediments because of dilution by the large input of planktonic foraminifera and terrigenous material. It is for these reasons that we advocate the use of a combination of species, both benthic and planktonic.

Vital Effects

Foraminifera undergo gametogenetic reproduction and exist in both juvenile and adult stages, which may have significant differences in the extent of oxygen fractionation. Migration of planktonic foraminifera during development is also common, especially in the genus *Globorotalia*, with juvenile stages inhabiting the euphotic surface waters and adult stages existing deeper in the water column. Together, these effects result in variations of oxygen isotope ratio with test size; adult stages (larger tests) having isotope ratios more depleted in ^{16}O than juvenile stages. Furthermore, the degree to which foraminifera precipitate $CaCO_3$ in isotopic equilibrium with the ambient sea water varies, due mainly to physiological differences, resulting in large deviations in oxygen isotope ratios between species. Such combined effects of developmental stage and species variations are termed "Vital Effects", and can give variations up to 1.2‰. They can be compensated for by comparison with extant species whose vital effects have been determined, and by selecting samples of homogeneous size.

Diagenesis and Dissolution

Diagenesis may affect the $\delta^{18}O$ signal by recrystallisation and dissolution (Baker et al., 1982, Elderfield and Gieskes, 1982, Killingly, 1983). The isotopic composition and gradient of pore waters differ between oceans, but in general, the diagenetic effects of these pore waters are assumed to be minor in comparison to the temperature and ice volume induced effects exerted on the planktonic surface dwellers. Generally, as sediment age and depth of burial increases, the diagenetic effect increases.

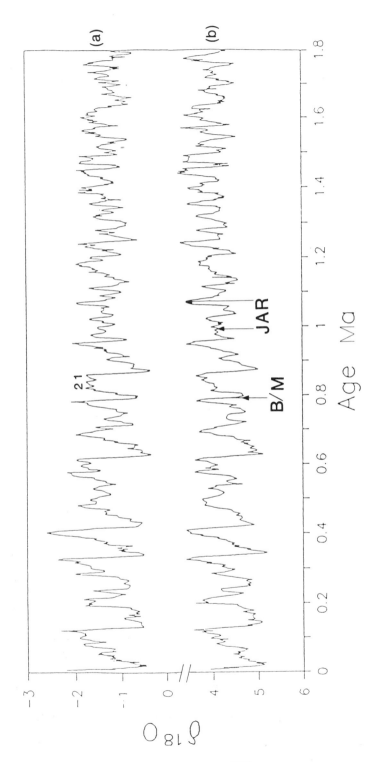

Figure 10.6 *Combined isotope stratigraphy in ODP hole 677.* **A:** *planktonic (Globigerinoides ruber) and* **B:** *benthic (Uvigerina. senticosa). B — Brunhes; M — Matuyama; JAR — Jaramillo subchron; 21 — isotope stage 21 with its three precessional peaks. Note the enhanced amplitude of the planktonic curve compared to the benthic curve as a result of temperature effects in the surface waters, and that the benthic curve is more positive because of a temperature fractionation effect in the cold bottom waters. Adapted from Shackleton and Berger (in press).*

ANALYTICAL TECHNIQUES

Today, analytical facilities for mass spectrometric determination of stable isotope ratios in $CaCO_3$ samples weighing tenths of milligrams are well established. For a detailed account of such techniques see Williams (1984 and accompanying references).

In summary, the recovered sediment core is cut in half along it's length and approximately 10-20 cm³ of wet sediment per horizon is sampled. This is subsequently washed using a 63 μm sieve and dried at around 40°C. Foraminifera are then sorted into size fractions (usually between 200-400 μm diameter), which are dependent on the species to be sampled, and 30-50 individuals of each species are hand picked for every sample. Several species may be required to enable $\delta^{18}O$ and $\delta^{13}C$ comparison between planktonic and benthic species.

A homogenised triplicate sample of 0.1-1.0 mg (5-15 foraminifera) is cleaned with alcohol and dried prior to being "roasted" (*in vacuo*) at c 380°C to remove organic contaminants. Purified phosphoric acid at c 60-90°C is then added (*in vacuo*) to dissolve the $CaCO_3$, liberating CO_2.

$$2H_3PO_4 + 3CaCO_3 \rightleftharpoons Ca_3(PO_4)_2 + 3H_2O \text{ (g)} + 3CO_2 \text{ (g)} \qquad (10.1)$$

Fractional freezing purifies the liberated CO_2 which is then transferred to an on line isotope ratio mass spectrometer. There it is ionised and separated into it's isotopic constituents (Figure 10.7).

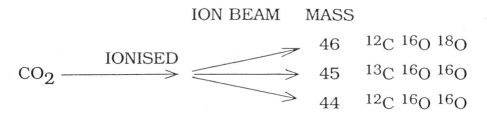

Figure 10.7 *Diagram showing the isotopic separation of liberated CO_2 during mass-spectrometry.*

The mass 46/44 ion beam ratio-intensity gives the $^{18}O/^{16}O$ ratio, and the 45/44 ion beam ratio-intensity produces the $^{13}C/^{12}C$ ratio of the CO_2. These ratios are repeatedly compared to a known CO_2 reference standard. Oxygen isotope ratios are usually expressed as an enrichment or depletion of the minor isotope relative to a standard (commonly the reference carbonate PDB) in parts per thousand (commonly abbreviated δ per mil or ‰). This δ value is calculated using equation 10.2.

$$\delta^{18}O = 1000 * \left[\frac{{}^{18}O/{}^{16}O \text{ sample } - {}^{18}O/{}^{16}O \text{ reference}}{{}^{18}O/{}^{16}O \text{ reference}} \right] \qquad (10.2)$$

CONSTRUCTION OF A STANDARD REFERENCE CURVE

To enable correlation of late Cenozoic marine sedimentary records, a standard, globally applicable isotopic template was required. Such a requirement led Imbrie et al. (1984) to generate the "SPECMAP" curve (Figure 10.8a) which encompasses the last 800 ka and is based on averaging (stacking) several low latitude oxygen isotope profiles derived from shallow-dwelling planktonic foraminifera (*Globigerinoides sacculifer* and *Globigerina bulloides*). They then used the theory of orbital forcing to tune each curve and thus developed an age model. It was hoped that the resulting timescale would act as a type section, against which other curves (e.g. isotopic, geochemical, palaeomagnetic) could be readily compared. Some important points in the methods used in the successful development of such an age model are outlined below.

Critical Reliance on Independent Age Dates

For the SPECMAP reference curve, an initial time scale was achieved by selecting six easily recognisable control points (dated radiometrically) and assuming linear sediment accumulation rates between control points. Stratigraphic inconsistencies in each raw isotopic profile as a result of coring or sedimentation disruption (e.g. stretching, breaks, slumping) were crucial to the selection of such control points, all of which were chosen from undisturbed parts of the selected cores.

Five of the control points were dated using ^{14}C techniques, whereas the Bruhnes-Matuyama magnetic reversal was dated independently by the K-Ar method. Thus, although the overall structure of the SPECMAP curve (Figure 10.8a) may be a good approximation of the global signal, the absolute ages and positions of the stage boundaries may be erroneous because of linear interpolation between the four ^{14}C dated control points (0-35 ka) and the K-Ar dated 730 ka Bruhnes/Matuyama magnetic reversal time control. Furthermore, recent mass spectrometric uranium series ages of ^{14}C dated corals indicate systematic differences greater than 3.5 ka between radiocarbon and true ages for dates older than 20 ka (Bard et al., 1990). After conversion from depth to time, the record must then be further adjusted such that it forms a time series with equally incremented data points.

Nature and Timing of Filtering Process

Subsequent to development of the initial age model, the SPECMAP authors were forced to decide on a tuning strategy which would ultimately determine the accuracy

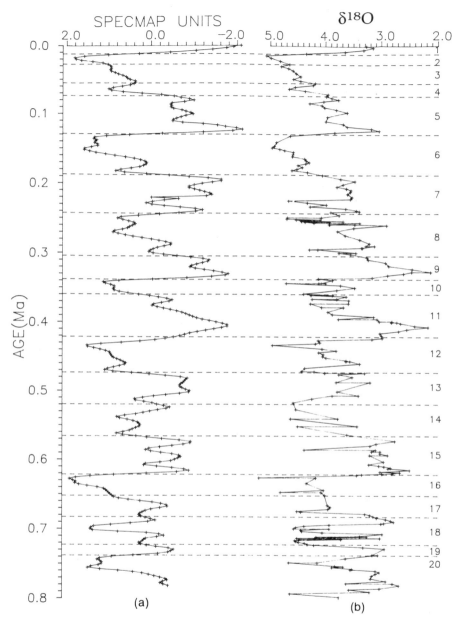

Figure 10.8 *Oxygen isotope curves spanning the last 800 ka. A: the SPECMAP stack generated from data in Imbrie et al. (1983). B: A composite curve generated from uncorrected δ18O data of two benthic foraminifera species from DSDP hole 607 in Ruddiman et al. (1989). The top 250 ka are from cores V30-97 and CHN82-24-4. Numbers 1-20 indicate oxygen isotope stage stratigraphy. The allocation of oxygen isotope cycles in DSDP hole 607 seems relatively easy for the last 600 ka, but at the base of the Brunhes problems occur (see also Figure 10.12).*

211

of the final model. They chose the target curve approach of Hays et al. (1976) and Morley and Hays (1981) which matches isotopic observations against the obliquity and precessional rhythms. Least square noise minimisation filters (Wiener filters) were used to remove any high frequency noise from the signal. Then Fourier transform techniques converted the data from the time to the frequency domain. An iterative process (120 steps) was employed to tune the isotopic signal to the orbital frequencies. Control points were moved to attain a maximum phase lock coherency between the orbital frequencies (Figure 10.2) and the isotopic record. As Imbrie et al. (1984) pointed out, the 120 iterations required to achieve the optimum phase lock raises questions as to the validity of the method. Once an optimum correlation between orbital frequencies and the isotope observations had been attained, depth versus age plots were studied for the stacked curve. It was shown that no sharp inflections occurred and the plots were generally smooth which, according to Imbrie et al. (1984), tenuously implies a relatively constant accumulation rate.

There are two schools of thought as to when is the best time to perform the filtering process. Imbrie et al. (1984), and most subsequent authors, filter in the time domain, whereas Shackleton and Berger (in press) advocate a depth domain filtering method. They argue that their depth domain model requires less change in the accumulation rate of reference core V28-238, which is believed to have an exceptionally constant accumulation rate, than do time domain filtered models. Further work to identify the advantages and disadvantages of both methods is needed, but the implication of such models should be considered carefully by users.

Imbrie et al. (1984) used fixed phase lag times for $\delta^{18}O$ events of around 8 ka behind for obliquity forcing and 4-5 ka behind for precessional forcing. These fixed (presumed constant) phase lag times which are based on the ice sheet model of Weertman (1964), have been shown by Pisias et al. (1990) to vary through time. Pisias et al. (1990) also throw doubt on the assumption of a constant response by the climate system to orbital forcing (see below). Finally, the curves were normalised to a zero mean and unit standard deviation before being superimposed and averaged. Suspect data points were removed prior to smoothing with a 9-point Gaussian filter.

CORRELATION OF "NEW" CURVES WITH THE REFERENCE CURVE

A bewildering variety of methods for correlating newly generated curves with the reference type section are employed today. Most attempt to quantify the degree of correlation between at least two signals often from separate locations. The main methods used and their associated problems are outlined below.

Visual Inspection

The human visual system is remarkably efficient at recognising similarity in patterns, enabling a rapid initial approximation as to the correlation of two records. Emiliani and Shackleton (1974) employed visual analysis to define the isotope stages and substages. Shaw (1964) and Prell et al. (1986) used a graphical correlation method which compares common isotopic events in the "New" curve with those in a reference section.

Stage Boundary Positioning and Tuning

Perhaps the most fundamental weakness in the whole age model development process is the subjectivity of the positioning of isotopic stage boundaries and substages, which are the tielines between any core and SPECMAP. The adoption of the standardised stratigraphic nomenclature of Emiliani (1955) and Shackleton (1969) for stages (numbered from the top of the core with even numbers equivalent to cold stages and odd numbers equivalent to warm) and substages (lettered sequentially, with (a) the highest substage in a given stage) in the curve reduces confusion during correlation. Pisias et. al. (1984) have preferred to use a wholly numerical format for substage and within substage events (e.g. 5.31 for the first event within substage 5.3 which is equivalent to the peak of substage 5e in the Emiliani (1955) scheme) and, although this does not create any great confusion, adoption of a single standard is desirable. There are, however, no standard guidelines which define what is a real positive or negative $\delta^{18}O$ excursion or, indeed, the criteria with which stage boundaries are positioned. Prell et al. (1986) define stage boundaries as being centred on peaks (the events of the Pisias scheme), which is less subjective than placing stage boundaries at the midpoints of anomalies, the scheme utilised by Shackleton and Opdyke (1977). Consequently, errors are almost inevitable in stage boundary positioning and stage numbering, especially in those models which date back millions of years.

Inverse Signal Correlations

Inverse signal correlation (Martinson et al., 1982, 1987) correlates any set (or pair) of isotopic records by defining a continuous non-linear mapping function which maximises the correlation coefficient between data sets being compared. Similarly, semblance methods correlate a reference type section with a "New" data set, and map the coherency as a time difference at any one location against age. The result is a map (Figure 10.9) showing coherency-chrons between the reference and "New" curves (Williams et al., 1988b).

Power Spectral Analysis

There are two common quantitative methods of correlation in the frequency domain; power spectral and cross (power) spectral (or spectral coherency) analysis. Each method plots the amount of spectral power (concentration of variance) present against a harmonic number (1/time window). Power spectral methods thus analyse data sets for the degree of power exhibited by a particular frequency in the frequency domain. Cross spectral analysis quantifies the degree of similarity between two records in

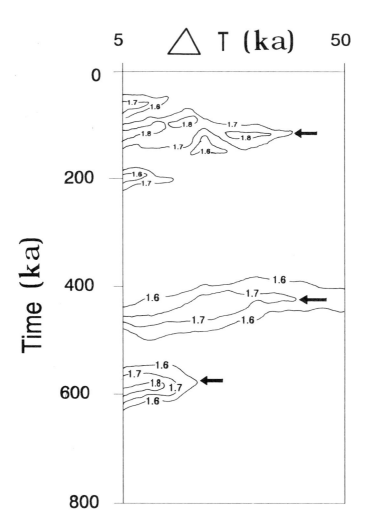

Figure 10.9 *Diagram illustrating the degree of semblance (coherency) between events in a "type" section and any other comparable data set. Contours represent coherency chrons and arrows indicate high coherency events. (Adapted from Williams et al., 1988b.)*

the frequency domain as measured by the spectral coherency measures. A coherency of 1 is indicative of perfect correlation whereas a coherency of zero indicates no correlation. Figure 10.10 presents power spectral analyses of the oxygen isotope composition of planktonic foraminifera, bulk $CaCO_3$ and magnetic susceptibility records from the western Arabian sea ODP hole 728, as previously shown in Figure 10.5.

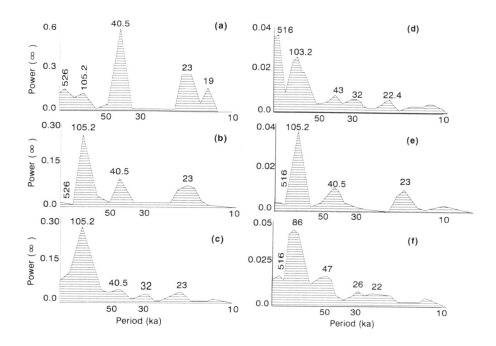

Figure 10.10 *A series of power spectral analyses with period (ka) along the x-axis and power along the y-axis based on a time interval from 12-524 ka and smoothed by a Hanning filter. ODP hole 728A adapted from Steens et al. (1990). (a) Summed normalised values of orbital parameters calculated at intervals of 2 ka (b) SPECMAP δ18O stacked curve calculated at intervals of 2 ka (c) Magnetic susceptibility sampled with a lag of 2 ka (d) δ18O ratios G. ruber sampled with a lag of 6 ka (e) δ18O ratios N. dutertrei sampled with a lag of 6 ka (f) δ18O ratios G. bulloides sampled with a lag of 6 ka. Power spectra (b) and (e) show that there is no direct link between the insolation record and the oxygen isotope records; the eccentricity frequency (100 ka) is much more pronounced in the isotope records. The power spectrum of the magnetic susceptibility record shows the potential for use in dating since all peaks match the Milankovitch rhythms. Nevertheless, one should be very careful in using this kind of parameter, especially where there is no oxygen isotope record available. The power spectra of the different species (d-f) show that the deep dweller N. dutertrei rather than the surface dwellers G. ruber and G. bulloides more accurately document ice volume changes and hence will improve the age model for this core.*

As shown in Figure 10.10, such techniques may be used to quantitatively measure the degree of similarity between two sets of data with respect to the frequencies that are present. Modern computer programmes can vary the time window on which the spectral analysis is performed, which allows comparison of small sections of the record with other parts of the "type" section or theoretical frequency model (e.g. solar input variation, Figure 10.10a). The ability to vary the time window is clearly an advantage but can lead to difficulties when making correlations because any variation in the time window invariably results in subtle or, in some cases, major changes in the structure of the power spectra. Further problems arise as a result of the necessity of spectral analysis programmes to deal only with equally spaced data. That is to say; if, for example, an ash layer or turbidite interrupts normal deposition, and analyses from this horizon are omitted from the data set, the resulting data available to the spectral analysis program will be unevenly spaced. Despite these drawbacks, power spectral analysis does provide a powerful tool to measure quantitatively the degree of similarity in the frequency structure of two records.

Power spectral analysis of curves can also assist in stage boundary positioning and identification because peaks in power should be sharp and well defined if stage boundaries are correctly positioned. However, this process is critically dependent on the time window being analysed and any slight change in this window can affect spectral peaks and boundary positioning. The extensive stretching and condensing of parts of the curve during the tuning process lead one to question to what degree the final timescale actually represents the original data and, indeed, the validity of the timescales.

Sequence Slotting

Sequence slotting is an objective method of comparison which has become possible through the development of computerised dynamic algorithms (Delgoigne and Hansen, 1975). Essentially these combine two records to produce a single "Master" curve which retains the original internal ordering. Problems occur when long blocks (groups) of horizons develop especially in cases of extreme variance. Single or simultaneous multi-core sequence correlations are possible. For an extensive overview of this method see Gordon (1973) and Thompson and Clark (1989).

Bioturbation, Reworking and Accumulation Rate Variation.

Three major potential sources of error in oxygen isotopes stratigraphy are the effects of bioturbation, reworking and accumulation rate variations. Benthic organisms which feed and burrow in the accumulating sediment, cause effective mixing and homogenisation of the upper 1 to 20 cm. This results in a time averaging effect which can be very important, but the extent to which it will blur the global isotopic signal is dependent on the sediment accumulation rate. A rapid accumulation rate renders bioturbation effects almost negligible whereas a slow rate will seriously alter a record. Increasing the sampling density can improve the time resolution, but this cannot compensate for the bioturbation effect. The bioturbation rate has serious implications for the maximum time resolution (Nyquist frequency) attainable in age models. A high bioturbation rate results in a reduction of the time resolution.

Reworking by, for example, current scouring can result in hiatuses in the record which are often difficult to detect, and which may lead to erroneous estimates of sedimentation rates. Oxygen isotope records can show where these breaks in sedimentation occur and help to counteract the potential errors, but significant variations in accumulation rate can also occur. Ruddiman et al. (1987) outline some of the problems resulting from coring which include variable compression and disturbance.

MORE ANCIENT RECORDS

Following the development of the SPECMAP time scale for the Brunhes chron attempts have been made to extend the $\delta^{18}O$ age models into the upper Pliocene (and older), an objective greatly aided by the immense quantity of core material available from DSDP and ODP legs. Underlying the obvious intrinsic scientific interest were many unanswered questions. Today isotope stage nomenclature is well documented throughout the Pleistocene (Shackleton and Opdyke, 1976, 1977, Williams et al., 1988a) and into the upper Pliocene from many of the world's oceans (Van Donk, 1976, Vergnaud-Grazzini et al., 1983, Prell, 1982, Keigwin, 1979, 1982, 1987 and Thunnell and Williams, 1983, Ruddiman et al., 1989, Raymo et al., 1989, Shackleton and Berger, in press, Sarnthein and Tiedeman, 1989). The most recent of these long term records was obtained from ODP hole 625 (Gulf of Mexico) which gave a high resolution oxygen isotopic record spanning the last 5.35 Ma. (Joyce et al., 1990). These studies have focussed on the nature and timing of variations and transitions in climatic periodicity, their relationships to orbital forcing and the possible existence of other longer term oscillations due to non-orbital forcing (e.g. tectonic), associated with the general evolution of the climate system.

Continuation of isotopic stages back to stage 137 (Sarnthein and Tiedeman, 1989) is regarded with some scepticism because of the ease with which a single excursion may be omitted or misinterpreted, but derivation of such long time scales should nevertheless be encouraged, provided they are treated with caution.

Combining Other Records

Although $\delta^{18}O$ curves potentially produce the most globally consistent signal, other records (e.g. $\delta^{13}C$, geochemistry, magnetic susceptibility, biostratigraphy, tephrochronology) should be used as corroborative evidence and studied in conjunction with the isotope profiles (e.g. Figure 10.5). Of these, perhaps magnetic susceptibility (Ledbetter, 1984a) has the greatest potential. However, tephrochronology (Ledbetter, 1984b, Ninkovitch and Shackleton, 1975) and even bulk $CaCO_3$ content, which suffers from dissolution and geographic variation, can have some use. If one could demonstrate a linear relationship between isotope ratios and bulk $CaCO_3$ in the Pleistocene, there is potential to extrapolate the isotope record back into much older sediment using the bulk $CaCO_3$ curves which have been determined back in time for many millions of years. One cannot, however, be sure that the linearity persists during the period when an oxygen isotope profile is not available.

In a recent discussion of the SPECMAP age model Imbrie et al. (in press) advocate a combined use of many records (e.g. geochemistry, oxygen isotopes, magnetic susceptibility) each reflecting different parts of the climate system. With such a spectrum of climatic tracers they propose careful examination of the structure of the climatic cycles (whether progressive or stationary oscillations), the spatio-temporal pattern of the 23 ka and 41 ka cycles in relation to forcing by external radiation in order to identify any latitudinal or seasonal Milankovitch pressure points, duration of climate regimes and the identification of monotonic trends especially over the last 400 ka. They go on to question to what degree filtering methods contribute to the wave forms of the observed cycles, the extent to which these oscillations may be accounted for by summation of the various cycles and if any other records (e.g. carbonate cyclicity, see Nelson et al., 1986 or species abundance profiles, see Morley and Shackleton, 1976) fit neatly into the global pattern.

CLIMATE VARIATIONS

Climatic variations are well documented in oxygen isotope profiles during the last 3.5 Ma. Several major isotopic shifts have been identified, one at 2.5 Ma (Shackleton and Cita, 1979, Thunell and Williams, 1983) the other at 3.2-3.0 Ma (Shackleton and Opdyke, 1977). The shift at 2.5 Ma was believed to have resulted from an increase in northern ice-sheet development (Thunell and Williams, 1983); whereas the earlier shift was described as resulting from a cooling of oceanic surface waters (Prell, 1982).

Perhaps one of the clearest examples of climate change is that reported by Ruddiman et al. (1986, 1989) and Raymo et al. (1989) in their analysis of northern hemisphere ice-sheet development. They document the "switch" in dominance from the 100 ka (eccentricity) rhythm in $\delta^{18}O$ during the Brunhes chron (0.735-0 Ma), to the dominance of the 41 ka (obliquity) rhythm during the Matuyama chron (2.47-0.735 Ma). It was as if the climate system had become somewhat unstable and less sensitive to obliquity forcing. Although Figure 10.11 was generated using raw data from Ruddiman et al. (1989), one can clearly see the different periodicities of the $\delta^{18}O$ cycles with Figure 10.11b displaying a marked dominance in the 41 ka rhythm. So how has this transition evolved? Pisias and Moore (1981), Prell (1982) and Maasch (1988) all favour a rapid (several 10^4 years) "switch" around 0.9 Ma, whereas Imbrie (1985) and Ruddiman et al. (1986, 1989) favour a more gradual transition between 0.78-0.4 Ma, which was accelerated from 0.7-0.6 Ma. Both models agree that by the base of the Brunhes, the 100 ka rhythm was an important feature in climatic variability.

The origin of the 100 ka cycle has long been a contentious issue (Sergin and Sergin, 1976, Pisias and Moore, 1981, Watts and Hayner, 1983, Saltzman, 1987 and Raymo et al., 1989); especially as a direct linear linkage to Milankovitch forcing appears to be very unlikely because insolation spectra (Figure 10.10a) have very low energy in the 100 ka band. However a strong association exists between the 100 ka cycle and the 23 ka cycle envelope (Imbrie et al. in press). It is hypothesised that the 100 ka cycle is internally driven and amplified by climatic instability (Broecker et al., 1985), interactions between climate and forcing mechanisms (Peltier, 1982, Peltier and Hyde, 1984, Saltzman, 1987), and a combination of positive and negative feedback mechanisms within the CO_2-Ice-Ocean system. Computer modelling by Saltzman and Maasch (1988) and Maasch and Saltzman (in press) support the latter idea. Indeed, Saltzman's model results confirm the importance of variations in the amplitude (envelope) of the 23 ka radiation cycle, perhaps in combination with some tectonic forcing (Ruddiman et al., 1989).

As a consequence of variations in the climate system, dating methods which use the Milankovitch theory become less tenable back through time, with the result that discrepancies appear in age estimates. For instance, Black et al. (1988) and Ruddiman et al. (1986, 1989) encountered difficulties when comparing their isotopic record to the SPECMAP stack between 0.8-0.6 Ma especially at the stage 17/16 boundary, despite having used the SPECMAP strategy in developing their age models. This led to tuning problems which forced them to propose that the SPECMAP stage 17/16 boundary date may be 15 ka too young and, although Ruddiman et al. (1989) retain the SPECMAP curve below this point, Black et al. (1988) query the stage 18 boundary age. However, as Ruddiman et al. (1989) point out, a proposed revision of the SPECMAP timescale would not be recommended in light of evidence from a single, potentially atypical, core.

According to Ruddiman et al. (1989), both the 23 ka and 19 ka components of the precessional rhythm increase their amplitude over the Matuyama/Brunhes boundary, especially between 0.8-0.7 Ma, although neither are as prominent as eccentricity or obliquity. Raymo et al. (1989) further extend the $\delta^{18}O$ curve to 2.73 Ma (Figure 10.8b) at stage 116. Between 2.73-1.6 Ma the 41 ka obliquity cycle dominates and only after 2.1 Ma do the 100 ka and 23 ka rhythms show any significant appearance.

The Brunhes/Matuyama boundary appears to be one of climatic disorder with several anomalous rhythms occurring between 0.9-0.6 Ma. Periodicities of 70 ka, 54 ka and 30 ka are reported by Ruddiman et al. (1989) and, of these, only the 54 ka cycle would seem to have the potential to result from orbital forcing as obliquity contains a small insolation component in this band (Berger, 1978). Apart from this minor

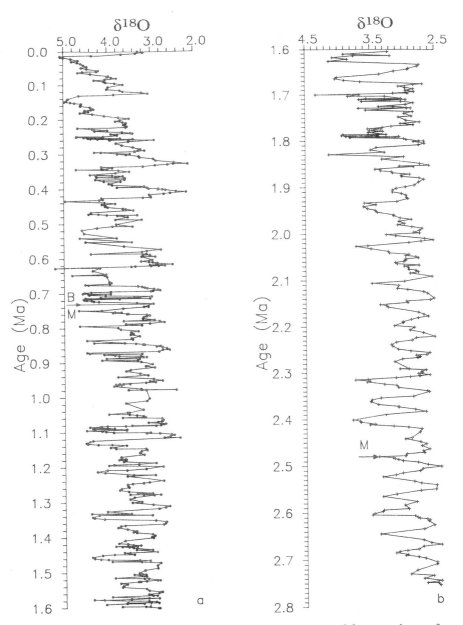

Figure 10.11 $\delta^{18}O$ *curves from 2.8 Ma to present generated from analyses of two benthic species (DSDP hole 607) by Ruddiman et al. (1989) dating from 0-1.6 Ma. Top 250 ka are from cores V30-97 and CHN82-24-4. B/M — Brunhes/Matuyama boundary. Continuation of the record from 1.6 Ma to 2.8 Ma by Raymo et al. (1989). M — base of the Matuyama chron. Note the strong dominance of the obliquity periodicity (41 ka) during the Matuyama which is manifest in the much smoother appearance of the older half of the record.*

220

association, these anomalous rhythms do tend to suggest that climate tracers such as the oxygen isotope record and the methods of age model development may produce an unknown amount of artefact.

The Brunhes/Matuyama transitory boundary period (0.8-0.6 Ma) has also received attention from Shackleton and Berger (in press), who use planktonic and benthic $\delta^{18}O$ records dating back to the upper Pliocene. Their approach differs from previous models in that they filtered in the depth domain. The net effect of this step is that, in contrast to Imbrie et al. (1984) and Ruddiman et al. (1986), the ages of the magnetic reversals were calculated after tuning and filtering. A good correlation is attained with the models of Imbrie et al. (1984) and Ruddiman et al. (1986, 1989) down to stage 116 (2.73 Ma) but below this point discrepancies appear. The main points on which the revised chronology differs from previous work (e.g. Mankinen and Gromme, 1982), is the inclusion of an extra tilt cycle in the lower Brunhes, allocation of three precessional peaks during stage 21 and the definition of stage 35 as encompassing a single tilt rhythm (Figure 10.6). As a result of these discrepancies, Shackleton and Berger (in press) conclude that currently adopted radiometric dates for the Brunhes/Matuyama boundary and the Jarmillo and Olduvai subchrons underestimate their true astronomical ages by around 6%.

CONCLUDING CONSIDERATIONS

There appears to be a need for a standardisation but not dogmatism in the methods of age model development. Until a more successful method of dating marine sedimentary records is found one must make the most of what is available despite the limitations. The numerous factors which affect the $\delta^{18}O$ signal together with analytical limitations must always be considered carefully.

The great advantage of the SPECMAP curve is that it provides a global reference section to which any core can be compared. The success with which such comparisons have been undertaken is evidence of the validity of applying Milankovitch Theory to age model development and climate research, although many problems remain. For instance, when an unknown record is correlated with the Milankovitch tuned SPECMAP stack, it is not surprising that Milankovitch cyclicities often appear in the unknown profile. The dangers of such circular arguments has led to some speculation regarding the authenticity of the SPECMAP model. Some authors (Pisias et al., 1984, Prell et al., 1986, Ruddiman et al., 1989, Sarnthein and Tiedemann, 1989, Shackleton and Berger, in press) developed their own oxygen isotope-based age models, some of which continue back into the upper Pliocene. Such alternative models rely on essentially the same strategy as SPECMAP but tend to combine planktonic and benthic isotope records and filter raw data in the depth domain rather than in the time domain. This similarity of strategies results in new age models running into essentially the same problems as SPECMAP. The great majority of stack records using floating time horizons then convert to time with radiometrically defined datum horizons and most then refine the curve by tuning to orbital frequencies.

Although the theoretical basis for isotopic fractionation and orbital variation would seem unequivocal, the degree of coherency between the Milankovitch rhythms and the climate system depends on the degree of linearity of the response to external forcing. Despite the presence of Milankovitch frequencies in the $\delta^{18}O$ record of foraminifera (e.g. Imbrie et al., 1984, Ruddiman et al., 1989) a discordance exists in linearly linking such records to climatic variability. This is manifest in the different spectral composition of the power spectral analysis of the solar input and $\delta^{18}O$ profiles from sediment cores (compare Figures 10.10a and 10.10b-f). Also Pisias et al. (1990) show that any change in phase shifts has serious implications for any age model, as do variations in sensitivity to orbitally induced insolation, which manifests itself in at least two internal feedback mechanisms. One (probably derived from lithospheric movements) enhances the 100 ka rhythm by increasing the rate of climatic change at glacial terminations. The other, which enhances the 41 ka rhythm, accelerates ice sheet growth and slows melting. Such problems can result in discrepancies of several thousand years which are cumulative down core. Thus, linking climate variability to Milankovitch forcing has many problems, some of which may prove to be forever enigmatic. The climate system appears to have varied through time and it is likely that its response to orbital forcing has changed. This has serious implications for age model developmental strategy.

Also, problems are especially acute with respect to the nature and timing of the filtering and tuning processes, and in the positioning of isotopic stage boundaries. The current debate as to the authenticity of the SPECMAP timescale can only be a healthy one. With the knowledge gained from previous attempts, future models are likely to be improvements if they are produced using several lines of corroborative evidence together. Until such models are developed, the SPECMAP curve and other isotope chronologies must be regarded with positive criticism.

More researchers are turning to either a combination of planktonic and benthic (Sarnthein and Tiedemann, 1989, Shackleton and Berger, in press, Zahn and Pederson, in press) or solely benthic curves (Pisias et al. 1984, 1990, Ruddiman et al. 1989, Raymo et al. 1989) to develop their age models. Benthic isotopic signals are less affected by temperature than the planktonic signal. Thus the stacking of benthic curves and their use in conjunction with planktonic stacks can only lead to improvements in timescales.

Oxygen isotopic ratio curves are potentially a powerful tool for dating and correlating ocean sediments through time, but they must be used in conjunction with other corroborative evidence such as carbon isotope ratios, magnetic susceptibility, geochemistry and power spectral analysis to enable the production of a reliable age model. Until a more precise method of dating sediments is found, oxygen isotope stratigraphy must be used and regarded with positive criticism.

REFERENCES

Baker, P., Gieskes, J., and Elderfield, H. 1982. Diagenesis of carbohydrates in deep sea sediments-evidence from Sr/Ca ratios and interstitial dissolved Sr^{2+} data. *Journal of Sedimentary Petrology*, **52**, 71-82.

Bard, E., Hamelin B., Fairbanks, R.G., and Zindler, A. 1990. Calibration of the ^{14}C timescale over the past 30,000 years using mass spectrometric U-Th ages from Barbados corals, *Nature*, **345**, 405-410.

Berger, A.L. 1976. Obliquity and Precession for the last 5 000 000 years. *Astronomy and Astrophysics*, **51**, 127-135.

Berger, A.L. 1977. Support for the astronomical theory of climate change. *Nature*, **269**, 44-45.

Berger, A.L. 1978. Long-term variations of caloric solar radiation resulting from the earth's orbital elements. *Quaternary Research*, **9**, 139-167.

Berger, W.H. 1979. Stable isotopes in foraminifera. In *Foraminiferal Ecology and Paleoecology, SEPM Short Course No. 6*, Houston, 156-198.

Berger, A.L. 1984. Accuracy and frequency stability of the earth's orbital elements during the Quaternary. In *Milankovitch and Climate, Part 1*, (ed. Berger, A.L.), Reidel, Hingham, Mass., 3-39.

Berger, A.L. 1988. Milankovitch theory and climate. *Reviews in Geophysics*, **26**, 624-657.

Black, K.P., Nelson, C.S., and Hendy, C.H. 1988. A spectral analysis procedure for dating Quaternary deep-sea cores and it's application to a high-resolution Brunhes record from the southwest Pacific. *Marine Geology*, **83**, 21-30.

Bloom, A.M., Broecker, W.S., Chappell, J.M.A., Matthews, R.K., and Mesolella, K.J. 1974. Quaternary sea level fluctuations on a tectonic coast: New $^{230}U/^{234}Th$ dates from the Huon Peninsula, New Guinea. *Quaternary Research*, **4**, 185-205.

Broecker, W.S., Peteet, D.M., and Rind, D. 1985. Does the ocean-atmosphere system have more than one stable mode of operation? *Nature*, **315**, 21-26.

Broecker, W.S., Thurber, D.L., Goddard, J., Ku, T.L., Matthews, R.K., and Mesolella, K. 1968. Milankovitch hypothesis supported by precise dating of coral reefs and deep-sea sediments. *Science*, **159**, 297-300.

Broecker, W.S. and Van Donk, J. 1970. Insolation changes, ice volumes and the ^{18}O record in deepsea cores. *Reviews of Geophysics and Space Physics*, **8**, 169-191.

Croll, J. 1864. Climate and Time. *Philosophical Magazine*, **28**, 121-137.

Delcoigne, A., and Hansen, P. 1975. Sequence comparison by dynamic programming, *Biometrika*, **62**, 661-664.

Duplessy, J.C., Lalou, C., and Vinot, A.C. 1970. Differential isotopic fractionation in benthic foraminifera and paleotemperatures reassessed. *Science*, **168**, 250-251.

Elderfield, H., and Gieskes, J.M. 1982. Sr isotopes in interstitial waters of marine sediments from Deep Sea Drilling Project Cores. *Nature*, **300**, 493-497.

Emiliani, C. 1955. Pleistocene Paleotemperatures. *Journal of Geology*, **63**, 539-578.

Emiliani, C., and Shackleton, N.J. 1974. The Brunhes epoch: Isotope paleotemperatures and geochronology. *Science*, **183**, 511-514.

Epstein, S., Buchsbaum, R., Lowenstam, H., and Urey, H.C. 1953. Revised carbonate-water temperature scale. *Geological Society of America Bulletin*, **64**, 1315-1325.

Fairbanks, R.G., and Matthews, R.K. 1978. The marine oxygen isotope record in Pleistocene coral, Barbados, West Indies. *Quaternary Research*, **10**, 181-196.

Gordon A.D. 1973. A sequence-comparison statistic and algorithm. *Biometrika*, **60**, 197-200.

Hays, J.D., Imbrie, J., and Shackleton, N.J. 1976. Variations in earth's orbit: Pacemaker of the ice ages. *Science*, **194**, 1121-1132.

Hemleben, C., and Spindler, M. 1983. Recent advances in research on living planktonic foraminifera. In *Reconstruction of Marine Paleoenvironments*, (ed Meulenkamp, J.E.), *Utrecht Micropalaeontlogy Bulletin*, **30**, 141-170.

Imbrie, J. 1985. A theoretical framework for the Pleistocene ice ages, *Quarterly Journal of the Geological Society of London*, **142**, 417-432.

Imbrie, J., Boyle, E., Clemens, S., Farrell, J., Kutzbach, J., MacIntyre, A., Martinson, D., Mix, A., Molfino, B., Pisias, N.G., Prell, W.L., Shackleton, N.J., and Toggweiler, J.R. 1990. Structure of the late Pleistocene climate cycles: major features of the marine record (0-400 ka). *Paleoceanography* (in press).

Imbrie J., and Imbrie, J.Z. 1980. Modelling the climate response to orbital variations. *Science*, **207**, 943-953.

Imbrie, J., Shackleton, N.J., Pisias, N.G., Morley, J.J., Prell, W.L., Martinson, D.G., Hayes, J.D., MacIntyre, A., and Mix, A.C. 1984. The orbital theory of Pleistocene climate: support from a revised chronology of the marine w^{18}O record. In *Milankovitch and Climate, Part 1*, (ed Berger A.), Reidel, Hingham, Massachusetts, 269-305.

Jansen, E. 1989. The use of stable oxygen and carbon isotope stratigraphy as a dating tool. *Quaternary International*, **1**, 151-166.

Joyce, J.E., Tjalsma, L.R.C. and Prutzman, J.M. 1990. High resolution planktic stable isotope record and spectral analysis for the last 5.35 m.y.: Ocean Drilling Program Site 625, Northeast Gulf of Mexico, *Paleoceanography*, **5**, 507-529.

Keigwin, L.D. Jr. 1979. Late Cenozoic stable isotope stratigraphy and paleoceanography of DSDP sites from the east equatorial and central North Pacific ocean. *Earth and Planetary Science Letters*, **45**, 361-381.

Keigwin, L.D. Jr. 1982. Isotopic paleoceanography of the Caribbean and East Pacific: Role of Panama uplift in late Neogene times. *Science*, **217**, 350-353.

Keigwin, L.D. Jr. 1987. Pliocene stable isotope record of DSDP 606: ^{18}O enrichment 2.4, 2.6 and 3.1 My ago. *Initial Reports of the Deep Sea Drilling Project*, **94**, 911-920.

Killingley, J.S. 1983. Effects of diagenetic recrystalisation on $^{18}O/^{16}O$ values of deep sea sediments. *Nature*, **310**, 504-507.

Ledbetter, M.T. 1984a. Pleistocene magnetostratigraphy. In *Principles of Pleistocene Stratigraphy Applied to the Gulf of Mexico*, (ed Healy-Williams, N.), IHRDC Press, Boston, Massachusetts, 1-24.

Ledbetter, M.T. 1984b. Late Pleistocene tephrochronology in the Gulf of Mexico region. In *Principles of Pleistocene Stratigraphy Applied to the Gulf of Mexico* (ed. Healy-Williams, N.), IHRDC Press, Boston, Massachusetts, 119-148.

Maasch, K.A. 1988. Statistical detection of the mid-Pleistocene transition. *Climate Dynamics*, **2**, 133-143.

Maasch, K.A., and Saltzman, B. (1990). A low-order dynamical model of climatic variability over the full Pleistocene. *Journal of Geophysical Research* (in press).

Mankinen, E.A., and Gromme, C.S. 1982. Paleomagnetic data from the Coso Range, California, and current status of the Cobb Mountain normal geomagnetic polarity event. *Geophysical Research Letters*, **9**, 1279-1282.

Martinson, D.G., Menke, W., and Stoffa, P. 1982. An inverse approach to signal correlation. *Journal of Geophysical Research*, **87**, 4807-4818.

Martinson, D.G., Pisias, N.G., Hays, J.D., Imbrie, J., Moore, T.C., and Shackleton, N.J. 1987. Age dating and the orbital theory of the ice ages: development of a high resolution 0-300 000 year chronostratigraphy. *Quaternary. Research*, 27, 1-29.

Milankovitch, M. 1941. *Canon of Insulation and the Ice-Age Problem*, Koninglich Serbische Akademie, Beograd, pp. 484. (English translation by the Israel program for scientific translation and published for the U.S. department of commerce and the national science foundation).

Morley, J.J., and Hays, J.D. 1981. Towards a high-resolution global, deap sea chronology for the last 750 000 years. *Earth and Planetary Science Letters*, **53**, 279-295.

Morley, J.J., and Shackleton, N.J. 1976. Extension of the radiolarian *Stylatractus universus* as a biostratigraphic datum to the Atlantic ocean. *Geology*, **6**, 309-311.

Nelson, C.S., Hendy, C.H., Cuthbertson, A.M., and Jarret, G.R. 1986. Late Quaternary carbonate and isotope stratigraphy, subantarctic site 594, southwest Pacific. *Initial Reports of the Deep Sea Drilling Project*, **90**, 1425-1436.

Ninkovitch, D., and Shackleton, N.J. 1975. Distribution, stratigraphic position and age of ash layer "L", in the Panama basin region. *Earth and Planetary Science Letters*, **27**, 20-34.

Peltier, W.R. 1982. Dynamics of the ice-age earth. *Advances in Geophysics*, **24**, 2-146.

Peltier, W.R., and Hyde, W. 1984. A model of the ice cycle. In *Milankovitch and Climate, Part II*, (eds Berger, A., Imbrie, J., Hays, J., Kukla, G., and Saltzman, B.), Plenum, New York, 565-580.

225

Pisias, N.G. 1976. Late Quaternary sediment sedimentation rates, periodicities, and controls of carbonate and opal accumulations. *Memoirs Geological Society of America*, **145**, 375-391.

Pisias, N.G., Dauphin, J.P., and Sancetta, C.S. 1973. Spectral analysis in late Pleistocene-Holocene sediments. *Quaternary Research*, **3**, 3-9.

Pisias, N.G., Martinson, D.G., Moore, T.C. Jr., Shackleton, N.J., Prell, W.L., Hayes, J., and Boden, G. 1984. High resolution statigraphic correlation of benthic oxygen isotope records spanning the last 300,000 years. *Marine Geology*, **56**, 119-136.

Pisias, N.G., Mix, A.C., and Zahn, R. 1990. Non-linear response in the global climate system: evidence from benthic oxygen isotope records in core RC13-110. *Paleoceanography*, **5**, 147-160.

Pisias, N.G., and Moore, T.C. 1981. The evolution of the Pleistocene climate: A time series approach. *Earth and Planetary Science Letters*, **52**, 450-458.

Prell, W.L. 1982. Oxygen and carbon isotope stratigraphy for the Quaternary of hole 502B: Evidence for two modes of isotopic variability. *Initial Reports of the Deep Sea Drilling Project*, **68**, 455-464.

Prell, W.L., Imbrie, J., Martinson, D.G., Morley, J., Pisias, N.G., Shackleton, N.J., and Streeter, H.F. 1986. Graphic correlation of oxygen isotope stratigraphy application to the late Quaternary. *Paleoceanography*, **1**, 137-162.

Raymo, M.E., Ruddiman, W.F., Backman, J., Clement, B.M., and Martinson, D.G. 1989. Late Pleistocene variation in northern hemisphere ice sheets and north Atlantic deep water circulation. *Paleoceanography*, **4**, 413-446.

Ruddiman, W.F., Cameron, D., and Clement, B.M. 1987. Sediment disturbance and correlation of offset holes drilled with the hydraulic piston corer. *Initial Reports of the Deep Sea Drilling Project*, **94**, 615-634.

Ruddiman, W.F., MacIntyre, A., and Raymo, M.E. 1986. Matuyama 41 000-year cycle: north Atlantic ocean and northern hemisphere ice-sheets. *Earth and Planetary Science Letters*, **80**, 117-129.

Ruddiman, W.F., Raymo, M.E., Martinson, D.G., Clement, B.M., and Backman, J. 1989. Pleistocene evolution:northern hemisphere ice sheets and north Atlantic ocean. *Paleoceanography*, **4**, 353-412.

Saltzman, B. 1987. Carbon dioxide and the $\delta^{18}O$ record of late Quaternary climate change: a global model. *Climate Dynamics*, **1**, 77-85.

Saltzman, B. and Maasch, K.A. 1988. Carbon cycle instability as a cause of the late Pleistocene ice age oscillation: modeling the asymmetric response. *Global Biogeochemical Cycles*, **2**, 177-185.

Sarnthein, M. and Tiedemann, R. 1989. Towards a high-resolution stable isotope stratigraphy of the last 3.4 million years:sites 658 and 659 off northwest Africa. In *Proceedings of the Ocean Drilling Program, Scientific Results*, **108**, 167-185.

Sergin, V.Y., and Sergin, S.Y. 1976. Systems analysis of the problem of large scale oscillations of the climate and glaciations of the earth (in Russian). In *Modelirovaine Planetarnoi Sistemy "Ledniti-Okean-Atmosphera"*, (ed Sergin, S.Y.), USSR Academy of Sciences, Moscow, 5-51.

Shackleton N.J. 1967. Oxygen isotope analyses and Pleistocene tempeatures re-assessed. *Nature*, **215**, 15-17.

Shackleton, N.J. 1969. The last interglacial in the marine and terrestrial records. *Proceedings Royal Society London Series B*, **174**, 135-154.

Shackleton N.J. 1977. The oxygen isotope stratigraphic record of the late Pleistocene. *Philosophical Transactions of the Royal Society London*, **280**, 169-182.

Shackleton, N.J., Berger, A. and Peltier, W.A. 1991. An alternative astronomical calibration of the lower Pleistocene timescale based on ODP site 677. *Transactions of the Royal Society of Edinburgh: Earth Sciences*, **81**, 251-262.

Shackleton, N.J., and Cita, M. 1979. Oxygen and carbon isotope stratigraphy of benthic foraminifers at site 397: Detailed history of climatic change during the Neogene. *Initial Reports of the Deep Sea Drilling Project,* **47**, 433-459.

Shackleton, N.J., and Matthews, R.K. 1977. Oxygen isotope stratigraphy of late Pleistocene coral terraces in Barbados. *Nature*, **268**, 618-620.

Shackleton, N.J., and Opdyke, N.D. 1973. Oxygen isotope and paleomagnetic stratigraphy of equatorial Pacific core V28-238: oxygen isotope temperatures and ice volume on a 10^5 and 10^6 year scale. *Quaternary Research*, **3**, 39-55.

Shackleton, N.J., and Opdyke, N.D. 1976. Oxygen isotope and palaeomagnetic statigraphy of Pacific core V28-239 late Pliocene latest Pleistocene. *Memoirs Geological Society America*, **145**, 449-464.

Shackleton, N.J., and Opdyke, N.D. 1977. Oxygen isotope and paleomagnetic evidence for early northern hemisphere glaciation. *Nature*, **270**, 216-219.

Shaw A.B. 1964. *Time in Stratigraphy*, Mcgraw-Hill, New York, pp. 365.

Steens, T.N.F., Kroon D., Ten Kate, W.G., and Sprenger, A. 1990. Late Pleistocene rhythmicities of oxygen isotope ratios, calcium carbonate contents and magnetic susceptibilities of western Arabian sea margin hole 728A, (ODP leg 117). *Proceedings of the Ocean Drilling Program, Part B: Scientific Results, Leg 117*, (in press).

Thompson, R., and Clark, R.M. 1989. Sequence slotting for stratigraphic correlation between cores: theory and practice. *Journal of Paleolimnology*, **2**, 173-184.

Thunell, R.C., and Williams, D.F. 1983. The stepwise development of Pliocene-Pleistocene paleoclimatic and paleoceanographic conditions in the Mediterranean. *Utrecht Micropaleontological Bulletin*, **30**, 111-127.

Urey, H.C. 1948. Oxygen isotopes in nature and the laboratory. *Science*, **108**, 489-496.

Van Donk, J. 1976. ^{18}O record of the Atlantic ocean for the entire Pleistocene Epoch. *Memoir of the Geological Society America*, **145**, 147-163.

Veeh, H.H and Chappell, J. 1970. Astronomical theory of climatic change: Support from New Guinea. *Science*, **167**, 862-865.

Vergnaud-Grazzini, C., Grably, M., Pujol, C., and Duprat, J. 1983. Oxygen isotope stratigraphy and paleoclimatology of southwestern Atlantic Quaternary sediments (Rio-Grande Rise) at Deep Sea Drilling Project Site 517. *Initial Reports of the Deep Sea Drilling Project*, **72**, 871-884.

Watts, R.G., and Hayner, M.E. 1983. The origin of the 100-kiloyear ice sheet cycle in the Pleistocene. *Journal of Geophysical Research*, **88**, 5163-5166.

Weertman, J. 1964. Rate of growth or shrinkage of non-equilibrium icesheets. *Journal of Glaciology*, **38**, 145-158.

Williams, D.F. 1984. Correlation of marine Pleistocene sediments of the Gulf of Mexico and other basins using oxygen isotope stratigraphy. In *Principles of Pleistocene Stratigraphy Applied to the Gulf of Mexico*, (ed Healy-Williams, N.), IHRDC Press, Boston, Massachusetts, 67-188.

Williams, D.F., Lerche, I., Full, W.E. 1988b. *Isotope Chronostratigraphy: Theory and Methods*, Academic Press, New York, pp. 345.

Williams, D.F., Moore, W.S., and Fillon, R.H. 1981. Role of glacial Arctic ocean ice sheets in Pleistocene oxygen isotope and sea level records. *Earth and Planetary Science Letters*, **56**, 157-166.

Williams, D.F., Thunell, R.C., Tappa, E., Rio, D., and Raffi, I. 1988a. Chronology of the oxygen isotope record, 0-1.88 million years before present. *Palaeogeography, Palaeoclimatology and Palaeoecology*, **64**, 221-240.

Zahn, R., and Pedersen, T.F. 1990. Late Pleistocene evolution of surface and mid-depth hydrography at the Oman margin: Planktonic and benthic records at ODP site 724. *Proceedings of the Ocean Drilling Program, Part B: Scientific results, Leg 117*, (in press).

INDEX

229

233